Geology of the
Brighton and W

The Brighton and Worthin꜀
variety and includes parts of the Weald Clay vale, the South
Downs, the Sussex coastal plain and some sandy heathland on
the Lower Greensand outcrop. The area is mainly drained by
the River Adur and its tributaries, which reach the sea via a
gap in the Chalk escarpment near Bramber. Dry valleys are
widespread in the Chalk downland in the south.

Rocks exposed at the surface range from Wealden (Lower
Cretaceous) to Eocene in age. Superficial deposits are locally
extensive, especially on the coastal plain where Brickearth
overlies Raised Beach Deposits. In this account the
stratigraphy of the Cretaceous and Tertiary strata is described, and the results of BGS boreholes in the Cretaceous
rocks are reported. Detailed mapping of the Lower
Cretaceous rocks has enabled improved interpretations of
their structure to be made, notably in the folded ground between Thakeham and Henfield.

Frontispiece   View west along the South Downs escarpment from near Poynings. The escarpment is formed by the basal beds of the Upper Chalk together with the whole of the Middle and Lower Chalk. In the distance the prominent clump of trees at Chanctonbury Ring is on the escarpment beyond the Adur gap [A13380]

BRITISH GEOLOGICAL SURVEY

Natural Environment Research Council

B. YOUNG and R. D. LAKE

Geology of the country around Brighton and Worthing

Memoir for 1:50 000 geological sheets 318 and 333
(England and Wales)

CONTRIBUTORS

Stratigraphy
R. A. Ellison
R. W. Gallois
T. E. Lawson
D. Millward
R. N. Mortimore

Palaeontology
B. M. Cox
H. C. Ivimey-Cook
A. A. Morter
R. N. Mortimore
G. Warrington
C. J. Wood

Economic geology
P. M. Harris
R. A. Monkhouse

LONDON: HER MAJESTY'S STATIONERY OFFICE   1988

First published 1988

ISBN 0 11 884407 5

Bibliographical reference

Young, B. and Lake, R. D. 1988. Geology of the country around Brighton and Worthing. *Mem. Br. Geol. Surv.*, Sheets 318 and 333 (England & Wales).

Authors

B. Young, BSc
British Geological Survey, Newcastle upon Tyne
R. D. Lake, MA
British Geological Survey, Keyworth

Contributors

B. M. Cox, BSc, PhD, R. A. Ellison, BSc, P. M. Harris, MA, H. C. Ivimey-Cook, BSc, PhD, and G. Warrington, BSc, PhD
British Geological Survey, Keyworth

R. W. Gallois, BSc, DIC, PhD, FIMM
British Geological Survey, Edinburgh

D. Millward, BSc, PhD
British Geological Survey, Newcastle upon Tyne

R. A. Monkhouse, MSc
British Geological Survey, Wallingford

T. E. Lawson, BSc
A. A. Morter, BSc
C. J. Wood, BSc
formerly of the British Geological Survey

R. N. Mortimore, BSc, PhD
Brighton Polytechnic, Moulsecoomb, Brighton BN2 4GJ

Other publications of the Survey dealing with this district and adjoining districts

Books

Memoirs
Haslemere (301), 1968
Tunbridge Wells (303), 1972
Lewes (319), 1987
British Regional Geology
The Wealden District, 4th Edition, 1965

Maps

1:625 000
Solid geology of Great Britain (South)
Quaternary geology of Great Britain (South)
Sheet 2 Aeromagnetic

1:50 000 and 1:63 360 (Solid and Drift)
Sheet 301 (Haslemere), 1981
Sheet 302 (Horsham), 1972
Sheet 303 (Tunbridge Wells), 1971
Sheet 317 (Chichester), 1972
Sheet 318/333 (Brighton and Worthing), 1984
Sheet 319 (Lewes), 1979
Sheet 332 (Bognor), 1975
Sheet 334 (Eastbourne), 1979

1:250 000
Wight (Solid Geology)
Wight (Seabed Sediments)
Wight (Gravity)
Wight (Aeromagnetic)

Printed in the United Kingdom for Her Majesty's Stationery Office.
Dd 0240410 C20 2/88 3933 12521

CONTENTS

FIGURES

TABLES

PLATES

PREFACE

This memoir describes the geology of the district covered by the Brighton and Worthing (318/333) New Series sheets of the 1:50 000 Geological Map of England and Wales. This area was included in the Old Series Sheets 5 and 9, which were surveyed on the scale of one inch to one mile (1:63 360) and published in 1864. Parts of the district were surveyed on the six-inch scale (1:10 560) in the period 1873 to 1890 and New Series sheets of the component areas were published in 1924. A later edition of the Brighton (318) Sheet included revised six-inch mapping of the Lower Greensand in 1938. The original memoir for the Brighton and Worthing district by H. J. O. White was published in 1924.

The full six-inch survey of the district was carried out by Messrs R. A. Ellison, R. D. Lake, T. E. Lawson, Dr D. Millward and Mr B. Young in 1973–1979 under Dr W. A. Read and Dr R. A. B. Bazley as District Geologists. Small areas had been surveyed in 1962–1973 as overlap from the adjacent Horsham (302), Tunbridge Wells (303) and Lewes (319) districts. A list of six-inch maps and the names of the surveyors is given in Appendix 3. The 1:50 000 map was published in 1984. Messrs R. D. Lake and B. Young have compiled the memoir, which was completed under Dr R. G. Thurrell as Regional Geologist and edited by Mr G. Bisson.

Palaeontological work has been the responsibility of the Biostratigraphy Group of the British Geological Survey. Dr H. C. Ivimey-Cook, Dr G. Warrington, Dr B. M. Cox and Mr A. A. Morter have reviewed the faunas of the Henfield Borehole. Mr Morter has also reported on the faunas of the Weald Clay, Lower Greensand and Gault with assistance from Dr E. F. Owen of the British Museum (Natural History) on the brachiopods of the Lower Greensand and from Dr H. G. Owen (BMNH) and Mr R. A. Milbourne (Reading University) on the Gault. Mr C. J. Wood has reviewed the palaeontology of the Chalk, with assistance from Dr R. N. Mortimore of Brighton Polytechnic. Dr Mortimore has also provided stratigraphical information and his contributions are particularly acknowledged. Mineralogical determinations of certain Lower Greensand lithologies were made by Dr D. J. Morgan of the Mineral Sciences and Isotope Geology Group. The hydrogeology of the district has been described by Mr R. A. Monkhouse and other economic aspects by Mr P. M. Harris. The most recent photographs were taken by Mr C. J. Jeffery. Several boreholes were drilled by the BGS drilling rig under the supervision of Mr S. P. Thorley.

We gratefully acknowledge information afforded by various local government authorities and the cooperation of landowners and quarry operators during the course of the survey.

G. I. Lumsden FRSE
Director

British Geological Survey
Keyworth
Nottingham
NG12 5GG

14 August 1987

NOTES

The word 'district' is used in this memoir to mean the area represented by the 1:50 000 geological sheets 318 and 333 (Brighton and Worthing). In some places the expression 'Brighton and Worthing district' is shortened to 'Brighton district' for the sake of brevity.

National Grid references are given in square brackets throughout the memoir. They all lie within the 100-km square TQ (or 51), except where otherwise indicated.

Numbers preceded by A refer to photographs in the Geological Survey collections.

The word 'bostall', which appears in the descriptions of some Chalk localities, means 'a track up the escarpment'.

CHAPTER 1

Introduction

The district represented by the 1:50 000 Geological New Series Sheet Brighton and Worthing (318/333) lies within the counties of West and East Sussex. It extends from the margins of the central Weald across the Weald Clay vale and the South Downs escarpment and dip-slope to the south coast and includes the eastern part of the Sussex coastal plain (Figure 1). Much of it retains a pleasant rural aspect, with farming the dominant occupation. North of the South Downs both dairy and arable farming are prevalent, with market gardening and fruit growing of local importance. Much of the population here is scattered in isolated farms and small villages, and the town of Burgess Hill, together with the villages of Steyning, Henfield and Hurstpierpoint, serve as centres for the farming community. Hassocks and the neighbouring village of Keymer are popular residential settlements for travellers to London, a role that is shared by Burgess Hill. Industries include light engineering and the manufacture of bricks and tiles at Burgess Hill and the quarrying of sand near Washington. On the South Downs, sheep farming was formerly an important activity but has been largely replaced in recent years by the cultivation of cereal crops. Cement manufacture near Shoreham is a major industry.

The densely populated conurbations of the coastal plain support a variety of industries, including light engineering and the manufacture of pharmaceuticals and clothing. The busy port of Shoreham is a centre for the importation of a variety of commodities, notably timber, oil products, coal, sea-dredged aggregates, and wine, as well as handling miscellaneous imports and exports.

Brighton, the largest town in the district, is a commercial centre and the home of the University of Sussex, but is probably best known as a holiday and conference centre. It was not until the latter half of the 18th century that Brighton, then a small fishing community known as Brighthelmstone, attracted attention as a resort. The practice of sea bathing and 'the Use of Sea Water in Diseases of the Glands' was encouraged here in 1753 by Dr Richard Russell, a physician from Lewes. Some years later George, Prince of Wales, later Prince Regent, established a royal residence in Brighton, which between 1815 and 1820 was transformed by the architect John Nash into the highly distinctive Royal Pavilion. By then Brighthelmstone and its neighbour Hove were fashionable resorts, becoming famous for their fine Regency terraces, crescents and squares, many examples of which survive as graceful features of modern Brighton and Hove. Both

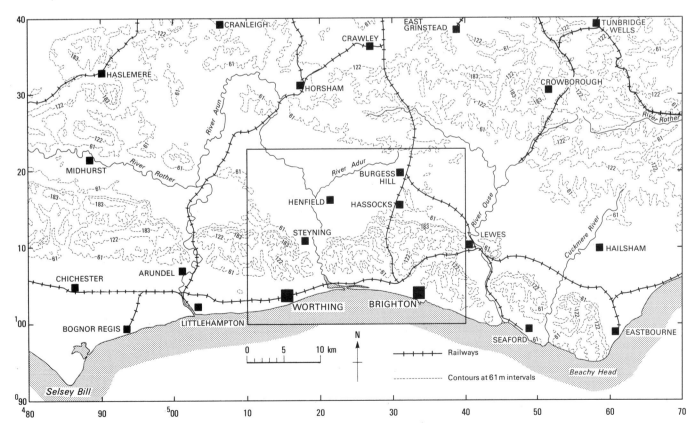

Figure 1   Topographical setting of the Brighton and Worthing district

towns retain their. individual identities and continue as popular and fashionable residential towns and seaside resorts. An excellent account of the history and development of Brighton has been given by Gilbert (1954). The smaller resort of Worthing, in the south-western corner of the district, is a popular residential town.

PHYSIOGRAPHY AND DRAINAGE

The district lies on the southern limb of the Wealden anticlinorium, the overall regional dip of the included formations being to the south. There are two broad physiographical belts which run approximately west to east across the area of the map (Figure 2).

The northern belt comprises the outcrop of beds between the escarpment of the Chalk and the high ground of the central Weald. In the district here described, the oldest formation at the surface, the Tunbridge Wells Sand, crops out only in the extreme north-east and forms a gentle dip-slope descending to the extensive Weald Clay outcrop to the south. The sands within the Tunbridge Wells Sand give rise to well drained soils and in the North Common area support shrubby heathland. The mudstones that make up the major part of the Weald Clay give rise to undulating country generally less than 60 m above OD, interrupted locally by low 'scarp and dip' features produced by beds of sandstone and limestone. The outcrop of the overlying Lower Greensand is marked by an escarpment prominent in the west and clearly marking the outcrop around the Henfield syncline in the centre of the district, but becoming low and relatively inconspicuous in the east. Light, free-draining soils on the Lower Greensand

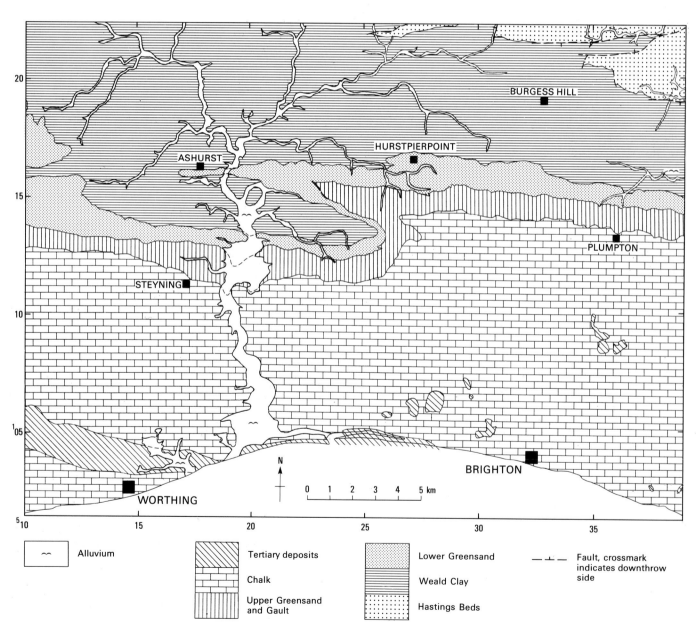

Figure 2 Geological sketch-map of the Brighton and Worthing district

enjoy a high reputation for arable farming, though the poorer sandy soils on the Folkestone Beds in the west mainly support woodland and heath. Between the Lower Greensand and the base of the Chalk, the Gault outcrop is marked by relatively featureless clay land, generally covered by permanent pasture; west of Hassocks the Upper Greensand intervenes between the Gault and the Lower Chalk, giving rise to a low but usually steep scarp feature.

The southern part of the district is underlain by the Chalk and includes the steep north-facing escarpment of the South Downs (Frontispiece) and the long rolling dip-slope. Within the district the South Downs reach their greatest elevation of 248 m at Ditchling Beacon. Other prominent hills along the ridge are Chanctonbury Ring (238 m), near Devil's Dyke (217 m), and Wolstonbury Hill (206 m). Numerous corrie-like valley heads or coombes interrupt the steep face of the Downs, the well known Devil's Dyke being a striking but rather atypical example. A rectilinear network of steep-sided dry valleys covers the dip-slope. East of Brighton marine erosion has produced spectacular sea-cliffs, leaving truncated dry valleys 'hanging' above the modern beach. West of the River Adur the main Chalk dip-slope is interrupted by a secondary escarpment caused by differential erosion of beds high in the Upper Chalk. Around Cissbury Ring (183 m) this escarpment forms as prominent a topographic feature as the main escarpment to the north. Between the western edge of the district and Brighton the Chalk dip-slope passes southwards into the drift-covered eastern end of the Sussex coastal plain.

All the surface drainage of the district is to the English Channel, with the greater part drained by the River Adur, though the area east of Burgess Hill and Hassocks drains eastwards to the River Ouse. The headwaters of the Adur rise in the area between Billingshurst, Horsham and Haywards Heath and flow south as two main tributaries which drain most of the area north of the South Downs and unite near Henfield. Between Upper Beeding and Shoreham the Adur flows through a wide gap in the South Downs. At Shoreham a long shingle spit deflects the river eastwards parallel to the coast to enter the sea between Shoreham and Portslade. Advantage has been taken of the sheltered stretch of water behind this shingle spit to construct the port of Shoreham.

Apart from the main channel of the River Adur, there is virtually no surface drainage across the Chalk outcrop, although a stream flowed from Patcham to the sea at Brighton until it was enclosed in a brick culvert in the 1790s. The extensive system of dry valleys on the Chalk bears witness to the abundant surface drainage at a period of higher water table during Pleistocene times. The coastal plain between Durrington and Shoreham is drained directly to the sea by a number of small streams.   BY

GEOLOGICAL HISTORY

The oldest rocks known in the district are of late Triassic or earliest Jurassic age and were proved in the Henfield Borehole [1799 1457] (p.5). By analogy with adjacent districts these sediments are assumed to overlie a surface of folded and faulted Palaeozoic rocks, probably of Devonian and Carboniferous age. The interbedded marls, breccias and limestones encountered at Henfield reflect a marginal continental facies, whereas the succeeding Jurassic strata were laid down in a fully marine environment in which shelf limestones and mudstones were deposited.

In late Portland Beds times a major regression occurred and the succeeding mudstones and limestones of the Purbeck Beds show evidence of a persistent lagoonal environment. The basal part of the Purbeck succession includes beds of anhydrite which point to a hot climate with restricted circulation of the basin-waters. Above this level the sequence contains faunas which reflect conditions ranging from brackish to freshwater. However, from one horizon, that of the Cinder Bed, a fully marine fauna has been obtained generally in the Weald; the transitory transgressive phase indicated by this bed has been considered to mark the base of the Cretaceous System (Casey, 1963), although recent work suggests that the underlying Purbeck strata may also be Cretaceous (Lake and others, 1987).

Above the Purbeck Beds the formations of the Wealden Series were laid down in a continuing shallow lagoonal environment in which coarse sediments, silts and fine-grained sands, were intermittently deposited. In the earlier deposits such sediments are sufficiently thick to be classed as formations, whereas in the Weald Clay only thin sheet-like bodies of sand occur within a dominantly argillaceous sequence. Incursions of brackish water occurred at times during the deposition of the Weald Clay and the highest example heralded a major environmental change described below. Allen (1949 and subsequent papers) has made detailed studies of the Wealden sediments; in his earlier works he ascribed the influxes of coarse sediment to deltaic advances but latterly to invasions by braided or meandering river systems which locally deposited coalescent alluvial fans.

At the end of Wealden times an important non-sequence was followed by a major marine transgression. The resultant Lower Greensand deposits are dominantly arenaceous, although argillaceous sediments (of the Atherfield Clay) are preserved in the western part of the district. A further hiatus of deposition occurred prior to the accumulation of the clays of the Gault, which indicate a more extensive transgression. The Gault passes upwards into the calcareous siltstones of the Upper Greensand in the western part of the district.

A further still-stand is indicated by the Glauconitic Marl at the base of the Chalk. The succeeding chalk sediments mainly comprise debris of marine micro-organisms and were laid down in wide, relatively shallow seas which extended across much of Europe. Within this relatively uniform succession periods of non-deposition are marked variously by thin seams of marl, burrowed horizons or encrusted and mineralised surfaces.

Towards the end of the Cretaceous, major uplift and warping occurred and created more restricted sedimentary basins. Above the resultant surface of unconformity, the Woolwich and Reading Beds comprise dominantly brackish to freshwater lagoonal deposits which were probably subject to intermittent exposure, leading to soil-forming processes. The succeeding London Clay was deposited in fully marine, relatively deep-water conditions. Younger Tertiary deposits are lacking because of subsequent uplift, deformation and erosion, and the early Tertiary deposits were originally far more extensive than at the present time. It is not known to what extent the Pliocene/Pleistocene (Calabrian) transgression affected this district. During subsequent times the Wealden area has suffered extensive subaerial erosion, producing the present-day scenery and drainage pattern. In the later part of the Pleistocene the area was subjected to intermittent periglacial conditions, with the probable development of local snow-fields on the higher ground. During one warmer climatic phase higher sea level gave rise to an extensive wave-cut platform in the area of the present coastal plain. The deep buried valley of the River Adur records a subsequent period of lowered sea level. In Flandrian times the progressive rise of sea level has resulted in the silting up of this channel.

Structurally, the district lies near the southern margin of the Wealden Basin which was formed in Triassic times in response to crustal extension. In the Jurassic, downwarp of the basin permitted almost continuous deposition of marine sediments. The southern limit of this trough, which is probably fault-bounded, is difficult to define precisely. It is likely that a structural high, the Portsdown–Paris Plage ridge, which lies near and parallels the Sussex coast, had considerable influence on sedimentation at times.

Faulting and localised structural warping evidently affected the Wealden Basin after late Jurassic times, but in the late Cretaceous the downwarping ceased and more positive movements initiated the 'inversion' of the basin which culminated during the Miocene and formed the anticlinorial dome structure. The structures observed at the surface are probably weak reflections of features present in the Palaeozoic basement.   RDL

PREVIOUS RESEARCH

Aspects of the geology of the district have attracted the attention of geologists from an early date. Gideon Mantell, perhaps best known for his discovery of the dinosaur *Iguanodon*, made his home in Brighton for a short time and many of his works refer to the present district (1818 to 1836). Other early general references to the district are made in Dixon's publications (1850; 1878), Martin's *A Geological Memoir on a part of Western Sussex* (1828), Topley's *The Geology of the Weald* (1875), and papers by Howell (1873; 1878). Allen (1949 and later papers) has made an important study of the Wealden Beds. The Weald Clay of the whole of the southern Weald was discussed by Reeves (1949; 1958) and notable accounts of the Lower Greensand and Gault were given by Jukes-Browne and Hill (1900), Kirkaldy (1935; 1937), Casey (1961) and Owen (1971; 1975). Many important works on the Chalk contain references to the district. Of particular interest are those by Mantell (1822; 1846), Barrois (1876), Rowe (1900), Jukes-Browne and Hill (1903; 1904), Gaster (1924 to 1951), Kennedy (1969) and Mortimore (1979). The Tertiary deposits were briefly mentioned by Prestwich (1854) and more recently Thomas and Gray (1974) have described the concealed outcrop beneath Shoreham Harbour.

The drift deposits of the coastal plain have been studied by Godwin-Austen (1857), Reid (1892), Edmunds (1930) and Hodgson (1964; 1967), and several authors, including Prestwich (1859), Chapman (1900), E.A. Martin (1929) and Smith (1936), have concentrated on the Brighton Raised Beach. Geomorphological studies of the district include accounts by Bull (1936), Kirkaldy and Bull (1940) and Wooldridge and Linton (1955).

The original Brighton and Worthing memoir by H.J.O. White was published in 1924.   BY

CHAPTER 2

Concealed formations

Within the district only one borehole has penetrated beneath the oldest rocks now exposed at the surface. This is the Henfield Borehole [1799 1457], drilled by the D'Arcy Exploration Company in 1936–37 (Lees and Cox, 1937; Taitt and Kent, 1958). Only short intervals were cored and the description and interpretation of much of the sequence are based on rock cuttings (Figure 3). The sequence penetrated can be summarised as follows:

	Thickness m*	Depth m*
CRETACEOUS		
Weald Clay	71.6	71.6
Tunbridge Wells Sand	80.8	152.4
Wadhurst Clay	42.7	195.1
Ashdown Beds	about 148.1	about 343.2
JURASSIC		
Purbeck Beds	about 95.7	438.9
Portland Beds	29.9	468.8
Kimmeridge Clay	about 323.2	about 792.0
Corallian Beds	about 138.0	about 930.0
Oxford Clay	about 119.7	1049.7
Kellaways Beds	11.0	1060.7
Great Oolite limestones and		
?Cornbrash	67.1	1127.8
Fuller's Earth	35.9	1163.7
Inferior Oolite	about 84.3	about 1248.0
Upper Lias	about 62.0	about 1310.0
Middle Lias	about 33.0	about 1343.0
Lower Lias	about 147.5	1490.5
?Late Triassic to early		
Jurassic rocks (see below)	65.5	1556.0

The borehole commenced in Weald Clay and was continued into beds thought, in 1937, to be of Carboniferous age but later re-identified (see below). In this chapter only those formations below the Wadhurst Clay are discussed; the higher beds crop out in the district and will be dealt with in the appropriate sections on later pages.

?LATE TRIASSIC TO EARLY JURASSIC ROCKS

The beds below 1490.5 m were originally considered to be Upper Carboniferous(?) in age down to 1542.3 m and Lower Carboniferous(?) below that depth (Pringle and Stubblefield, *in* Lees and Cox, 1937; Taitt and Kent, 1958; Falcon and Kent, 1960). However, the revised determinations of plant remains from 1505.7 to 1506.0 m and the evidence afforded by miospores recovered from 1505.9 to 1522.8 m indicate a 'Rhaeto-Liassic' or late Triassic to early Jurassic age

(Chaloner, 1962). The only macrofossils from below 1522.8 m are from limestone clasts derived from Palaeozoic strata.

The borehole was ended at a depth of 1556 m, having touched a dark red shaly clay of unknown age (Figure 3). Overlying this was a breccia, 1.8 m thick, composed of angular fragments of chalcedony, dolomite, oolitic limestone and limestones containing the compound corals *Alveolites* and *Thamnopora*, brachiopods (*Ambocoelia?*, *Martiniopsis?* and *Tylothyris?*), possible gastropods and crinoid debris. Dr D. E. Butler has reported that the coral genera are common in Britain in the Middle and early Upper Devonian, although quite long ranging, and that a late-Devonian or Carboniferous age is suggested by the whole fauna. Dr A. R. E. Strank has identified foraminifera including *Nodosarchaediscus sp.* and *Archaediscus grandiculus* and the alga *Koninckopora inflata* which suggest a Holkerian (Lower Carboniferous) age for some of the limestone fragments.

This breccia is overlain sharply at 1554.2 m by a conglomerate composed of large limestone cobbles and pebbles, much resembling the underlying bed, in a matrix of red marl. Thin limestone beds, or very large cobbles, occur within the conglomerate. Above this a pale brown fine-grained crystalline limestone some 6.7 m thick was penetrated, which was likened to the Viséan limestones recorded in the Penshurst Borehole (Taitt and Kent, 1958, p.37). At Henfield the limestone exhibits red staining in its top part and includes streaks of maroon marl. It is overlain by 3.0 m of red, green and brown marl with a sharply marked top, so forming a fining-upwards rhythm.

The beds between 1522.5 m and 1539.2 m form another rhythm, with breccia overlain by variegated marls, clay with plant fragments and a marine grey shale (Figure 3). The basal unit comprises 0.6 m of breccia, with angular fragments of cherty limestone and red marl in a calcareous matrix. The topmost bed is 0.6 m of grey shale with argillaceous limestone nodules; it has yielded diademopsid spines and bivalves including *Modiolus* cf. *minimus* and *M.* cf. *laevis*, and the gastropods *Neridomus?* and *Promathildia?*, which suggest a late Rhaetian or early Jurassic age.

Between 1506 and 1522.5 m there is a similar rhythmic sequence (Figure 3). This rhythm is cross-bedded in part and plant fragments which include *Equisetites* cf. *grosphodon* occur at about 1508 m (Chaloner, 1962). Between 1490.5 and 1506 m a further rhythm occurs, although the sequence is finer in grade. A thin limestone conglomerate (0.3 m thick) at the base is followed by a grey-brown shale with plant fragments and also a grey silty limestone at 1503.6 m which yielded the rhynchonellid *Calcirhynchia calcaria*, so indicating a Hettangian or early Sinemurian age. However, the overlying beds are logged as 2.4 m of pale red and green gritty sandstone, followed by about 11 m of red, purple and dark green marl and greenish grey clay indicating a significant terrestrial influence. These beds have not been given a

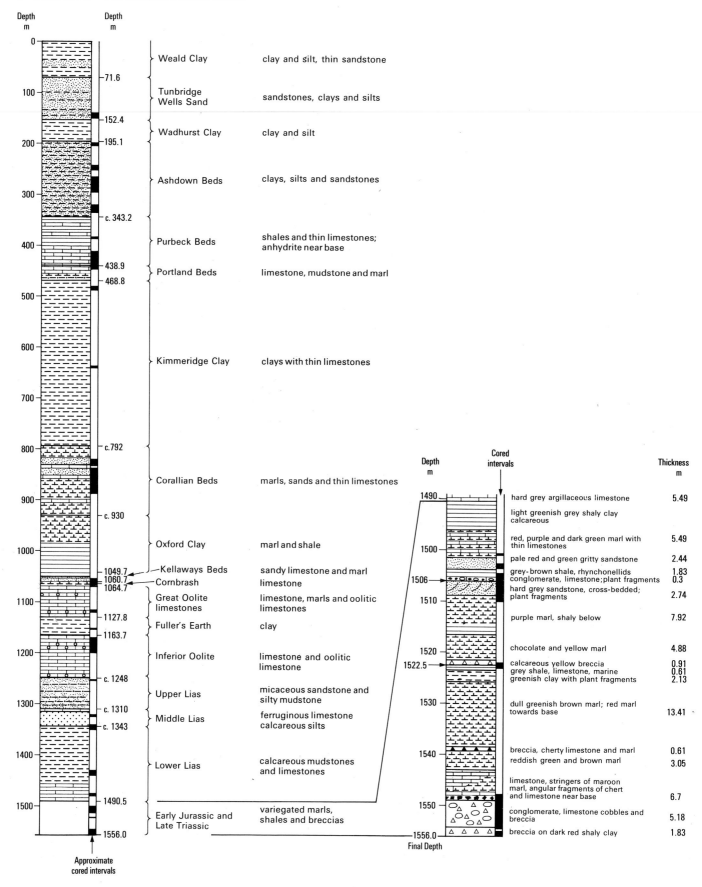

Figure 3   The lithological sequence proved in the Henfield Borehole (after Taitt and Kent, 1958)

formal name but lithologically they are distinct from the Lower Lias. Traces of them have been found in other boreholes in Surrey and Sussex. A palynological study of the beds below 1490.5 m has been made by Dr G. Warrington, following earlier work by Chaloner (1962). Dr Warrington reports a profuse and varied assemblage of miospores with some acritarchs from material labelled 1503 m. The acritarchs are indicative of a marine depositional environment; the miospores are dominantly bisaccates, but *Chasmatosporites magnolioides*, *Classopollis torosus*, *Leptolepidites argenteaeformis*, *Lycopodiacidites rugulatus*, *Osmundacidites wellmanii*, *Quadraeculina anellaeformis*, *Retitriletes austroclavatidites* and *Tsugaepollenites mesozoicus* are also present. Miospores including *O. wellmanii* and *Kraeuselisporites reissingeri* were recovered from 1508.5 m and a sample from about 1522.8 m yielded *C. torosus* with sporadic *C. magnolioides*, *Alisporites spp.*, and *?Q. anellaeformis*. By comparison with the succession of palynomorphs known from the late Triassic to early Jurassic sequence in west Somerset (Warrington, 1983) the assemblage from 1503 m indicates a Sinemurian, possibly post-*Arietites bucklandi* Zone, age, and those from 1508.5 m and about 1522.8 m are indicative of the presence of beds of Sinemurian to late Rhaetian age to the latter depth.

Fourteen samples were examined by Dr Warrington from lower beds (1523.1, 1523.4 and 1547.8 to 1555.4 m). Poorly preserved and indeterminate bisaccate miospores from 1549.6 to 1551.7 m may indicate a post-Carboniferous age, but simple laevigate trilete spores from between 1547.8 and 1554.5 m are of no stratigraphic value; some, from 1549.6 to 1550.6 m, are dark and may be reworked.

LIAS

The calcareous mudstones and limestones found above 1490.5 m show that a marine facies was firmly established and these rocks may be referred to the Lower Lias. A short length of core from between 1475.2 and 1476.7 m shows two non-sequences. A pale grey, very calcareous mudstone at 1476.3 m is overlain by a grey, calcareous mudstone with a basal layer of mud pellets. Above, pale grey limestones contain a grey conglomerate at 1475.5 m, with lignite and pyritous shale clasts in a limestone matrix. The fauna from this core includes fragments of a terebratuloid and the bivalves *Camptonectes?*, *Cardinia?*, *Gryphaea sp.*, ostreids and *Plicatula*; it is not diagnostic of age but may be Lower Sinemurian. Chaloner (1962, p.17) recorded the leaves of *Cheirolepis* (now *Hirmeriella*) *muensteri* at 1475 m and also at 1505 m.

The beds between 1408.2 and 1450.8 m comprise marls and clays with limestone beds. The grey, calcareous, slightly pyritic mudstones, with some silty limestones were cored between 1432.2 and 1436.5 m. They yielded a macrofauna of *Asteroceras obtusum* Zone age, including *Lingula sp.*, *Cuneirhynchia* cf. *oxynoti*, *Zeilleria?*, *Spiriferina verrucosa*, *Camptonectes sp.*, *Chlamys sp.*, *Gryphaea sp.*, *Modiolus sp.*, ostreids, *Pholadomya sp.*, *Plagiostoma sp.*, *Protocardia sp.*, *Pseudolimea sp.*, *Pseudopecten sp.*, *Aegasteroceras sp.* (at 1432.7 m), *Promicroceras?* (at 1434.4 m), belemnite fragments and *Promathildia?*. Above are dark silty marls with some limestone bands up to about 1408 m, and then dark shaly clays with a few bands of ferruginous nodules.

With the recent identification of an *Androgynoceras (Oistoceras) sp.* in grey mudstones at 1344.7 m, the *oistoceras figulinum* Subzone of the *Prodactylioceras davoei* Zone is proved, and the top of the Lower Lias lies between this level and the earliest Middle Lias fossil in the same core sequence at 1342.3 m (see below). The core between 1344.7 and 1346 m also yielded *Cardinia?*, *Modiolus sp.*, *Nuculana (Ryderia)* cf. *graphica* and *Palaeoneilo sp.*

Very little core or faunal evidence is available from the rocks attributed to the Middle Lias. The *Amaltheus stokesi* found in grey, slightly calcareous mudstone at 1342.3 m establishes the oldest subzone of the *Amaltheus margaritatus* Zone. Immediately above is up to 1 m of red-brown limestone, limestone containing pebbles of grey, burrowed limestone and also some ferruginous rubbly limestone with *Amaltheus sp.* at 1340.5 m and echinoderm and terebratuloid fragments, *Camptonectes sp.*, *N. (Ryderia) graphica* and a crustacean (*Eryma?*). The highest part of this core (1339.6 to 1340.5 m) is of finely silty and micaceous limestone; these lithologies are also logged as occurring above to a higher core (1320.2 to 1322.7 m) which was of dark grey micaceous mudstone and siltstone, locally purplish-stained, but yielding no macrofossils. At 1320.2 m the core is rather slickensided and contains small pebbles including 'pinkish' limestone fragments and fragments of serpulids and belemnites, against a slightly irregular surface which could be either erosional or faulted. The matrix also yields crinoid fragments and a *Gibbirhynchia*; this rhynchonellid is dominantly an Upper Pliensbachian genus but can occur in the Toarcian. The top of the Middle Lias has been taken at 1310 m, at a bed recorded as dark sandy limestone, so that all the silty marls and siltstones are referred to this unit.

The 'Upper Lias' is logged as dark grey, shaly clays and micaceous marls, silts and fine-grained sandstones, passing up into cross-bedded, micaceous, calcareous sandstones. A length of core (1247.2 to 1252.1 m) in the sandstones yielded *Lingula sp.*, *Camptonectes sp.*, *Meleagrinella sp.*, *Myophorella sp.*, *Oxytoma?*, *Propeamussium sp.* and ostreids. These are not diagnostic of age but similar beds in the Portsdown Borehole are of both late Toarcian and Aalenian age.

INFERIOR OOLITE

The 'Lower Inferior Oolite' of Taitt and Kent (1958, p.30) was not cored but was logged as grey micaceous sandstone overlain by pale brown, fine-grained limestone, oolitic limestone and oolitic marl. These were in turn overlain nonsequentially by ferruginous oolite, white, brown and grey, fine-grained oolites and a coarse shelly limestone which Taitt and Kent compared to the Middle Inferior Oolite although no palaeontological evidence of age was available. The Upper Inferior Oolite was cored and as the brachiopods between 1166.5 and 1169 m include *Stiphrothyris tumida*, *Acanthothyris spinosa* and *Sphaeroidothyris sphaeroidalis*, this indicates that all the limestones up to 1163.7 m may be late Bajocian in age. The underlying lithologies are buff-grey calcarenitic and locally oolitic or shell-fragmental limestones with a sparse macrofauna including echinoderm fragments, *Camptonectes sp.*, *Modiolus sp.*, ostreids, *Propeamussium (Parvamussium) sp.* and *Pseudolimea sp.*, above an horizon with pebbles of raggy and oolitic limestone; the latter rests on an erosion surface at 1199.0 m, so that the Upper Inferior Oolite is about 35.3 m thick.

FULLER'S EARTH

Although Taitt and Kent (1958, p.25) correlated the strata of Bathonian age with various named beds in the Great Oolite of the north Cotswolds, little material is now available to confirm this and a bipartite division into a lower unit of Fuller's Earth (of lower to middle Bathonian age) and an upper unit of Great Oolite limestones (late Bathonian) is used here.

The Fuller's Earth contains a lower unit of 4.9 m of soft dark clays overlain by 8.6 m of rubbly limestone and 22.9 m of dark silty clay. A core (1151.8 to 1153.0 m) from the limestone unit consists of grey argillaceous limestone with *Rhynchonelloidella wattonensis*, *Camptonectes sp.* and a gervillellid fragment. Muir-Wood (1936, p.62, and *in* Taitt and Kent, 1958, p.27) regarded *R. wattonensis* as indicative of the Fuller's Earth Rock and the top of the Lower Fuller's Earth. Penn (*in* Penn and others, 1979) also found this species principally in the Fuller's Earth Rock of the Bath–Frome area, so these limestones may also be of similar age and the overlying silty clays may be Upper Fuller's Earth Clay, contrary to the view of A. J. Martin (1967).

GREAT OOLITE LIMESTONES AND ?CORNBRASH

The Upper Fuller's Earth Clay is overlain at 1127.8 m by 7.6 m of dark grey, fine-grained, sandy limestones passing up into 4.6 m of pale grey oolitic limestones, rich in echinoid fragments. A core of the latter (1115.5 to 1121.6 m) shows pale grey, shell detrital and oolitic limestone with echinoderm and ostreid fragments. It is overlain by 21.3 m of fine-grained oolite, 8.5 m of soft white oolitic marl and 17.4 m of alternating grey oolitic and shelly limestones and marls capped by a green clay. No fauna was recovered from these limestones.

Core was taken between 1060.7 m to 1067.7 m. The lowest part of this sequence was described as cross-bedded, white oolite and contains shell detrital and oolitic limestones with a non-diagnostic fauna including terebratuloid fragments, *Corbula?*, *Limatula?*, ostreids and *Procerithium sp.* Between 1063.4 and 1064.7 m dark grey silty limestones rest non-sequentially on the oolitic limestones and these have yielded *Kallirhynchia?*, *Rhynchonelloidella sp.*, *Avonothyris?*, terebratuloid fragments, *Camptonectes sp.*, *Entolium corneolum*, *Meleagrinella sp.* and ostreids which only indicate a ?late Bathonian age. The *Kutchithyris* cf. *fulva* and *Cryptorhynchia bradfordensis* cited by Taitt and Kent (1958, p.24) as indicating a Bradford Clay fauna in a bed grading into Upper Cornbrash have not been found but the evidence for their being derived into the Cornbrash is unconvincing. The highest part of this unit (1060.7 to 1063.4 m) was described as 'massive' limestone; it contains some grey silty limestone beds, and locally rubbly and shell-fragmental beds. Only a sparse macrofauna is now available, comprising echinoderm fragments, a terebratuloid (*Cererithyris?* or *Obovothyris?*),

Camptonectes sp., *E. corneolum* and small ostreids. This bed may be of Cornbrash or older age.

KELLAWAYS BEDS

The specimens from 1054.0 to 1060.7 m show about 4.3 m of dark grey argillaceous limestone or slightly silty marl with *Mesosaccella.?*, *Modiolus* (several), *Pseudolimea*, *Thracia depressa*, crustacean fragments and pyritised trails, and harder concretionary layers and septarian limestone (Kellaways Clay), overlain by about 2.4 m of bioturbated, burrow-mottled, pale and dark grey calcareous sandstone, with muddy wisps, laminae and burrow-fills, and fossils including small oysters (cf. *Catinula alimena*), *Anisocardia?*, shell fragments including *Myophorella* and rhynchonellid brachiopods, and pyritised trails (Kellaways Rock). Ammonite fragments (*Macrocephalites?*) occur at 1058.6 m and 1059.2 m. Taitt and Kent (1958, p.24) recorded 'numerous light brown phosphatic nodules' from this level and at 1057.8 m there is a cream-coloured phosphatic shell-infilling. Finely disseminated pyrite and partially pyritised fossils and concretionary masses also occur. These may indicate the lower and phosphatic facies of the Kellaways Clay (Callomon, 1955, p.246; 1968, p.270) which belongs to the *Macrocephalites macrocephalus* Zone, *M. kamptus* Subzone, of the Lower Callovian. The highest part of the Kellaways Rock sequence was not cored but according to Taitt and Kent (1958, p.24) it consisted of '[4.3 m] of light grey calcareous sandstone, with clay partings in the lower part'.

OXFORD CLAY

No core was taken in the Oxford Clay and only small fossils or fossil fragments extracted from the rock cuttings are now available. They include tiny pyritised perisphinctid nuclei, *Cardioceras* inner whorls and a *Peltoceras* nucleus; an ammonite spine or tubercle fragment (maybe of *Peltoceras*); tiny bivalves including *Corbulomima*; tiny gastropods including *Chemnitzia?*, *Dicroloma*, *Procerithium?*; and a pyritised crustacean fragment. The specimens of *Cardioceras*, indicative of the Lower Oxfordian *Quenstedtoceras mariae* Zone are marked 1018.0 to 1018.6 m, 986.9 to 987.6 m and 973.5 to 974.1 m, and the whole assemblage is suggestive of the Upper Oxford Clay. If this were the case, the Upper Oxford Clay would have a disproportionately large thickness. Taitt and Kent's record (1958, p.23) of fragments of *Gryphaea* and a terebratulid fragment 'resembling *Aulacothyris*' from 990.6 to 999.7 m, which they suggested were 'reminiscent of the *Peltoceras athleta* Zone [Upper Callovian; Middle Oxford Clay] in the Midlands' (cf. Arkell, 1933, p.355; Neaverson, 1925, p.34), is *above* a sample containing pyritised *Cardioceras* indicative of the younger Upper Oxford Clay (Lower Oxfordian). Also included at 901.0 to 901.6 m is an iridescent ammonite fragment preserved in mudstone, ex gr. *Aulacostephanus eulepidus*, which is a caving from the much higher Kimmeridge Clay. There are thus some doubts about the stratigraphical validity of these specimens and no detailed interpretation can be attempted. However, from the specimens and Taitt and Kent's (1958) notes, it seems probable that a complete Oxford Clay sequence was present, ranging from Middle Callovian to Lower Oxfordian (inclusive), and that it was probably divisible into the three traditional divisions, Lower, Middle and Upper. The lower part of the sequence (about 42.7 m; assumed Lower Oxford Clay) consisted of 'dark and grey-brown shales' with a 'rich bituminous shale' near the base; the upper part (assumed Middle to Upper Oxford Clay) consisted of 'a uniform series of hard grey marls, with occasional septarian or ironstone nodules'.

CORALLIAN BEDS

The base of the Corallian Beds was fixed arbitrarily by Taitt and Kent (1958, p.23) at 889.7 m 'above the highest nodule bed of Oxford Clay appearance'. However, regional correlation of geophysical logs from other boreholes suggests that a depth of about 930 m would be more appropriate.

Coring began at about 820.8 m and continued with minor interruptions to about 887.0 m. In the beds below 877.5 m, the calcareous mudstones are shelly with partial pyritisation (including pyritised trails) and phosphatisation. The fauna includes the common bivalves '*Astarte*', *Corbulomima*, *Dacryomya*, *Entolium*, *Modiolus*, *Myophorella*, oysters (some in shell beds), *Palaeonucula?* and *Thracia*; echinoid (including cidarid) spines; *Dicroloma*; *Lingula* and serpulids. Perisphinctid nuclei or inner whorl fragments are also quite common.

At 877.5 m there is an horizon with marked chondritic burrow-mottling and a large fragment of lignitic wood.

In the beds up to 842.8 m, the specimens show about 35 m of more or less calcareous, medium and pale grey mudstone, with subsidiary cementstone bands some of which are nodular. The fauna includes the bivalves *Arcomya?*, '*Astarte*', *Camptonectes*, *Gervillella*, *Grammatodon?*, *Myophorella* (including *M.* cf. *clavellata*), nuculoids, oysters (including *Nanogyra*), *Pinna*, *Protocardia*, *Thracia* and *Trigonia*; the gastropods *Dicroloma*, '*Natica*' and cerithiids; a crustacean claw; brachiopods including a large specimen of the inarticulate *Discinisca*, and several terebratulids and rhynchonellids between 876.9 m and 877.2 m, and between 869.3 m and 874.5 m; serpulids; and other shell fragments together with pyritised trails. There are several poorly preserved and partially pyritised perisphinctid ammonites (mainly fragments or inner whorls) including a *Decipia?* at 873.6 m.

The next interval represented amongst the specimens (838.2 to 842.8 m) shows silty, calcareous mudstones with *Limatula?*, *Myophorella*, oysters, *Pinna*, *Trigonia*, crustacean and other shell fragments, and with partial pyritisation. These are overlain by about 2.4 m of grey hard calcareous sandstone or grit interbedded with siltstones and silty mudstones. The fauna in the latter lithologies includes fragments of *Myophorella*, *Nanogyra* and *Pleuromya* aff. *uniformis*, together with lignitic wood and plant fragments. Some of the fossils are preserved in dull brown pyrite and flecks and small fragments of similar pyrite are scattered throughout. There is bioturbation with muddy burrow-fills in the lowest beds.

The overlying beds (from 829.1 to 835.8 m), according to Taitt and Kent (1958, p.21), were 'hard argillaceous grey sandstone marly below'. From 821.1 to 827.2 m, the specimens show bioturbated siltstones, which are glauconitic in the uppermost 1.8 m, with subordinate thin cementstones

some of which are silty. The fossils include the bivalves *Entolium*, *Gervillella*, *Grammatodon*, *Nanogyra* and *Pinna*, a crustacean fragment, an ammonite (*Ringsteadia?*) at 821.1 m and scattered poorly preserved perisphinctid fragments, together with pyritised trails.

The top of the formation was taken by Taitt and Kent (1958, p.20) at 798.6 m, at an ill defined change in the rock cuttings from 'typical Kimeridge clay with cementstone bands to a hard micaceous marl'. They believed that specimens found in the rock cuttings from 808.3 to 813.2 m were the 'first fossils of Corallian appearance'. However all the specimens available from 804.7 to 814.4 m, which include fragments of the ammonites *Aspidoceras* and finely ribbed *Aulacostephanus*, almost certainly came from the Lower Kimmeridge Clay (*?Aulacostephanus mutabilis* Zone). These specimens cannot be relied upon as having been in situ, and so an arbitrary level at 792 m has been taken from regional geophysical log correlations.

The ammonite fauna of the Corallian Beds in this borehole is perisphinctid and poorly preserved. It allows neither recognition of a detailed ammonite zonation nor detailed correlation with other Oxfordian sequences in the Weald, where a more useful cardioceratid fauna occurs (for example at Grove Hill Borehole, Hellingly, in the adjacent Lewes district). Taitt and Kent (1958) believed they could recognise the divisions of the Dorset coastal Corallian Beds, and named them accordingly.

KIMMERIDGE CLAY

Tiny fossils and fossil fragments extracted from the rock cuttings between 764.4 and 790.0 m include iridescent fragments of finely ribbed *Aulacostephanus* (ex gr. *A. eulepidus*) and *Aspidoceras*, indicative of the Lower Kimmeridgian *mutabilis* Zone. Similar specimens, found between 808.3 and 813.2 m have been mentioned above.

A core run from 637.0 to 640.7 m shows mainly silty-textured calcareous or fissile grey mudstones with the bivalves *Corbulomima?*, *Liostrea*, *Nanogyra virgula*, *Protocardia morinica*; the inarticulate brachiopod *Discinisca*; the gastropod *Dicroloma*; faecal debris and shell fragments including the ammonite *Pectinatites*. The lowest specimen, from the base of the core, is a pale grey, fine-grained cementstone. The fauna indicates the Upper Kimmeridge Clay.

A second core, from between 481.6 and 487.7 m, shows more or less calcareous and shelly grey mudstones with the bivalves '*Astarte*', *Buchia*, *Camptonectes?*, *Grammatodon*, '*Lucina*', nuculoid?, *Oxytoma* and oysters including *Liostrea* (possibly in shell beds or epizoic on ammonites); brachiopods including *Rhynchonella* and a terebratulid?; and other shell fragments and debris. Ammonites, mainly fragmentary, include *Pavlovia* and pavlovids with common polygyrate ribs but without inner whorls visible; these are identified as *Virgatopavlovia?*. The fauna indicates a level high in the Kimmeridge Clay, and the sequence is assigned to the youngest Kimmeridgian zone of *Virgatopavlovia fittoni* or the next oldest *Pavlovia rotunda* Zone (Cope, 1978). Taitt and Kent (1958, p.20) recorded small brown limestone nodule casts of '*Pavlovia rotunda*' as caved material in later stages of drilling and concluded that these showed the presence in the Henfield sequence of 'rotunda nodules like those of Dorset' (rotunda Zone).

Two markers of stratigraphical interest can be picked out tentatively from Taitt and Kent's (1958, p.20) descriptive notes and figure. Between 587.7 and 598.6 m, rich bands of bituminous shale were recorded together with a specimen of the crinoid *Saccocoma* in cuttings from 596.2 to 597.4 m; these are suggestive of the oil shales which occur, associated with the Blackstone, at the *Pectinatites wheatleyensis – P. hudlestoni* zonal boundary. The 'Buff bituminous [limestone]' at about 551.7 m and the 'Brown bituminous argillaceous [limestone]' at about 536.5 m shown in figure 5 of Taitt and Kent (1958) are suggestive of the coccolith-rich bands of *P. pectinatus* Zone, the best known and lowest of which is the White Stone Band. This horizon has been recognised in boreholes in the Lewes and Hastings districts. These markers are well known in the Dorset coastal sections (Cox and Gallois, 1981). Although detailed information is not available, it is almost certain that a full Kimmeridgian sequence was present in the Henfield Borehole.

PORTLAND BEDS

According to Taitt and Kent (1958, p.19) the lower part of the Portland Beds (about 23.8 m) consisted of 'very calcareous sandy marl, with occasional limestone bands'. The base of the formation was taken at the base of the lowest distinctly sandy bed. This thickness, the greater part of which must belong to *Progalbanites albani* Zone (see below), seems rather great compared with other similar sequences known from the Weald (e.g. in the Fairlight [8592 1173] and Grove Hill [6008 1359] boreholes).

Only the uppermost part (about 6.1 m) of the Portland Beds, beneath the gypsiferous Lower Purbeck Beds, was cored. The lowest part of the core (about 442.6 to 445.0 m) consists of argillaceous and calcareous siltstones with shell fragments (some of which are encrusted with foraminifera) including *?Isocyprina (Venericyprina)*, *Isognomon* cf. *bouchardi*, *Modiolus* cf. *autissiodorensis*, oysters, pectinids (including *Camptonectes?* and *Entolium*); *Lingula*, rhynchonellid brachiopods (cf. *Rhynchonella portlandica*) and a fragment of a large ammonite tentatively included with *Glaucolithites*.

Above about 442.6 m there is about 1.8 m of calcareous and shelly mudstone with many bivalves and fossil fragments including *Corbulomima?*, *?Isocyprina (Venericyprina)* and ammonite inner whorls which probably belong to the genus *Epivirgatites*. The ammonites *Glaucolithites* and *Epivirgatites* suggest the *Glaucolithites glaucolithus* Zone of Wimbledon and Cope (1978), although the latter genus, together with the similar *Progalbanites*, is most common in, and generally taken to be indicative of, the underlying *albani* Zone.

The highest Portland Beds strata showed about 1.8 m of silty and argillaceous limestone with shell fragments including *Anisocardia?*, *Camptonectes?*, *Modiolus* cf. *autissiodorensis*, *Lingula*, and ammonite fragments identified as *Glaucolithites?* (Wimbledon, 1980, p.92; Wimbledon and Hunt, 1983, p.268). Small black ?phosphatic chips occur in the lower part.   BMC

PURBECK BEDS

The base of the Purbeck was penetrated at 438.9 m. The basal beds consist of impure limestones and marls with anhydrite beds and nodules in the lowest 16 m, though it is not possible to correlate in detail the evaporites at Henfield with those of the Purbeck inliers in the Battle area and the Fairlight Borehole.

The mudstones, siltstones and limestones between 404.7 m and 420.9 m yielded a limited macrofauna comprising the bivalves *?Corbula sp.*, *Protocardia purbeckensis* and *P. sp.*, and the isopod *Archaeoniscus sp.* This assemblage is probably typical of the Broadoak Calcareous Member (Lake and Holliday, 1978; Morter, 1984). *Archaeoniscus* occurs commonly in the 'Cypris Freestones' of the Lower Purbeck in Dorset.

Between 346.3 m and 390.8 m a sequence of grey marls, some bituminous, and shaly clays with subordinate limestones and calcareous sandstones was logged. Within this division, shelly limestones were noted in the lower part and dark grey argillaceous limestones in the upper part. No diagnostic macrofossils were identified from the cored interval between 382.5 m and 383.1 m and these beds probably fall within the Plant and Bone Beds Member. The marine interlude marked by the Cinder Bed Member was not recognised in the cuttings, but Taitt and Kent tentatively placed its base at 378.6 m in the borehole, within a sequence of argillaceous limestones and shales.

The various ostracod assemblages were described by Anderson *in* Taitt and Kent (1958), of which the 'Upper Purbeck' occurrences are now taken to represent the lowest Wealden beds (see below). A revised assessment, with ostracod zones, was given by Anderson *in* Anderson and Bazley (1971, Plate VI).

ASHDOWN BEDS

Taitt and Kent (1958) placed a rather arbitrary lithological Wealden/Purbeck boundary at 329.2 m, and this was taken by Howitt (1964) as the top of his Greys Limestones. However, the evidence from the late Dr F. W. Anderson's work on ostracods and the macrofossil assemblages (see below) shows that this depth is not the top of the Greys Limestones of Anderson and Bazley (1971) and Lake and Holliday (1978). In fact the mudstones present at this level are the upper clay division of Bazley (*in* Anderson and Bazley, 1971), and are now placed wholly within the Ashdown Beds (Wealden). (*See also* Anderson, 1985).

Between 328.5 m and 333.7 m mudstones, silty mudstones and occasional thin limestones yielded the bivalves '*Neomiodon*' *elongatus*, *Protelliptio (Pleisioelliptio)* cf. *porrectus* and *Unio* cf. *planus* and the common gastropods *Viviparus* cf. *cariniferus*. This assemblage shows a strong resemblance to the 'Upper Purbeck' faunas of Dorset, where *V. cariniferus* (= *V. sussexiensis*) is abundant and forms limestones. Only thin limestones are however present in this borehole. This cored portion of the borehole was placed wholly in the Upper Purbeck by Anderson and Bazley (1971 and notes) within the *Cypridea setina* Zone. The succeeding beds comprise clays, which are commonly calcareous, and thin limestones. Above

289.0 m, variegated clays and silts with sphaerosiderite dominate the sequence.

A specimen of '*N.*' *elongatus* was collected from 321.7 m and below 278.0 m mudstones with limestones yielded the bivalves '*N.*' *elongatus*, *Protelliptio* (*P.*) *sp.*, *P.* (*Plesioelliptio*) cf. *porrectus*, *Unio* cf. *compressus*, Unio aff. *cordiformis*, cf. *Unio planus* and indeterminate unionids, and the gastropods *Anisopis?*, *Viviparus cariniferus*, *Viviparus* cf. *cariniferus* (abundant), *Viviparus sp. indet.* (abundant), together with estheriids and fish scales.

Estheriids were obtained from argillaceous siltstones and mudstones between 199.0 m and 204.8 m, especially at 199.9 m. A medium-grained sandstone approximately 4.6 m thick has been taken as the top bed of this formation here. Parts of the Ashdown Beds have been proved in boreholes close to the Brighton district at Bolney [2800 2427] and Cuckfield [2962 2729]. The Bolney Borehole passed through the top and bottom parts of the formation but the sequence (about 82 m thick) is incomplete owing to faulting. Only the highest 41.7 m of the Ashdown Beds were penetrated in the cored borehole known as BGS Cuckfield No.1 (Lake and Thurrell, 1974). AAM

CHAPTER 3

Cretaceous: Wealden

In the Brighton and Worthing district and an area to the north, the Wealden succession is as follows:

	Thickness m
Weald Clay	172 to 275
Hastings Beds	
Tunbridge Wells Sand	
Upper Tunbridge Wells Sand	100
Upper Grinstead Clay	up to 11.5
Cuckfield Stone	8
Lower Grinstead Clay	0 to 6
Lower Tunbridge Wells Sand	27
Wadhurst Clay	54
Ashdown Beds	about 200

Within the district only one borehole, that at Henfield (p.5; Taitt and Kent, 1958), has penetrated the full thickness of the Hastings Beds, the lower, predominantly arenaceous part of the Wealden Series. There, 271.6 m of alternating mudstones, siltstones and sandstones are present in a sequence which, although it includes the main formations, is thinner and apparently overall more clayey and silty than that of the nearest outcrop. The Hastings Beds crop out only in the north-eastern part of the district, where about 400 m of strata are present (Figure 4). The Ashdown Beds do not crop out within the district and are described in Chapter 2. The remaining formations are poorly exposed and much affected by faulting, but individual sections can be matched with those of the adjacent Horsham district, where a complete sequence can be demonstrated. Beds ranging from high in the Wadhurst Clay up to the junction with the Weald Clay are exposed in a series of stream sections, old stone pits and road and railway cuttings around Brooklands Farm [320 217] and Folly Farm [324 218]. The strata in this block of ground are bounded on their northern side by the Sandrocks Fault and dip southwards at 8° to 10°.

The clay formations of the Hastings Beds are typically fresh- to brackish-water lagoonal deposits, whereas the Cuckfield Stone is apparently a channel-fill deposit (Allen, 1975; 1981). According to Allen's more recent model, the other thick arenaceous formations represent braided floodplain deposits which pass distally into a meanderplain of silts and clays. The source area for much of this sediment lay to the north in the London Platform.

The Weald Clay has an extensive outcrop in the northern part of the district. It comprises dominantly silty clays with thin beds of fine-grained sandstone, siltstone, shelly limestone and ironstone deposited in a lagoonal environment, subject to periodic brackish-water incursions, particularly in the upper part of the sequence.   RWG

OSTRACOD ZONES OF THE WEALDEN

Ostracods are the most abundant fossils in the Wealden Series and present such diversity of form that they have been used as a basis for its stratigraphical division (Anderson, 1940; 1985). In the Wealden, the ostracod genus *Cypridea*, which probably preferred mixohaline conditions, includes a large number of species and subspecies and so is ideally suited for the purpose. The stratigraphical divisions listed below are all recognisable by characteristic assemblages of ostracods named from species of *Cypridea*.

Zone	Lithological divisions
C. valdensis	
C. clavata	
C. marina	Weald Clay
C. tuberculata	
C. dorsispinata	
C. aculeata	Hastings Beds (Tunbridge Wells Sand including Grinstead Clay, upper and middle Wadhurst Clay)
C. paulsgrovensis	Hastings Beds (lower Wadhurst Clay)
C. brevirostrata	Hastings Beds (Ashdown Beds)

Of these zones, the *C. aculeata* Zone contains an ostracod fauna richer and more varied than in any other part of the Wealden. The eponymous fossil is a variable species and together with *C. recta* and *C. bispinosa* dominates the fauna. Other distinctive species, *C. arenosa* and *C. melvillei*, are also characteristic of the zone.

The sequence of ostracod faunas in the Purbeck and Wealden strata is characterised by repeated alternation between assemblages mainly composed of species of the genus *Cypridea* and those in which the dominant forms are species of genera other than *Cypridea*. In the latter case many genera are represented but few by more than two or three species. These variations in the composition of the fauna are thought to have been controlled by climatic factors, such as rainfall, which would have modified the salinity of the water in which the ostracods lived. These alternations, referred to as faunicycles, form a useful basis for correlation throughout southern England.

In the Weald Clay the faunas which favoured increased salinity comprise mainly species of *Miocytheridea*, and *Theriosynoecum*, whereas the other faunas (of *Cypridea*) form a rapidly changing complex, so that many of the faunicycles can be identified by the cypridean assemblage alone. In the Wadhurst Clay the non-cypridean forms include species of *Darwinula*, *Mantelliana*, *Rhinocypris*, and *Theriosynoecum*.

Detailed information on the Wealden faunas has been provided in Anderson (1962; 1985) and Anderson and others (1967).   RDL

WADHURST CLAY

The Wadhurst Clay consists of dark grey mudstones and pale grey silty mudstones with subordinate beds of siltstone, sandstone, shelly limestone and clay-ironstone. At the base of the formation, the Wadhurst transgression is marked over large parts of the Weald by a thin bed of pebbly sandstone or coarse ferruginous sandstone known as the Top Ashdown Pebble Bed.

Many of the mudstones are finely banded, owing to rhythmic variation in the coarseness of the sediment, which may have been caused by climatic changes. Siltstone bands

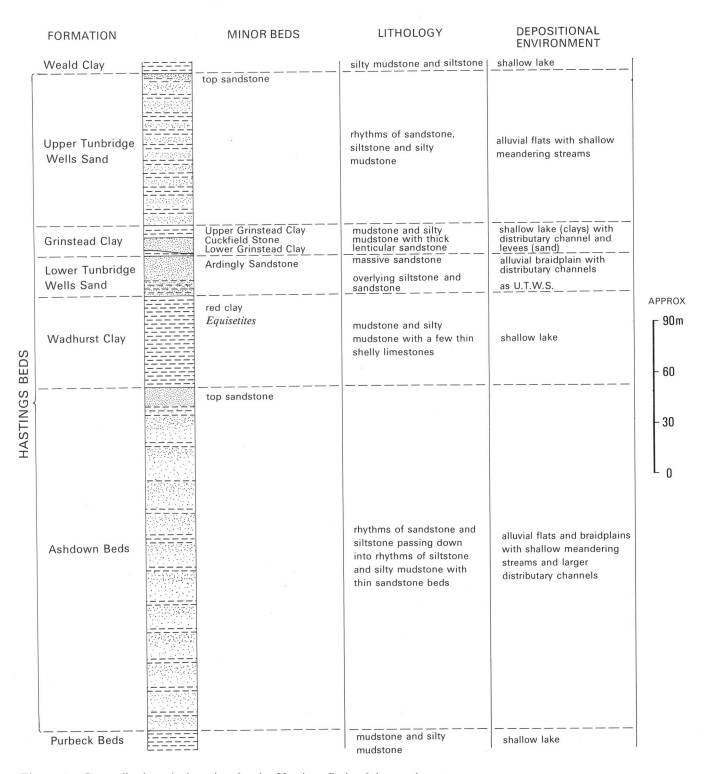

Figure 4   Generalised vertical section for the Hastings Beds of the north-eastern part of the Brighton district

occur throughout the sequence and are commonly calcareous and normally less than 0.1 m thick; these siltstones were deposited during times of greater current activity and in places the underlying shales were scoured to form groove casts and flute casts.

The brackish-water conditions of the Wadhurst Clay environment are reflected by the shelly fossils present: the non-marine bivalves *Neomiodon* and *Unio* and the ostracods *Cypridea aculeata* and *C. bispinosa* are predominant in the fauna, but gastropods also occur at some horizons. Winnowed accumulations of *Neomiodon*, and less commonly the gastropod *Viviparus*, form thin silty limestones with local concentrations of small phosphatised bone fragments, teeth and fish scales. Marsh-soil beds, crowded with rhizomes and rootlets of the horsetail *Equisetites lyelli* in position of growth, occur at several levels, notably in the upper part of the formation. A bed of red and green mottled mudstone up to 10 m thick commonly marks the top of the Wadhurst Clay and is a useful aid to field mapping.

TUNBRIDGE WELLS SAND

In the western part of the High Weald, the Tunbridge Wells Sand is divided into three, a lower and an upper sandy formation separated by the Grinstead Clay. In the Brighton and Worthing district, the Grinstead Clay itself is divided into lower and upper clayey parts separated by a sandstone, the Cuckfield Stone. A full sequence of the Tunbridge Wells Sand crops out in the north-eastern part of the Brighton district, but exposures are few and the outcrop is much disturbed by faulting. Outcrop and borehole data in the south-eastern part of the adjacent Horsham district suggest that the Tunbridge Wells Sand is about 150 m thick in that area. The fossils of the sandy formations consist mainly of poorly preserved plants. The fauna of the Grinstead Clay closely resembles that of the Wadhurst Clay, both in overall content and in the genera represented.

Lower Tunbridge Wells Sand

The Lower Tunbridge Wells Sand is up to 27 m thick and consists of interbedded siltstones and fine-grained silty sandstones overlain by a massive or thickly cross-bedded sandstone known as the Ardingly Sandstone. The latter is generally a distinctive clean white quartzose sandstone that forms small crags; locally it is more silty and less massive and gives rise to very steep slopes.

Grinstead Clay

The Grinstead Clay consists of mudstones and silty mudstones with subordinate beds of siltstone, clay-ironstone and shelly limestone, the last including one composed almost entirely of ostracod shells. The base of the formation is marked by a minor erosion surface and a pebble bed that is analogous to the transgressive base of the Wadhurst Clay. At its top there is a red-mottled clay like that at the top of the Wadhurst Clay. Thus the lithology of the Grinstead Clay is similar to that of the Wadhurst Clay, and only their relationships to the underlying and overlying strata make it possible to distinguish the two formations in individual sections.

In this district the Cuckfield Stone is a lenticular bed of sandstone, calcareous in part, that separates the Lower Grinstead Clay from the Upper Grinstead Clay. This stone was formerly extensively quarried at Cuckfield and in it Gideon Mantell (1822) first discovered the remains of the land dinosaurian reptile *Iguanodon*.

The thickness of the Grinstead Clay, including the Cuckfield Stone, is about 20 m in the Brighton and Worthing district. Of this, the lowest 9 m is made up of the Lower Grinstead Clay (up to 6 m) and the Cuckfield Stone (2 to 8 m), whose thicknesses vary in inverse relationship to one another. The thickness of the Upper Grinstead Clay typically remains relatively constant in the district at about 8 to 11.5 m.

Upper Tunbridge Wells Sand

The Upper Tunbridge Wells Sand is lithologically similar to the lower part of the Lower Tunbridge Wells Sand and consists of variegated soft mudstones, siltstones, thinly bedded sandstones and local clay-ironstones. The formation is poorly exposed in the district: its thickness is estimated to be about 100 m. No distinctive horizon is known within the formation and all the lithologies present are characteristically impersistent. The siltstones and mudstones commonly weather to red, grey and orange-mottled ('catsbrain') clays and silts.

The junction of the formation with the overlying Weald Clay is well defined at outcrop and is taken at the top of a massive sandstone that marks a change from the predominantly silty and arenaceous deposition of the Tunbridge Wells Sand to the silty and argillaceous deposition of the Weald Clay.   RWG

WEALD CLAY

The unweathered clay sediments of the Weald Clay are pale to dark grey, brown, greenish grey and red, but within the zone of surface weathering shades of yellow, buff and brown are assumed, owing to alteration of iron compounds; clays that are mottled red and green in the unweathered state tend to develop an overall deep red colouration, whereas 'catsbrain' mottling (weak red mottling on pale greenish grey) is assumed by some green clays.

The thickness of the formation probably ranges from 172 to 275 m in this district. A marked increase in thickness northwards has been demonstrated by Worssam (1978, fig.2). However, there are few reliable records of boreholes within the district and these figures are therefore approximations. The base of the Weald Clay is generally poorly defined and certain well logs may have included clayey transition beds of the Tunbridge Wells Sand in the Weald Clay. The top of the formation is typically marked by a sharp erosional contact with the Lower Greensand (see p.26).

The fauna of the Weald Clay includes ostracods, gastropods and bivalves. Ostracods are generally the most abundant fossils throughout the sequence and provide the basis of zonal classification (see p.12). Accumulations of the shells of the gastropods *Viviparus* and *Filosina*, formerly known as 'Paludina' and 'Cyrena' respectively, locally form shelly limestones. Large-'*Paludina*' limestone, also known as Petworth Marble, Sussex Marble or winklestone, is composed of closely packed shells of the globose gastropod *Viviparus fluviorum*; it typically forms the thickest limestones (up to 0.3 m) in the district and has been worked as a buildingstone in the past. *Filosina gregaria* and *Viviparus infracretacicus* (Small-'*Paludina*') are less common rock-forming fossils. Reptilean bones and fragmentary remains of fish and plants occur commonly in association with the arenaceous beds.

SUBDIVISION OF THE WEALD CLAY

This account follows the scheme adopted for the Haslemere district by Thurrell and others (1968, p.24), which was a modified version of that of Topley (1875, p.102).

The lithological marker horizons recognised within the dominantly clay sequence are as follows:

7 and above: alternating sands and Large-'*Paludina*' limestones
6 Large-'*Paludina*' limestone
5 Sandstone(s)
4 Large-'*Paludina*' limestone
3 Sandstone(s)
2 Small-'*Paludina*' limestones and '*Cyrena*' limestones
1 Horsham Stone

The distribution of these beds is shown in Figure 5. The Large-'*Paludina*' limestone units are individually restricted in vertical range, but the other horizons may comprise more than one intercalation within the sequence. To the east of Haslemere the sandstones are thick (up to 10 m) and form mappable units. Traced south-eastwards across the present district they become thin and impersistent. Farther to the east, in the Lewes district (Lake and others, 1987), the sands were difficult to trace and there marker clays, comprising red clays and greenish grey clays, were found to be mappable. In the present district, red clays are more common in the sequence but only certain marker clays have been locally depicted on the published map where other distinctive lithologies are absent. In other instances, clays which are solely greenish grey have also been shown as markers (see below).

A subdivision of the Weald Clay of Sussex by Reeves (1949; 1958) was based on the widespread occurrence of both red clay and 'catsbrain' horizons. This method of mapping met with criticism (Worssam, 1969) on the grounds that it gave only a rough indication of the stratigraphy and structure.

Lowest Weald Clay and Bed 1 (Horsham Stone)

The lowest beds of the Weald Clay of adjacent districts, seen in the Cuckfield No. 1 Borehole [2962 2729] (Lake and Thurrell, 1974), and in the Ripe [5059 1052] and Hailsham [5746 1083] boreholes (Lake and Young, 1978), consist of a monotonous sequence of alternating bioturbated and well laminated barren grey silty mudstones (65 m thick at the first locality). There is generally a gradational passage from the siltier beds of the Upper Tunbridge Wells Sand beneath. A prominent ironstone occurs 2 m below the Horsham Stone in

the Warninglid Borehole [2488 2701] (Lake and Thurrell, 1974), and this has been mapped locally.

The Horsham Stone is a flaggy calcareous sandstone up to 1 m thick, which splits into two leaves south and east of Christ's Hospital [148 285] in the Horsham district. An *Equisetites* soil bed has been recorded in the upper leaf from Slinfold [1253 3122] (Allen, 1959; 1975) and roots were recorded in the lower leaf in the Warninglid Borehole. The presence of *Ophiomorpha* at other localities in the Horsham district (Kennedy and MacDougall, 1969) may indicate brackish–marine conditions at this horizon.

Bed 2—Small-'*Paludina*' limestones and '*Cyrena*' limestones

Bed 2 comprises variably bioturbated, silt-laminated or homogeneous grey mudstones. The presence of the gastropod *Viviparus infracretacicus* characterises the succession, although it is rarely a rock-former at the surface in this district. The bivalve *Filosina* is also abundant locally and may form limestones. At Warnham Brickworks [174 350] near Horsham, clays with '*Cyrena*' limestones are overlain by 23 m of beds with Small-'*Paludina*' limestone. The bivalve *Cassiope* recorded in a '*Cyrena*' limestone at this brickworks (Worssam, 1978, p.17 and fig.5) indicates a brackish marine influence. A comparable thickness of beds with both *Viviparus* and *Filosina* was recorded in the Ripe Borehole. In the Hailsham Borehole *Viviparus* was noted in 49 m of beds, although the fossil was abundant in only 39 m of the strata.

Bed 3—Sandstone(s)

Bed 3 is characterised by thin sheet-like sandstones and associated red clays. The lowest red clay in the Weald Clay approximately coincides with the lower boundary of this sequence. The intervening grey silty mudstones seen in borehole samples show evidence of varying intensities of bioturbation and of channelling activity: silt-laminated beds commonly exhibit sharp, possibly erosional bases. Up to four mappable sandstones are present in this district, each up to 2 m thick; locally they are strongly ripple-marked and have a calcareous cement (see below). A borehole [1499 1868] 1 km from Dial Post showed these four sandstones in 12.2 m of strata.

Bed 4—Large-'*Paludina*' limestone

The gastropod *Viviparus fluviorum* apparently has a restricted occurrence in the Wealden, being present typically in well defined beds of the upper Weald Clay. This mode of occurrence may perhaps be related to its salinity tolerance, although it is known to occur in association with both *Unio* and *Filosina* (Worssam, 1978, p.7). In the Ripe Borehole, Bed 4 was a greenish grey marly mudstone 3.6 m thick with *Viviparus* and with strong red and brown mottling in the upper part. In the Henfield Brickpit [2197 1434] (see below) 0.54 m of *Viviparus*-bearing beds were overlain by more than 2 m of red-mottled clay. Generally the red mottling appears to be patchy at outcrop and where limestone fragments were not present in the soil this bed proved difficult to map. Locally, however, associated greenish grey or brown-mottled

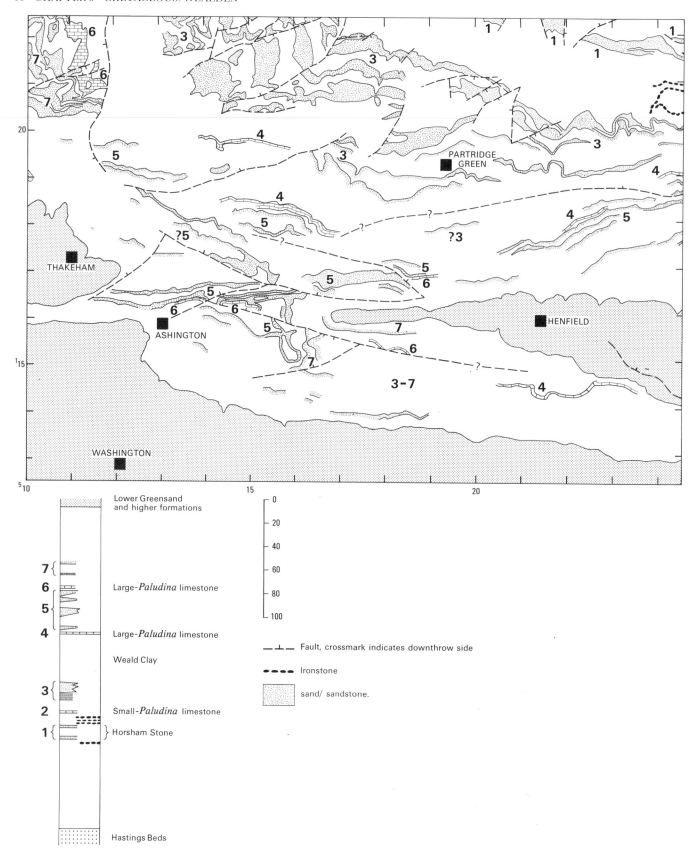

Figure 5 Distribution of the subdivisions of the Weald Clay

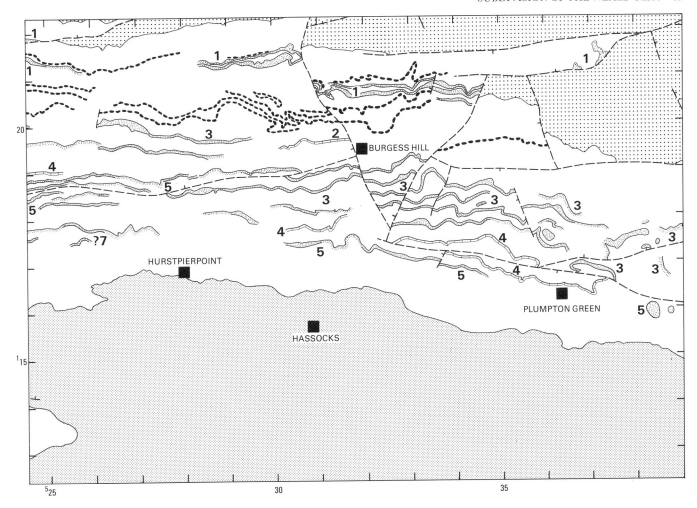

medium grey clays were augered which helped to distinguish this horizon. The evidence of ostracod faunas has confirmed that Bed 4 has been correctly correlated throughout the southern outcrop of the Weald Clay.

Bed 5 — Sandstone(s)

Up to four sandstones are present in this part of the succession within the district. They are commonly associated with red clays and locally pass into them. Whereas they generally consist of fine-grained sands and silts, the sands increase locally in thickness and grain-size, suggesting that both channel-fill and overbank flood deposits are represented. These sand bodies occur in some 30 m of strata in the Ashington area [13 16].

Bed 6 — Large-'*Paludina*' limestone

In the vicinity of Ashington [135 163], greenish grey clays with intercalations of Large-'*Paludina*' limestone have been shown to overlie directly the highest sandstone of Bed 5. Red mottling is patchily developed within these clays. It is not known whether *Viviparus* occurs widely at this level but locally clays with 'race' suggest the presence of calcareous beds. The limestones are common to the north-west of this district (Worssam, 1978, p.9).

Bed 7 — Sandstone(s)

Only one distinctive suite of rocks occurs within the grey clays that lie between Bed 6 and the base of the Lower Greensand. This suite consists of a red clay overlain by silty beds which in places contain sandy intercalations. Two sand beds have been mapped locally. In the Washington Borehole [1264 1345] brown and purple-mottled greenish grey mudstones are overlain by siltstones with a sandstone intercalation at a depth of 137.95 m. This horizon is 41 m below the base of the Lower Greensand. Higher in the succession fragmental bivalve limestones between 102.10 and 102.20 m depth are possibly equivalent to the shell beds noted in the Lewes district (Lake and others, 1987), where in the Ripe Borehole they contain a brackish-water fauna. A brackish fauna has been confirmed from the Thakeham Borehole [1084 1765] between 34.41 and 34.75 m depth, 0.9 m below the top of the formation. A comparable assemblage has been found elsewhere in the uppermost Wealden (White, 1921, p.6; Smart and others, 1966, p.48; Allen, 1976; Morter *in* Worssam, 1978).

Environment of deposition

The Weald Clay was laid down in shallow, fresh-water to brackish-water conditions. The sediments show evidence of cyclic deposition, reflecting the interaction of tectonic subsidence and sedimentation (Allen, 1975, p.412; Worssam, 1978, p.4). Worssam regarded the Weald Clay as comprising two megacycles, the lower characterised by '*Cyrena*' limestones and Small-'*Paludina*' limestones and the upper by Large-'*Paludina*' limestones. Brackish marine intercalations are present near the top of each megacycle. Smaller-scale cycles within the sequence show a rhythmic alternation of shallow-water deposits (sand bodies and red clays) and deeper-water deposits (shelly limestones) in periods of reduced influx of sediment (Worssam, 1978, p.5). This pattern is complicated however, particularly in the western Weald, by the interplay of fluvial and marine processes: much of the coarse sediment was derived from the west (see, for example, Allen, 1975, fig.3 and p.411), whereas the brackish-water clays are more common in the north-west Weald (Worssam, 1978, fig.5).

On the smallest scale, various idealised sedimentary cycles have been suggested by previous authors. In the Haslemere district, Thurrell and others (1968, pp.22–23) recognised the sequence:

Sand beds
—Sharp base—
Greenish grey clays with limestones
Grey clays
Red and grey mottled silty clays
Sand beds

In the Lewes district, Lake and others (1987) suggested the sequence of beds to be:

Sand bed
Grey silty clay, locally red-mottled
Red clay
Greenish grey to khaki, calcareous clay
Grey clays
Red and grey mottled silty clay
Sand bed

Allen (1975, pp.413–415, 419–422) has listed other examples of generally incomplete cycles, including for instance:

Clay
Erosion surface, locally with pebble bed
Sand bed, locally with *Ophiomorpha*, penetrated by rootlets

In the Brighton district there are few useful exposures but evidence obtained by augering suggests that red clays characteristically underlie many of the sand beds or interdigitate with them. Other red clays appear to be overlain with a sharp erosional base by silts and silty clays. Both examples indicate that the red clays reflect emergent conditions within the basin, followed by an influx of coarser sediment, locally with an intervening phase of erosion.

Whereas the ostracod faunas provide evidence of varying salinities within the basin, the macrofaunas cannot as yet be related to environmental conditions. It has been noted above that Large-'*Paludina*' has a restricted occurrence and Allen (1976, p.439) has suggested that *Filosina* is 'associated especially with early stages of brackish transgressions'. He further proposed that 'extensive developments of freshwater

Viviparus-habits . . . suggest facies-transgressions in a region remote from the sea'. Lake and Young (1978, pp.15–16) concluded, however, that the occurrences of Small-'*Paludina*' and *Filosina* are not comparable, even on a local scale, suggesting that they represent localised facies faunas and are not suitable for correlation purposes, other than in a broad 'zonal' sense. They considered that the occurrence of *Cyzicus (Lioestheria) subquadrata* (in the strata immediately above Bed 2) was more valuable for correlation purposes.   RDL

DETAILS

Wadhurst Clay

Deeply weathered grey and red fissile mudstones, disturbed by valley-bulging, crop out in the stream bed [3227 2229] north of Folly Farm. Siltstone casts of stems of *Equisetites* occur loose and have been derived from a nearby exposure. The junction with the Lower Tunbridge Wells Sand is obscured by a sandy and silty wash.

In the Henfield Borehole [1799 1457] 42.7 m of grey and green mudstones below 152.4 m which locally displayed red mottling have been assigned to the Wadhurst Clay. A red clay was observed at the base and a silty division about 4.6 m thick was recorded near the middle of the formation. At a depth of about 186 m fragments of *Cyrena sp.* were noted and ostracods identified from the Wadhurst Clay at Henfield include *Cypridea bispinosa*, *C. laevigata*, *C. menevensis*, *C. paulsgrovensis*, *C. tuberculata* and *Theriosynoecum fittoni* (Anderson *in* Taitt and Kent 1958).

Lower Tunbridge Wells Sand

About 1 m of thickly bedded fine-grained sandstone, close to the top of the Ardingly Sandstone, was exposed in the floor of the railway cutting [3255 2225] north of Folly Farm, and debris of similar lithology is common on the adjacent steep features formed by the Ardingly Sandstone.

Grinstead Clay and Cuckfield Stone

In the inlier north of Brooklands Farm [320 217] and Folly Farm [324 218] the Lower Grinstead Clay is typically grey, weathering to yellow and buff, but locally it contains nodules of brick-red clay-ironstone and is itself completely red stained. The Cuckfield Stone thickens rapidly eastwards at the expense of the Lower Grinstead Clay in this inlier. Cuckfield Stone debris is abundant along its outcrop, consisting usually of dark brown ferruginous-stained silty sandstone flags, and locally containing plant fragments and unionid bivalves. The Upper Grinstead Clay comprises grey clays passing up into red.

In this area a large number of old pits were dug through the Upper Grinstead Clay to work unweathered Cuckfield Stone for paving and roofing slabs, as well as marl from the Upper Grinstead Clay. Two quarries [3174 2224; 3193 2225] dug for Cuckfield Stone showed 1.4 m and 3.0 m respectively of trough cross-bedded ('festoon-bedded') fine-grained sandstone. The same stone was worked in several nearby pits [318 222 to 3235 2205] from beneath red clays of the Upper Grinstead Clay. Festoon-bedded Cuckfield Stone was well exposed in Rookery Lane [3247 2231 to 3236 2213] and in the adjacent railway cutting [3252 2219] near Folly Farm, where up to 6 m of sandstone was visible. The small inlier at Meadowland Farm [354 222] contains several pits dug for Cuckfield Stone, which here is up to 3.7 m thick and is overlain by about 8 m of predominantly red Upper Grinstead Clay.

Upper Tunbridge Wells Sand

East of the Garstons Farm Fault and between the Burgess Hill Fault and North Common, Chailey [390 210], sandstone beds within the Upper Tunbridge Wells Sand form a series of long dissected dip-slopes with the more silty and clayey beds cropping out in the valley sides.

East of Little Gravenhurst [273 221] and between the Burgess Hill Fault and the Lunce's Common Fault the top of the Upper Tunbridge Wells Sand is marked by a prominent thick bed of sandstone which is locally capped by a bed of very ferruginous sandstone or by clay-ironstone. A section at Bolney Mill Sluice [2632 2177], east of Garston's Farm, showed 0.9 m of khaki-brown fine-grained sandstone and siltstone with plant debris, close below the junction with the Weald Clay. Sandstone was probably worked in an old pit [2898 2230] at Leigh Manor; the adjacent roadside showed the following section in the beds immediately above the worked horizon, dipping southwards at 10°:

	Thickness m
Ironstone, limonitic, thinly bedded, sandy at base	0.30
Clay, silty, pale grey	0.05
Siltstone, pale grey, hard	0.30

An overlying sandstone was poorly exposed.

The road cutting [2963 2231] east of Leigh Manor showed:

	Thickness m
Sandstone, fine-grained, very ferruginous, with coarser lenses, flaggy	0.6
Beds obscured	0.6
Sandstone, silty, massive and thickly bedded, cross-laminated, grey with bright orange ferruginous staining	1.5

A section [3067 2168] in the top sandstone west of Hookhouse Farm showed 1.2 m of thickly bedded orange and grey silty sandstone, ferruginously cemented in part. Between there and the Lunce's Common Fault, the top sandstone makes a very strong feature, the dip-slope of which is littered with fragments of clay-ironstone and ferruginously cemented sandstone.

The steep, north-facing feature on the north side of the Townings ridge was referred to by Reeves (1953, pp.271–272) as formed by his 'Wivelsfield Sand', which he measured (presumably in the Slugwash Lane cutting, see below) as consisting of 28 ft (8.5 m) of sandstone and sand. The composite section given below encompasses most of the beds that crop out on this feature; it was measured in a cutting in Slugwash Lane [3492 2085 to 3496 2098] and an adjacent water-main trench [3503 2081 to 3495 2098] and totals about 19.8 m of typical Upper Tunbridge Wells Sand lithologies.

	Thickness m
Clays, silty, passing down into pale grey silts with thin beds of brown silty sandstone	about 3.7
Sandstone, silty, iron-stained, thickly bedded	0.15
Interbedded siltstone and silty sandstone, pale grey	0.6
Sandstone, silty, flaggy	0.2
Silts, mottled orange and pale grey, with interbedded thin silty sandstones	about 2.1
Sandstone, fine- to medium-grained, ferruginous, brown, coarsening downwards to a fine-grained pebble bed with mudflake pellets; erosive base and rolled flute casts and slump structures at base	0.5
Sandstones, silty, mottled orange and pale grey, flaggy bedded, with plant remains, irregular patchy iron-staining and shallow washout features	0.9
Interbedded pale grey siltstones and brown silty sandstones	about 3.7
Sandstones, silty, orange and grey, with plant fragments	0.6
Siltstones, clayey in part, mottled pale grey and red, with thin beds of silty sandstone	about 4.3
Clay, silty, brown	0.6
Sandstone, silty, fine- to medium-grained, brown and white, thickly and flaggy bedded, iron-stained in part, and with plant fragments	2.4
Fault (Holford Manor Fault)	
Weald Clay: shales, greyish green and brown, and soft mudstones; vertical dip	seen to 0.3

The top of the Upper Tunbridge Wells Sand is marked by a less well developed bed of sandstone, also locally capped by an ironstone, between the Wivelsfield Fault and the Strood Farm Fault north of Wivelsfield Green. Silty sandstones were noted in a road cutting [3487 2064] south of Townings, and in an old stone pit [3555 2048] at Strood Farm; west of the farm a section in a water-main trench [3530 2047] showed 0.05 m of clay-ironstone capping this sandstone.

A prominent bed of clay-ironstone, probably nodular, was traced by means of soil fragments, a feature and old workings, from a point [360 204] near Strood Farm to North Common, Chailey [379 210]. This bed is estimated to be in the middle part of the Upper Tunbridge Wells Sand. Large amounts of ironstone debris occur at Wivelsden Farm and a shallow pit there [3633 2069] may have been an opencast working. Similar shallow pits [3771 2076; 3770 2066] near Broadstone Farm appear to be entirely in siltstones but may have been dug for the ironstone; the feature and fragments can be traced from there to the Haywards Heath–Uckfield road [380 211], where the ironstone either dies out or is displaced by faulting.

A small roadside quarry [3752 2015] near Breens Cottages showed 1.2 m of flat-bedded, striped silts with small sandy washouts. Shallow pits in siltstone and clayey siltstone, possibly dug for ironstone, occur near Longridge Farm [3677 2034; 3713 2028], Townings Farm [3766 2016] and Leylands Farm [3812 2140].

Shallow pits [3867 2057; 3891 2083; 3900 2060; 3908 2081; 3908 2060] south-east of The Old Heritage showed only silts and silty sandstones, but they may originally have been dug for impersistent clay-ironstone seams at two separate horizons high in the Upper Tunbridge Wells Sand.   RWG

Weald Clay

Western outcrop: Thakeham – West Grinstead – Ashurst

The sandstones of Bed 3 have extensive outcrops between Shipley [145 218] and West Grinstead [173 207], broken by minor faulting. The wide outcrops of the individual beds reflect the dip-slopes present. Red clays are common, particularly below the sand bodies, and in places sandstone fragments in the soil are distinctly calcareous. Stream bank exposures of sandstones occur just east of Bay Bridge [1643 2070] near Knepp Castle.

The clays containing Large-'Paludina' limestone (Bed 4) are not generally distinctively coloured in the area between Lower Barn [1236 2010] and Dial Post [155 195]. Fragments of limestone and ironstone were present in the spoil from a water-main excavation [1222 2009] near Lower Barn, and red clay was augered slightly down-dip from here. The latter lithology probably gives rise to the break of slope present to the east between Lower Barn and Brookhouse Farm [1333 2005]. The mapped boundaries of this lithological unit between Bentons Place [1395 1975] and Dial Post are based largely on the presence of khaki clays. Limestone debris was noted at an old excavation [1428 1978] to the east of Bentons Place and in an old brick-pit [1435 1964] near Wickwood Cottages. Red-mottled pale grey clays apparently overlie the clays of Bed 4 near Dial Post.

Large-'*Paludina*' limestone of Bed 4 has been dug from pits [159 183] near Sand's Farm. This unit has given rise to bench features [163 182; 166 179] to the east of Eder Farm, where limestone brash is present in the soil. Elsewhere the outcrop has been traced by the presence of buff and greenish grey clays. A red-mottled pale grey clay caps these lithologies.

The succeeding Bed 5 consists of interbedded silty fine-grained sands and clays. The lowest sand bed caps the ridge to the north-east of Apsley Farm [117 194]. Red clays are particularly common beneath the second, more persistent sand bed to the south, which also forms an outlier at Gaston's Barn [145 191].

The sands of Bed 5 that are present in the tract of country between Goose Green [118 185] and Godsmark's Farm [1825 1680] are typically fine-grained. Red clays locally underlie all but the lowest sand bed. The road-cutting [1486 1795] near Woodman's Farm exposes 1.8 m of fine-grained sands dipping south at 8° beneath 1.8 m of ochreous pale grey clay. In the vicinity of Eder Farm [1580 1800] an apparent overall thickening of the sand unit suggests the presence of a channel-fill feature. A well [1782 1692] near Clayland Farm proved 22.9 m of Weald Clay, with sandy clay from surface to 6.1 m and sand from 21.3 to 22.3 m (in Bed 5).

Debris of Large-'*Paludina*' limestone (of Bed 6) is common in the soil in the Goringlee area [113 223]; fine-grained sands were augered locally in the beds below. In the faulted ground between Ashington [133 163] and Ashurst [176 163] two persistent sands are locally capped by clays with Large-'*Paludina*' limestone (Bed 6). These sands may be equivalent to the persistent uppermost two sands in the sequence immediately to the north near Coombewick. A well [1265 1640] at Ashington commenced in the clays between these two sands and proved the following sequence:

	Thickness m	Depth m
Clay, yellow	1.5	1.5
Clay, yellow, and brown sand (lower sand)	2.9	4.4
Sand, marl, clay and shale; with fossils from 15.5 to 16.8 m	26.7	31.1
Bed of shells and rock with fossils	2.4	33.5
Shale, blue	12.2	45.7

The penultimate lithology of this record is possibly the lower Large-'*Paludina*' limestone of Bed 4.

Large-'*Paludina*' limestone brash (Bed 6) was noted at two places [1350 1632; 1377 1637] near East Wolves Farm. Farther to the east, around Jessups Farm [158 161], sands are gently folded at the nose of the Henfield Syncline, but no evidence of the Large-'*Paludina*' limestone was found. Red clays above the higher sand (of Bed 5) to the south of the farm are capped by silts and very silty pale grey clays (Bed 7).

In the Bines Green area a shallow well [1875 1664] is reported to have struck two beds of Large-'*Paludina*' limestone at 6 to 10 m depth. New Barn [1894 1697], nearby, is built of dressed blocks of this material. Greenish grey and medium grey clays were augered to the north of the well, marking the limestone horizon. This unit is thought to be Bed 6 and overlies two sand beds separated by pale grey clays.

Clays probably somewhat higher in the succession are exposed in the brickworks [118 188] at Goose Green. The main face in 1978 exposed the following sequence below disturbed ground:

	Thickness m
Mudstones, silty, mottled ochreous and pale grey; passing down to	1.0
Siltstone, clayey, pale grey, laminated; passing down to	0.12
Mudstones, silty, mottled ochreous and pale grey, laminated	0.24
Siderite-mudstone, with an irregular base	up to 0.10
Mudstones, silty, grey, generally bioturbated; well laminated towards the base	0.7 to 0.8
Siderite-mudstone, impersistent	0 to 0.07
Mudstone, silty, grey, generally poorly laminated, bioturbated; siderite lenticles; ostracods in the upper part	0.5
Obscured strata	about 2.7
Mudstone, silty, grey, well laminated, with ostracod-rich partings	0.50
Siltstone, pale grey, weakly laminated	0.23
Mudstone, silty, grey, well laminated, slightly bioturbated	0.24
Siltstone, pale grey, laminated	0.10
Mudstone, grey	seen to 0.50

The overall sequence was affected by minor faulting and flexuring possibly related to nearby faults.

A well [1073 1861] at Goffsland Farm proved the following succession:

	Thickness m	Depth m
Made ground	0.8	0.8
Clays, blue, brown and grey	26.6	27.4
Clay, red	1.9	29.3
Clay, blue	12.8	42.1
Clay, red	1.5	43.6
Sand and stone	0.3	43.9
Clay, red	1.5	45.4
Clay, sandy	0.3	45.7
Sandstone and clay	3.7	49.4
Clay, sandy	2.1	51.5
Sandstone	0.6	52.1
Clay, sandy	seen to 0.6	52.7

The three sandstones proved probably belong to Bed 5, whereas the red clay beneath 27.4 m is considered to be that associated with Bed 7. A well [1131 1877] at nearby Laybrook Farm confirmed the presence of sands and clays of Bed 7 below 26.8 m depth.   RDL

The topmost part of the Weald Clay between 34.41 and 34.75 m in the Thakeham Borehole [1084 1765] yielded the following brackish marine shelly fauna: Bivalvia: *Corbula spp.* indet., *Pleuriocardia* cf. *ibbetsoni* (common) and *Pseudoptera subdepressa* (abundant on one surface at 34.62 m); Gastropoda: *Paraglauconia (P.) morteri* and *Paraglauconia (Diglauconia) fittoni* (abundant).   AAM

In the Washington Borehole [1264 1345] Weald Clay was penetrated from 95.63 m to a depth of 142.04 m, and consisted mainly of alternations of grey laminated silty mudstones and relatively massive strongly bioturbated mudstones. A few siltstone beds were recorded; these were mostly less than 0.2 m thick, but below 135.20 m they were up to 0.46 m in thickness. A fine-grained, silty, clayey sandstone 0.43 m thick and containing large partly pyritised wood and other plant fragments was recorded at 136.85 m. A mudstone between 138.70 and 141.50 m with brown and purplish mottling and rootlet traces at 140.75 m was near to seatearth in lithology. Throughout the sequence drilled, beds and partings rich in ostracods and fish debris were common locally. Bivalves were found between 97 and 105 m and between 124 and

129 m, and thin shelly limestones between 102.10 and 102.20 m. A specimen of *?Viviparus* was found at 101.97 m. Plant fragments were recorded at 135.46 m as well as in the sandstone at 136.85 m (see above).   TEL

Central outcrop: West Grinstead – Burgess Hill

Between the Bolney Fault and the Burgess Hill Fault, and between the latter and Wivelsfield, the Weald Clay sequence below the Horsham Stone appears to be unfaulted and can be divided into three parts. The lowest part is composed entirely of siltstones, the middle part of siltstones, silty mudstones and mudstones, and the topmost part predominantly of mudstones and silty mudstones, with subordinate amounts of siltstone, that weather to mottled brown and yellow silty clay. The more clayey topmost part has been worked extensively for brick clays, for example in Rushypit Wood [2956 2167], Kilnfield Pit [299 216] and at Lower Ridges [304 218].

At Bolney, in the Horsham district, the Horsham Stone (Bed 1) can be traced as two seams of sandstone separated by grey clays. Flags of laminated buff calcareous sandstone in a ditch section [2163 2227] at Eastlands Farm are within the upper stone seam.

The Horsham Stone outcrop has been displaced southwards by the Bolney Fault and has been traced from Bankfield Grange as far as the Burgess Hill Fault, where it has again been moved southwards. Between one and three stone seams are present, except in the area around Rice Bridge [266 211], where they appear to be absent or very thin over a distance of about a kilometre. Between the Bolney Fault and Coombe House numerous pits along the crest of the escarpment formed by one stone seam were probably dug for ironstone. A shallow digging at Coombe House [2481 2135] showed 0.1 m of calcareous sandstone set in grey clay. In the gap in the Horsham Stone outcrop near Rice Bridge, the ironstone bed below the Horsham Stone appears to continue without any break and can be traced by means of a continuous line of old pits running from Coombe House [2522 2136] to near Leigh Farm [2803 2155]. A thin, impersistent representative of one of the stone seams appears to be locally present.

Two stone beds are present between Leigh Farm and Lye's Farm where they cap a prominent feature. A small degraded quarry [2870 2123], in the upper stone seam, showed 1.5 m of pale grey silt overlain by 1 m of orange and dark brown decalcified sandstone. A similar section in an old quarry [2900 2137] near the base of the lower seam, 300 m east of Leigh Farm, showed 1 m of brown and orange decalcified flaggy sandstone. The lower seam has been worked from beneath a capping of clay in shallow pits [2967 2141; 2964 2132] at Paynes Place Farm, where the composite section is approximately as follows:

	Thickness m
Upper stone bed	
Sandstone, fine-grained, flaggy, calcareous in part, weathering to orange and dark brown	about 1.5
Clays, silty, and silts, red and grey mottled	2 to 3
Lower stone bed	
Sandstones, calcareous, flaggy, weathering to dark brown and passing down into less calcareous, orange and grey silty sandstones. An impersistent seam of mottled red and grey silty clay, up to 1 m thick, occurs locally within the sequence, separating the largely non-calcareous sandstones from the overlying calcareous sandstones	total about 3
Clays, stiff, mottled grey and brown	about 9
Clay-ironstone, impersistent, nodular	up to 0.1

At Lye's Farm several exposures showed southerly dips of 6° to 8°. The following section was measured in a quarry [3038 2169] that worked the lower sandstone seam:

	Thickness m
Siltstone, thinly bedded, with wisps of sand	0.3
Sandstones, thickly bedded, fine-grained, silty, cream- and orange-coloured, capped by ripple lenses up to 6 mm thick of coarser ferruginously cemented sand	0.6

A temporary section in a pylon foundation [3021 2159] at the farm exposed the following section:

	Thickness m
Clayey soil and subsoil	0.60
Clays and silty clays, mottled yellow and brown, weathered	2.70
Sandstone, fine- to medium-grained, brown, flaggy	0.66
Ironstone, sandy, deeply weathered, with ooliths of ?chamosite and limonite	0.02 to 0.05
Sandstone, as above	0.05
Clay, silty	0.15
Clay-ironstone, well bedded	0.08 to 0.13
Mudstone, silty, fissile, grey	0.50
Sandstone, silty, dark grey-brown, with plant fragments and disseminated carbonaceous material	0.30
Sandstone, white and orange, thickly bedded and flaggy, hard, compact, with plant fragments	0.90

In the area between Hickstead and Burgess Hill the strata between the Horsham Stone and the Small-'*Paludina*' limestone appear to dip regularly southwards at 3° to 5°, but there are few marker bands. Several well defined features trending roughly west–east coincide with the outcrops of discontinuous bands of clay-ironstone less than 0.1 m thick. The enclosing clays weather to mottled grey and brown, with at least one red and several grey silty horizons. It is possible that the ironstones are restricted to the more silty parts of the sequence and that these have given rise to the features.

White (1924, p.11) recorded 'Sussex marble' at St John's Common [310 195], Burgess Hill, and limestone is shown at this locality on William Smith's Map of Sussex (1815). A temporary trench section in Royal George Road [3013 1946], west of the common, exposed a bed of Small-'*Paludina*' limestone 80 mm thick. The occurrence in the Twineham (Great Wapses Farm) area of Large-'*Paludina*' limestone (see below) at what appears, on the basis of the regional strike, to be a similar stratigraphical level suggests that the structure of the area is more complex than that shown on the map.   RWG

In the area between West Grinstead and Partridge Green, the succession including Bed 3 is probably duplicated by unmapped strike faulting. Ripple-marked calcareous sandstone debris is abundant in the soil on a prominent dip-slope near Joles Farm [189 197] and this rock was formerly dug at the farm for walling material. Large flags of sandstone are present in a ditch-section [1852 1950] south-west of Jolesfield House.

The succeeding sand bed, which is present eastwards of St Michael's Church [189 194], Partridge Green, is apparently thinner and locally passes into silty beds. Red clays commonly underlie the higher sand beds which are present between Hobshort's Farm [165 191] and Cornerhouse [205 189]. A section [1762 1856] above the highest sandstone of Bed 3 exposed 1.5 m of medium grey clay with siltstone partings. This lithology is probably present throughout much of the sequence up to Bed 4; locally, however, slightly red-mottled clays occur.

South-west of Brightham's Farm [1945 1790] a sandstone forms a dip-slope feature overlying a red clay. To the east the sand possibly splits and locally peters out. Greenish grey clays were augered in the area [1975 1790] adjacent to the abandoned railway line and red clays occur extensively on the lower slopes to the south. Reeves (1958, p.12) noted the presence of 'Paludina Limestone' at this locality and inferred the presence of a fault, the Chesham Park Fault, nearby. Although no evidence for this major strike fault was found, this ground may be structurally disturbed and also affected by valley-bulging on the lower slopes.

In a ditch [2344 1983] at Frylands Farm, Wineham, yellowish fawn, fine- to medium-grained, massive sandstone within Bed 3, of which 0.4 m was exposed, was overlain with a gently undulating, possibly ripple-marked base by 1.5 m of fine- to medium-grained, flaggy sandstone. Iron-staining here emphasised small-scale cross-bedding in the flaggy sandstone.

A small and partly overgrown quarry [2192 1921] in the upper part of the river bank near Shermanbury Place exposed 1.3 m of friable, yellowish orange, silty, flaggy, fine-grained sandstone within Bed 3. Faint cross-bedding was visible in the lowest 0.3 m of the section. At Sakeham Farm, Twineham, the pond [2229 1905] was dug in the same sandstone and it was reported that gold-coloured sand was dug during the construction of the new barn nearby. The sand is approximately 2.5 m thick and contains a lens of grey clay; it is underlain by red clay.

To the south of the Sayers Common Fault, the following section (believed to be in Bed 3) was exposed in the west bank of the Danworth Lane [2871 1861]:

	Thickness m
Sandstone, very fine-grained, silty, pale grey and fawn, laminated; sharp base	0.25
Sandrock, pale yellowish fawn, massive; traces of lamination locally; sharp base	0.38 to 0.44
Sandstone, fine-grained, silty, brown, ferruginous; crudely laminated; passing down to	1.00
Sandrock, fine-grained, yellowish grey	seen to 0.8

In the spoil from excavations for a new electricity pylon [2468 1907] ESE of Great Wapses Farm, numerous blocks of Large-'Paludina' limestone (Bed 4) up to 70 mm thick were found, together with red and grey mottled clay and greenish grey clay. The limestone forms a distinct ridge feature between this point and Gratten Lane [2533 1907], where shallow pits [2506 1905; 2522 1906] may mark the site of workings for the limestone. A bed of Large-'Paludina' limestone, presumed to be at the same stratigraphical level, has given rise to a slight ridge feature to the east of Chestham Park [2185 1790].

A disused quarry [2115 1751], west of Chestham Park exposed 2.1 m of fine- to medium-grained sand and sandstone in Bed 5. Some small-scale 'herringbone' cross-bedding was noted in the top 0.3 m.   TEL

An old sand-pit [2995 1900] near Eastlands Farm, on the north side of the Sayers Common Fault, exposed about 1.5 m of yellowish fawn, fine-grained sand, believed to be in Bed 5. Fragments of dark brown, micaceous sandstone occur at the southern end of the pit but were not seen in situ.   BY

Central outcrop: Ashurst–Poynings

The structure and stratigraphy of the Weald Clay within the Pyecombe Anticline (Figure 24) is not fully understood., The problems are probably exacerbated by undetected strike faults and local steep dips. The Henfield Borehole [1799 1457], 450 m ENE of Calcot Farm, proved the sequence:

	Thickness m	Depth m
WEALD CLAY		
Clay, bluish grey with ostracods, silty near base	36.27	36.27
Sandstone, calcareous, very fine-grained, white (Horsham Stone: Bed 1)	0.31	36.58
Clay, bluish grey, silty near top; some brown ferruginous clay	35.05	71.63
TUNBRIDGE WELLS SAND	—	—

Dr F. W. Anderson reported that this borehole started some 20 m above the Cypridea dorsispinata Zone, that is in beds towards the top of the Small-'Paludina' limestones (Bed 2). It follows that the red clay marker horizon mapped adjacent to the borehole is the lowest horizon of Bed 3. To the south of the borehole site only one substantial sand body has been mapped within the Weald Clay. This sand forms a small scarp north of Huddlestone Farm [1800 1355] and has been traced for 1 km eastwards. Red-mottled pale grey clay underlies the sand bed and red marker clays have been mapped further north of it.   DM,RDL

A marker bed of buff and greenish grey clays mapped west and east of the Ashurst–Steyning road north of Horsebridge Common [183 153] may represent Bed 6. Slightly higher in the sequence, to the south and west of the Lower Greensand outcrop in the Henfield Syncline, a further red clay has been traced, overlain by silty or sandy beds; these beds approximately follow the line of the unnamed stream south of Pepper's Farm [1705 1590].   RDL

The Nep Town Borehole [2112 1562] at Henfield penetrated 72.55 m of Weald Clay beneath the Lower Greensand at 76.80 m. Much of the sequence drilled comprised alternations of massive, bioturbated silty mudstones and laminated silty mudstones. No sandstone or limestone beds were encountered.

The abandoned pit [2197 1434] adjacent to the disused Henfield Brickworks formerly provided good sections through the Weald Clay (Kirkaldy and Bull, 1937; Reeves, 1958; Milbourne, 1961). The pit was closed during the 1960's and has since been used as a rubbish tip. At the time of the survey (1975) the following section was measured in the north-eastern corner of the pit:

	Thickness m
Sand, fine-grained, silty, grey, micaceous, with some low-angle cross-bedding; some impersistent clay laminae near base	1.50
Sand and siltstone, grey and brown; some lignite near top	0.18
Sand, fine- to medium-grained, yellowish brown; locally well cemented and laminated in lower part	1.50
Obscured	1.50
Silt, clayey, yellowish brown, with pockets of lignite	0.90
Clay, silty, grey, with lignite and clay-ironstone nodules	0.50
Sand, fine-grained, silty, mottled grey and brown	0.30
Silt and clayey silt, grey and brown, micaceous	0.40
Clay, grey	0.15
Obscured	1.00
Silt and micaceous clayey silt, grey and fawn; ferruginous cement in top 0.2 m	0.30
Sandstone, fine-grained, pale olive-grey, well cemented	0.60
Clay, silty, laminated, grey, micaceous, with clay-ironstone nodules	at least 2.00
Obscured	1.00

Clay, grey, yellow-weathering, micaceous; locally weathering dark brown	1.20
Clay, mottled red and grey, stiff, with bands of clay-ironstone, passing down into grey clay	at least 2.00
Large-'*Paludina*' limestone	0.17
Clay, silty, greenish grey, with ostracods, impressions of *Viviparus sp.* ('*Paludina*') and indeterminate plant fragments	0.15
Shale, grey, with ostracods becoming more numerous downwards and occasional bivalves	1.80
Siltstone, grey, massive	0.23
Mudstone, silty, grey, laminated, bioturbated	1.70
Shale, grey, with occasional ostracods, bivalves and fish fragments	5.00
Siltstone, grey, finely laminated	0.30
Shale, grey, with bored calcareous siltstone nodules up to 0.1 m thick near base	0.80
Mudstone, silty, pale to dark grey, bioturbated, laminated, with calcareous siltstone nodules up to 30 mm thick at base	2.50
Shale, dark grey	0.50
Mudstone, silty, pale grey, bioturbated	1.20
Mudstone, dark grey, massive	0.30
Mudstone, silty, pale to dark grey, laminated	seen to 2.00

The beds dip to the north at 5°.

The following fish fauna from the clays immediately above and below the Large-'*Paludina*' limestone was described from this pit by Patterson (1966). Actinopterygians: *Caturus tenuidens*, *Clupavus sp.*, *Coelodus mantelli*, *Lepidotes mantelli*, *Pachythrissops sp.*; Sharks: *Hybodus basanus*, *H. brevicostatus* (holotype), *H. parvidens*, *Hylaeobatis ornata*, *Lonchidion breve breve* and *Lonchidion striatum* (holotype). Subsequently Hollis (1971) detailed a comparable fauna from this pit.

On ostracod evidence, Anderson (*in* Patterson, 1966) placed the Large-'*Paludina*' limestone at Henfield Brickworks at about 170 m below the top of the Weald Clay. Large fragments of pyritised wood have been recorded from the pit (Milbourne, 1961) and former workmen recall the finding of large bones, presumably reptilean, during 1959.

The Large-'*Paludina*' limestone exposed in the Henfield Brickworks pit forms a distinct ridge feature that has been traced eastwards along the northern limb of the Pyecombe Anticline as far as Bramlands Lane [2347 1435]. Blocks of the limestone occur in the soil north of Oreham Common [2249 1446] and at Bramlands Lane. The limestone has not been found on the southern limb of the Pyecombe Anticline, although 'winklestone' is said to have been encountered in a well dug at Catsland Farm [2339 1342] 1.3 km south of Terry's Cross.

Temporary excavations in the eastern bank of Clappers Lane [2488 1342] exposed up to 3.5 m of grey and fawn silty clays with sand-grade sphaerosiderite and occasional thin lenticular beds of grey, micaceous, silty, fine-grained sand.   TEL

Eastern outcrop : Burgess Hill – Plumpton Green

A section near the top of the siltstone beds near the base of the Weald Clay occurs in a waterfall [3195 2112] near Holmbush Farm, where about 5 m of siltstones and predominantly silty mudstones are overlain by weathered brown clay.

A number of temporary sections in pylon foundations proved up to 6 m of clays and silts in the long fault-bounded outlier of Weald Clay that runs from Lunce's Common to Teague's Farm. At each locality weathering extended to a depth of 3 to 5 m. The lowest part of the Weald Clay, consisting of pale grey and cream-coloured siltstones, silty mudstones and striped beds, was proved at six localities on the south side at Lunce's Common [3311 2142 to 3488 2134]. Poorly preserved plant fragments were the only fossils

recorded. Exposures at a higher level, up as far as the ironstone below the Horsham Stone, consisted predominantly of dark grey shales and silty mudstones with lesser amounts of pale coloured siltstones, and were recorded at four localities north of Wivelsfield Hall [3519 2133; 3552 2134; 3576 2135; 3610 2135]. Ostracods, worm tubes, fish and plant debris were common in the more fissile parts of the sequence at these levels; the last two localities yielded ostracods determined by Dr F. W. Anderson to be indicative of the Zone of *Cypridea tuberculata*. The mudstones and silty mudstones below the Horsham Stone have been worked for brick clays north of the Lowlands Farm to Lunce's Hall ridge at Goose Pit [326 211], Tile Barn [3315 2125] and Fatting Hovel [336 212; 339 212].

The precise stratigraphical position of the beds that crop out on the ridge running from Lowlands Farm to Wivelsfield and thence to North Common, has been the subject of some discussion. Topley (1875, p.98 and Old Series Sheet 9) considered them to be lithologically like the Upper Tunbridge Wells Sand and thought they might represent an unusual example of interdigitating on a large scale of the sediments near the Upper Tunbridge Wells Sand – Weald Clay boundary. White (1924, pp.12–13) agreed that they were Upper Tunbridge Wells Sand, but suggested that the ridge was separated from the Weald Clay to the north of it by faulting. Reeves (1953), using the name Wivelsfield Sand, considered that the ridge between Lowlands Farm and Wivelsfield was capped by a lenticular bed of sandstone within the Weald Clay; he suggested that this sandstone was 28 ft (8.5 m) thick at Wivelsfield and that it was faulted against Grinstead Clay and Upper Tunbridge Wells Sand near Wivelsfield Hall [357 208].

The results of the present survey suggest that all three interpretations are partly correct. Between the Burgess Hill Fault and Wivelsfield the outcrop consists of thin sandstone beds in an argillaceous sequence, at the same stratigraphical level as the Horsham Stone as suggested by Reeves (1953, p.274). The remaining eastern part of Topley's Tunbridge Wells Sand outcrop remains as Upper Tunbridge Wells Sand, faulted against the lower part of the Weald Clay on its northern side between Townings [349 209] and Teague's Farm [374 213]. The section recorded at Townings by Reeves (1953, p.271) as 28 ft [8.5 m] of Wivelsfield Sand is within the Upper Tunbridge Wells Sand (see p.19). The name Wivelsfield Sand is unnecessary.

Small exposures in both the lower and upper seams of the Horsham Stone crop out in stream sections [3108 2067; 3100 2062] near Lowlands Farm. A section in the upper seam was recorded in a stream bed [3131 2054] south-west of the farm as follows: sandstone, flaggy, with plant fragments, 0.5 m, overlain by grey silty shales and mudstones, weathering to yellow and brown mottled clays, 1.8 m.

Both seams have been worked in shallow pits in the past, the upper seam much more extensively than the lower. Pits in the lower seam occur near Bedelands Farm [3216 2083; 3229 2081] and in the upper seam at Theobalds [3246 2059; 3265 2061], Antye Farm [3283 2069] and at Lunce's Hall [3347 2075; 3351 2084]. A small exposure in the last of these pits showed 0.6 m of dark brown ferruginous sandstone which originally may have been calcareous.

Both seams are again exposed in a stream section west of Lunce's Hall. The lower seam [3308 2068] consists of 0.3 m of white, silty, very fine-grained sandstone overlain by 0.9 m of brown and white medium-grained sandstone with plant fragments. The exposure of the upper seam [3312 2058] showed 1.5 m of white, clean, cross-laminated, hard, fine-grained sandstone, with ripple marks and small washouts.

Between Bedelands and Lunce's Hall the two stone seams are separated by about 6 m of silt and silty clay. South of Wivelsfield church [342 204] a third, higher, sandstone bed, up to 1 m thick and about 9 m above the second stone bed, crops out for about 800 m.

A borehole at Leylands Park [316 201], near Wivelsfield railway station, appears to have intersected two thin sandstone beds at about the level at which the Horsham Stone would be expected to occur, based on a 6° to 8° southerly dip between the borehole and the nearest outcrop. The beds between 41.3 and 43.0 m depth were described as 'Hard Weald clay and sand conglomerate', they were separated by 0.6 m of 'Weald clay' from 'Weald clay and sand' between 43.6 and 45.1 m (Whitaker and Reid, 1899, p.58). The remainder of the sequence was described almost entirely as clays, much of the lowest 18 m being termed 'Very hard', a feature that probably refers to the hard siltstones at the base of the Weald Clay. The junction with the Upper Tunbridge Wells Sand was probably in the interval between 112.1 and 114.7 m, described as 'Hard clay and brownish sand'. This classification, if correct, gives a thickness of about 67 m for the Weald Clay below the Horsham Stone, a figure similar to that proved (about 68 m) in the Cuckfield No. 1 Borehole in the Horsham district.

East of the Burgess Hill Fault, the persistent ironstone that occurs a little below the Horsham Stone, has been worked in large open pits north of Lowlands Farm [3130 2090], north-west of Bedelands Farm [3172 2088; 3188 2094] and by means of bell-pits [3178 2088] in Big Wood. This same ironstone was probably worked in deep pits in Wilderness Wood [3564 2121; 3578 2119], north of Wivelsfield Hall, and at Holford Manor [3680 2107]. Dark brown flaggy sandstone, the lower seam of the Horsham Stone, forms a small outlier at Holford Manor [3675 2113] and large amounts of this sandstone form a capping to the ridges there and near Teague's Farm [372 215]. A clay-ironstone low in the Weald Clay sequence has given rise to a strong scarp feature between St George's Retreat [3387 1941] and Wivelsfield Green [3608 1947]. RWG

At Burgess Hill the clay-pits of the Maidenhead Brick and Tile Co. Ltd. are in mudstones and sands at the level of Bed 3. Of the extensive excavations, the northern pits [3236 1930; 3258 1931] were degraded and in part filled in 1977; the following section was measured in the southern corner of the pit [3254 1890]:

	Thickness m
Sand, fine-grained, clayey, pale grey and fawn	0.45
Clay, mottled reddish brown and pale grey, massive; sharp base	1.00
Sand, fine-grained, pale fawn; sharp ?channelled base	0 to 0.70
Mudstone, silty, pale fawn and grey, some reddish brown mottling; passing down to	0.25
Mudstone, silty, reddish brown; passing down to	0.80
Mudstone, silty, pale fawn and grey, becoming sandy towards base; sharp base	0.35
Sandstone, fine-grained, pale fawn, calcareous; ripple-marked top, sharp base	0.04
Mudstone, silty, yellowish fawn, with calcareous sand laminae; sharp base	0.16
Sandstone, fine-grained, pale fawn, calcareous; ripple-marked top, sharp base	0.09
Mudstone, silty and sandy, yellowish fawn; sharp base	0.25
Sand, fine-grained, yellowish fawn, with some clay laminae; sharp base	0.35
Mudstones, pale fawnish grey, with nodular beds of dark brown-weathering clay-ironstone	0.37
Mudstone, pale fawnish grey, with some laminae of fine-grained sand and a little scattered sphaerosiderite near base; sharp base	0.06
Mudstone, very pale grey, soft; sharp base	0.07
Mudstone, pale fawnish grey, with abundant scattered fine-grained sphaerosiderite locally aggregated into nodules 2 to 3 mm in diameter; sharp base	0.05

	Thickness m
Mudstone, pale greyish fawn, laminated with silt; slightly to strongly bioturbated	1.04
Sand, fine-grained, clayey, pale grey	0.09
Mudstone, pale grey, with fine-grained sphaerosiderite	0.12
Sand, fine-grained, fawn; passing down to	0.07
Mudstone, silty, pale grey, faintly laminated; passing down to	0.35
Mudstone, chocolate-brown, massive, with some ?rootlet traces; sharp base	0.90
Clay-ironstone, dark brown, compact; sharp base	0.03
Mudstones, pale to medium grey, in alternately massive, strongly bioturbated beds and laminated beds with silt laminae	4.00
Mudstone, dark grey, shaly, with greyish fawn tabular clay-ironstone beds; occasional bone and fish fragments and some rootlet traces in the ironstones	seen to 1.96

The beds dip at 5° WSW. There was an unexposed vertical interval of about 2 or 3 m between the base of this section and a bed of sand and sandstone which cropped out in the floor of the pit. This sandstone was exposed in the partially slipped and obscured north-eastern face of the pit [3261 1902], where the section measured showed:

	Thickness m
Sand, fine-grained, brownish yellow	about 2.00
Sandstone, fine-grained, pale fawn, very hard, flaggy	0.10
Sand, fine-grained, brownish yellow, with some fawn silty clay laminae; passing down to	0.70
Mudstone, pale greenish grey, with sand laminae; passing down to	0.55
Sandstone, fine-grained, yellowish fawn, massive, with occasional pale grey clay laminae; passing down to	0.42
Mudstone, pale greenish grey, with sand laminae; passing down to	0.88
Mudstone, pale grey, laminated, with beds of tabular clay-ironstone	seen to 5.20

The upper sand is more strongly cemented in the western face of the pit [3237 1900], where it comprises 1.5 m of pale grey, hard, flaggy sandstone, underlain by 0.3 m of grey mudstone.

A trench excavated on a building site [3240 1848] north-west of Folder's Farm provided a temporary section through a sand bed 2 to 3 m thick. The sand was seen to dip gently southwards and to pass upwards and downwards into grey and fawn sandy clays.

Red-brown clays within Bed 3 are exposed in the sides of the road [3390 1797] that crosses Ditchling Common. A persistent red clay, also within Bed 3, has been traced eastwards from near St Helena Farm [3550 1819] into the Lewes district. This red clay lies a few metres above a sand between St Helena Farm and Hatton's Green [3740 1767], east of which the sand appears to die out.

Red clays have been traced for short distances near Hunt's Wood [3500 1841] and Gallops Farm [3504 1780]. The clay-pits [3620 1720] worked by the Keymer Brick and Tile Company until about 1920 in the fields north-west of the Fountain Inn are now degraded but red clays may be seen locally in the north-eastern banks.

East of the church at Plumpton Green a ditch [3677 1676] exposed about 0.4 m of pale fawn, soft, flaggy sandstone overlain by 1.5 m of pale fawn, micaceous, clayey, fine-grained sand. BY

The log of a well [3829 1720] at Pouchlands Hospital, formerly Lewes District Workhouse, was discussed by Edmunds (1928, pp.86–88). He considered that the apparently excessive thickness of dominantly clay lithologies (273 m) was due to the Weald Clay resting directly on a lower clay-rich division of the Hastings Beds, possibly as a consequence of faulting. However, regional correlations suggest that the base of the Weald Clay may lie at a depth of about 110 m, overlying beds assigned to the Tunbridge Wells Sand. It is possible that certain beds near the assumed base of the Weald Clay represent 'passage beds' into the formation beneath.   RDL

A bed of Large-'*Paludina*' limestone (Bed 4) was tentatively traced between Clayton Priory [3030 1775] and Keymer road, Burgess Hill [3155 1804]. Two outcrops of Large-'*Paludina*' limestone (Bed 4), separated by a west – east strike fault, have been mapped between Wellhouse Farm [3257 1742] and North Barns Farm [3735 1658]. The northernmost outcrop is marked by a persistent scarp feature which becomes especially prominent in the Blackbrook Wood area [346 176]. The southern outcrop extends eastwards from south of Clearview Farm [3376 1724] to near North Barns Farm [3738 1661]. Several small pits have been dug for limestones, notably near Clearview Farm [3381 1722], Kent's Lane [3490 1685], and at North Barns Farm [3707 1632; 3705 1642]. Blocks of limestone in the soil around these pits show that a bed of limestone up to at least 0.38 m thick was worked. Slabs of Large-'*Paludina*' limestone up to 0.3 m thick and 1.0 m across are abundant in the small stream [3544 1658] immediately north of the railway east of Streat Lane and similar limestone debris was noted in spoil from the ditch [3523 1673] on the east side of Streat Lane north of the railway bridge.

The topmost 25.85 m of the Weald Clay were drilled in the Streat Borehole [3492 1485]. The Weald Clay there consisted of grey laminated silty mudstones alternating with more massive silty mudstones commonly exhibiting strong bioturbation. Burrows filled with glauconitic sand penetrated the formation to a depth of 0.25 m below the base of the Lower Greensand at 69.65 m. Several siltstone beds up to 0.46 m thick occurred and clay-ironstones with a maximum thickness of 0.18 m were recorded throughout the sequence. Rootlet traces were common, particularly between 84 m and 90 m. Ostracods were locally common, as was fish debris. Bivalves and *?Euestheria* were noted at a number of levels between the base of the Lower Greensand and 80 m, and small gastropods were found in partings at around 78.35 m.   BY

Concealed crop south of the South Downs

In the Sompting Borehole [1661 0636] the contact between the Atherfield Clay and the Weald Clay at 456.5 m appeared to be faulted (Young and Monkhouse, 1980). Laminated silty mudstones similar to those described in the Washington, Nep Town and Streat boreholes (pp. 20, 22 and above) were present near the bottom of the borehole at 457 m. Dr F. W. Anderson (personal communication) identified the ostracods *Cypridea valdensis*, *C. tenuis*, *Mantelliana mantelli* and *Theriosynoecum ?fittoni* and regarded the Weald Clay proved at Sompting as belonging to the *Cypridea valdensis* Zone.   BY

CHAPTER 4

Cretaceous: Lower Greensand

The Weald Clay is succeeded by the predominantly arenaceous deposits of the Lower Greensand. Within the district the well established subdivisions, Atherfield Clay, Hythe Beds, Sandgate Beds and Folkestone Beds, are represented, although the Atherfield Clay is present only in the west and the Hythe and Sandgate beds have not been separated over much of the area. The palaeontological zonation of the Lower Greensand in the district is summarised in Figure 8 and on p.33.

The predominantly non-marine to brackish conditions of Weald Clay sedimentation were brought to a relatively abrupt end by the Lower Aptian marine transgression. Middlemiss (1962; 1973) suggested that the transgression covered the area between the London Platform and Brittany within the timescale of one ammonite zone. Prior to this event some gentle folding was followed by slight erosion of the Weald Clay locally. In the western Weald there is evidence of unconformity between the Weald Clay and Atherfield Clay of the Haslemere district (Holmes, 1959). To the east of the present district, Kirkaldy (1937, p.106) described and figured a section at Berwick which showed Weald Clay overlain unconformably by Lower Greensand; also Dr F. W. Anderson (*in* Lake and others, 1987) estimated that the top 10 m of Weald Clay present in the Ripe Borehole [5059 1052] had been removed by pre-Lower Greensand erosion in the Hampden Park Borehole [6120 0204] near Eastbourne. White (1924, p.18) described a section [119 158] near Warminghurst where the lowest few centimetres of the Atherfield Clay consisted of a breccia (p.34). However, where seen in boreholes the Lower Green-sand usually displays a sharp burrowed contact with the Weald Clay. In addition, examination of the ostracod faunas by Dr Anderson suggested that the Lower Greensand rested on the same Weald Clay faunicycle in the Washington, Streat and Sompting boreholes. Thus within the present district there is little evidence of significant erosion of the Weald Clay before deposition of the Lower Greensand began.

The extent of the initial phase of the Lower Aptian transgression within the South Downs area is unclear. It is not known whether the present eastern limits of the Atherfield Clay represent the original spread of deposition or whether early Aptian erosion removed Atherfield Clay from areas farther east. Casey (1961, p.556) suggested that grey nodules and rolled specimens of *Prodeshayesites sp.* and *Deshayesites forbesi* from the base of the Lower Greensand at Berwick might represent a condensed remanié of the Atherfield Clay; if so this may indicate that the cover of Atherfield Clay was formerly more extensive. The overstep of the Hythe Beds over the Atherfield Clay presumably reflects a later pulse in the Lower Aptian transgression. The later overstep of the Sandgate Beds in the Streat area described by Kirkaldy (1937) has not been confirmed by the recent survey.

The sedimentology of the Lower Greensand of the Weald has been studied by Narayan (1963; 1971) and Allen and Narayan (1964), with particular reference to analysis of cross-bedding structures in the Folkestone Beds. They concluded that the Folkestone Beds were deposited as migrating mega-ripples or sand waves in a shallow marine environment, perhaps similar to parts of the present-day North Sea (Narayan, 1971).

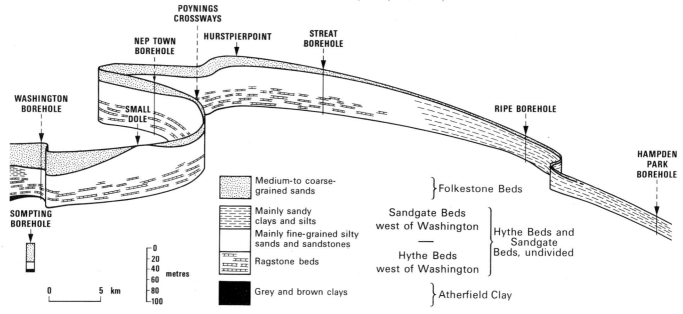

Figure 6 Lithological variations in the Lower Greensand of the Brighton and Lewes districts

The Lower Greensand reaches its thickest development in this district around Washington, where up to 120 m are present. A progressive eastward thinning reduces this figure to around 90 m in the Henfield area and to about 75 m in the east of the district around Streat (Figures 6, 7). This progress is part of an overall eastward or south-eastward thinning of the Lower Greensand along the whole of the southern Weald outcrop, where the thickness decreases from over 150 m in the Petersfield area to only 20 m in the Eastbourne area. There is evidence that the Lower Greensand also thins southward beneath the South Downs; a maximum of only 28.04 m of Lower Greensand was proved in the Portsdown borings to the west of the present district (Lees and Cox, 1937; Taitt and Kent, 1958; Falcon and Kent, 1960), and at Sompting [1661 0636], in a borehole that penetrated the complete Lower Greensand sequence beneath the Chalk cover, only 52.5 m were present (Young and Monkhouse, 1980). This thickness variation has been related to thinning against a structural 'high' thought to be a western extension of the Paris Plage ridge structure of northern France (Kent, 1949; King, 1954; Owen, 1971), which is known to have influenced sedimentation for long periods during the Cretaceous. Dr Anderson (personal communication) considered that thinning in the upper part of the Weald Clay in the Streat Borehole may have been related to contemporaneous uplift on the northern flank of this structure and Casey (1961) suggested that this ridge formed a barrier between the Wealden and Vectian basins of Lower Greensand deposition. On occasions at least, a land area on this structural line may have acted as a sediment source during Lower Greensand times (Kirkaldy, 1933). Indeed, farther west, near Midhurst in Sussex, the Selham Iron Shot Sands give some evidence of derivation from the south (Young and Morgan, 1981, p.36).

ATHERFIELD CLAY

The Atherfield Clay crops out as a narrow belt along the lower slopes of the main Lower Greensand escarpment in the Thakeham and Ashington areas but it is generally covered by superficial 'wash' from the escarpment and it is commonly landslipped. Although there are no good permanent exposures of the Atherfield Clay in the district, details of the sequence have been obtained from cored boreholes at Thakeham [1084 1765] and Sompting [1661 0636]. In unweathered borehole cores the beds consist mainly of massive yellowish brown to pale grey mudstones. At outcrop samples of the clay obtained by hand augering commonly have a chocolate-brown colour.

The junction with the Weald Clay is sharp. Near Warminghurst a thin breccia composed of fragments of fine-grained silty sandstone of possible Wealden origin was noted at the base and bivalve casts were obtained from nodules near the base of the mudstones by G.W. Lamplugh (White, 1924, p.18). A Lower Aptian *Deshayesites forbesi* Zone fauna was obtained from the Thakeham Borehole and the upper part of the Atherfield Clay here appears to correlate with the Lobster beds and Crackers horizon of the Isle of Wight (p.34; cf. Casey 1961). This accords with palaeontological evidence from the Hurlands Farm Borehole [SU 9413 2104],

some 19 km to the west in the Chichester district, where the bulk of the Atherfield Clay falls within the *D. callidiscus* Subzone but the lowest 0.5 m above the Weald Clay may belong to the *D. kiliani* Subzone and thus may be the correlative of the Lower Lobster Bed of the Isle of Wight.

In the present district the top of the Atherfield Clay has only been seen in the Thakeham Borehole, where the contact with the Hythe Beds was sharp and possibly erosional. Thus, at least locally, the overstep of the Hythe Beds over the Atherfield Clay may have been preceded or accompanied by some erosion.

The 9.47 m of Atherfield Clay proved in the Thakeham Borehole is the greatest thickness known in the district. Only 3.5 m were found at Sompting, though this thickness may have been reduced by faulting. Boreholes in the Petworth area have shown between 13 and 18 m of Atherfield Clay, demonstrating the overall westward thickening of the formation.

HYTHE BEDS

The Hythe Beds have been mapped separately from the Sandgate Beds only around Thakeham and Warminghurst. There they are about 40 m thick and consist typically of alternations of soft, weakly cemented, fine-grained sandstone, termed 'hassock', with hard or very hard calcareous fine-grained sandstone, known as 'rag' or 'ragstone' (Figure 7). Individual ragstone beds are up to 1 m thick and the intervening beds of hassock are up to 4 m.

The sandstones are commonly silty and locally clayey. Scattered glauconite of fine sand grade is generally present, giving the characteristic 'pepper and salt' appearance to these beds. A little white mica occurs locally and scattered hollow casts of sponge spicules have been noted. Moderate to intense bioturbation is almost invariably present and little original lamination has been preserved, though some small-scale cross-bedding has been observed. Dark grey silty clay wisps are abundant and represent remnants of original lamination and burrow-linings. Well preserved discrete burrows are not uncommon, and in places burrow-fills have been phosphatised. Where unweathered, almost all of the beds are calcareous to some extent, though the calcareous cement is most abundant in the ragstone beds. The rag and hassock alternation is considered to be a cementation feature, secondarily superimposed on the 'background' of sandy sediment. In some of the ragstone beds the calcareous cement is so abundant that the rock is a sandy limestone. Some of the ragstone beds of the Maidstone and Sandgate areas of Kent contain as much as 85 per cent of calcium carbonate. No figures are available for the ragstones of the present district, but the carbonate content is considerably less than this. The strong calcareous cement is patchy in places, giving lenticular, flattened 'dogger'-like beds of ragstone. The origin of the calcareous cement and the development of the 'rag and hassock' alternations in the Hythe Beds of Kent has been discussed by Wooldridge (*in* discussion of Kirkaldy, 1937) and Worrall (1954; 1957). The latter thought that the alternations were caused by groundwater movement because they were apparently absent in the subcrop.

No chert nodules have been recorded in the Hythe Beds of the present district, though they are common in places in the

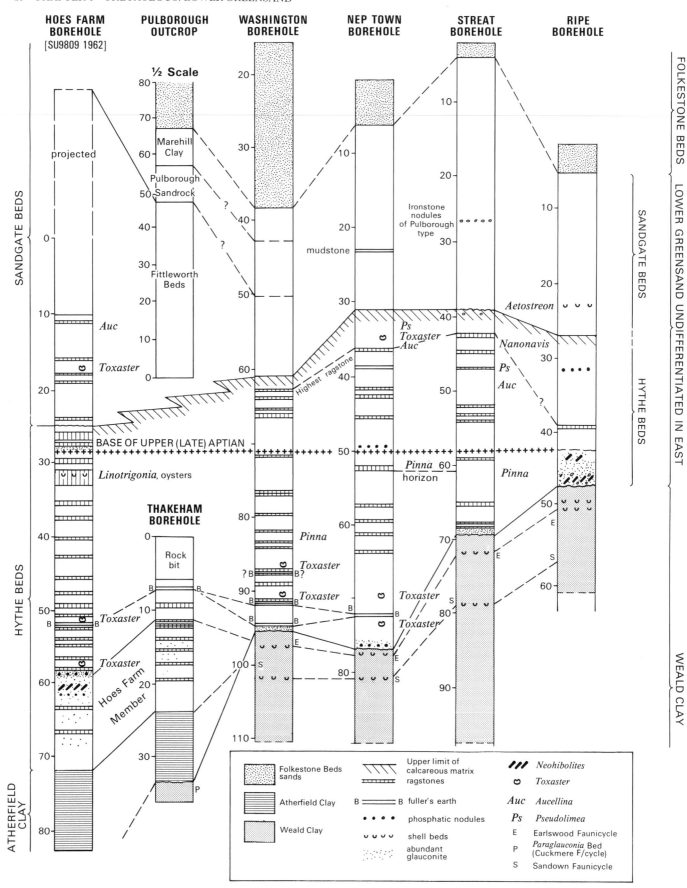

Figure 7   Correlation of the Lower Greensand of the Brighton and adjoining districts

Chichester district. A thin bed of fuller's earth was present in the Hythe Beds of the Thakeham Borehole (p.34), and thin beds of fuller's earth are relatively common in the Lower Greensand of western Sussex (Young and others, 1978).

SANDGATE BEDS

Like the Hythe Beds, the Sandgate Beds have only been mapped separately in the extreme west of the district. In this area the Hythe Beds are overlain by about 17 m of sandy and silty clays, clayey sands and glauconitic silts. Immediately to the west of this district, at Pulborough and Storrington, the Sandgate Beds have been subdivided as follows (Figure 7; Bristow and Wyatt, 1983):

	Thickness m
Marehill Clay: grey silty clay	3 to 11
Pulborough Sandrock: fine-grained sands	0 to 10
Fittleworth Beds: grey sandy clays and clayey sands	10 to 52

The Pulborough Sandrock is absent east of Cootham [0728 1467], whereas the Marehill Clay is present as a persistent unit in the Storrington area and is probably thinly represented in the extreme western margin of this district, for example at Thakeham Tileworks [102 149].

East of Heath Common the Sandgate Beds become rather coarser grained and at outcrop are indistinguishable from the underlying equivalent of the Hythe Beds.

HYTHE BEDS AND SANDGATE BEDS UNDIVIDED

The present survey has revealed that over much of the district the Hythe Beds and Sandgate Beds are not sufficiently distinct at outcrop to enable them to be mapped separately. Difficulty in subdividing the Lower Greensand of eastern Sussex was experienced by Topley (1875, p.126), who suggested that the group was incapable of subdivision east of Henfield, and White (1926) found problems in correlating the Lower Greensand of the Lewes district with the accepted lithological divisions.

East of Heath Common the Lower Greensand sequence beneath the Folkestone Beds is poorly exposed; the limited field evidence available suggests that it consists essentially of a succession of silty fine-grained sandstones, up to 70 m thick, in which scattered glauconite of fine sand grade is common and bioturbation is usually intense. Much of the sediment closely resembles the 'hassock'-type sandstone described from the Hythe Beds (p.27). Locally, and particularly in the Henfield area, beds of hard calcareous sandstone identical to the Hythe Beds ragstones crop out, but over much of the outcrop the lime content has been leached out by deep weathering, so that these Lower Greensand sediments present a strikingly uniform appearance.

Cored boreholes at Washington [1264 1345], Nep Town [2110 1564] and Streat [3492 1485] have confirmed that the dominant sediment throughout the sequence is a bioturbated, glauconitic, silty, fine-grained, 'hassocky' sandstone. In all three boreholes very hard calcareous ragstone beds alternate with much softer hassock-type sandstones in the lower part of the sequence (Figure 7). These beds are evidently the correlatives of the Hythe Beds, though there is a progressive upward reduction in calcareous cement over an interval of 10 or 20 m above the highest ragstone bed in each of the three boreholes, so that even in continuous borehole cores it is difficult to fix an upper limit. In both the Washington and Nep Town boreholes a few beds of clayey sand and one or two beds of silty and sandy clay, up to 0.15 m in thickness, were noted in the beds above. Compared with the Sandgate Beds of the Thakeham area, the beds which occupy the comparable stratigraphical position beneath the Folkestone Beds east of Heath Common are considerably more sandy. It seems, therefore, that east of Washington the Sandgate Beds become coarser grained and are indistinguishable from the Hythe Beds.

FOLKESTONE BEDS

The Folkestone Beds constitute the most persistent and most easily mappable division of the Lower Greensand within the district. They consist mainly of medium- to coarse-grained sands and weakly cemented sandstones known as 'sandrock'. The sands are coarsest in the west around Washington and become progressively finer grained towards the east. In addition White (1924, p.17) remarked that the Folkestone Beds as a whole tend to coarsen upwards. The topmost few centimetres of the formation, immediately beneath the Gault, are characteristically very coarse grained, with sand grains generally about 1 to 2 mm in diameter. The sand grains are generally relatively well rounded and well sorted. Grains of quartz and grey chert up to 4 mm in diameter occur in some laminae. Quartz pebbles up to 10 mm across, accompanied by siltstone fragments, were noted in the Sandgate Pit [1049 1407], near Washington, as was a single pebble of oolitic limestone (p.37). Glauconite grains occur in places and abundant grains of dark brown limonite possibly represent oxidised glauconite. Lignite fragments are common. White (1924, p.17) noted that 'white friable phosphatic concretions with indefinite boundaries occur sporadically in the highest few feet of the Folkestone Sand'.

Cross-bedding, usually on a large scale, may be seen in most of the pits in the Folkestone Beds (Plate 2). The cross-bedded sets are up to 4 m thick and the cross-bedding dips to the south-east or east-south-east. Traces of bioturbation are present locally. In the Streat sand-pit [3483 1482] structures interpreted as dewatering features have been observed.

Thin, impersistent partings of smooth grey to purplish grey 'pipe clay' occur in places. These are usually only a few millimetres in thickness but some are up to about 20 mm thick. In places they form drapes on the foresets of the sands. Similar clays in the Folkestone Beds of the Chichester district consist essentially of kaolinite (Dr D. J. Morgan, personal communication).

The sands are generally pale fawn or pale yellow in colour but in places, notably around Washington, Hassocks and Streat, they show a secondary patchy bright red staining (Plate 1). A very hard dark brown secondary ferruginous cement is common, giving irregular anastomosing networks of 'carstone' or 'clinker'. Some of these carstone veins follow

Plate 1 Ferruginous staining in Folkestone Beds. Concentrically banded iron-staining largely obscures the cross-bedding in this face at Rock Common Quarry, Washington [A13347]

the foresets of cross-lamination, others occur adjacent to clay laminae, but usually they appear to have random shapes. The carstone is locally sufficiently abundant to have been used as a building stone; however, it is an undesirable constituent of the sands in the working sand quarries. The reddish brown ferruginous sandstone described by White (1924, p.17) as occurring at the top of the Folkestone Beds was referred to as the 'iron-grit' by Kirkaldy (1935), and was regarded by him as the basal member of the Gault. In the present account this bed is described with the Gault.

A general eastward thinning of the Folkestone Beds is apparent across the district, though there are considerable local thickness variations (Figure 6). The beds are thickest around Washington, where between 40 and 70 m are present. They are 35.1 m thick in the Sompting Borehole (Young and Monkhouse, 1980). Farther east, in the Henfield and Poynings areas, their thickness is at most 20 to 25 m, but may be reduced to 10 m or less in places. Beneath the Horton Clay Pit [2100 1245], near Small Dole, the beds may be entirely absent (see p.38). In the east of the district around Streat, the formation has thinned to about 15 m. The sand-wave depositional model proposed by Allen and Narayan

(1964) and Narayan (1971) for the Folkestone Beds may, in part, account for these local thickness variations. Scouring and removal of sediment prior to the deposition of the Gault may also have played a part.   BY, AAM

STRATIGRAPHICAL PALAEONTOLOGY

The Lower Greensand of the Brighton district embraces the Lower (Early) Aptian, the Upper (Late) Aptian and the lowest of the Lower (Early) Albian substages, which have been subdivided into ammonite zones and subzones (Figure 8). This zonation was based mainly on the thick Lower Greensand succession in the Isle of Wight, supplemented by information from successions in Kent and Surrey. The scheme tabulated below largely follows Casey (1961), though some amendments have been made following taxonomic revisions by Casey (1978) and work in northern France by Destombes (1973; 1979), particularly on the Lower Albian. Owen (1984) has reviewed the Lower Albian of north-west Europe and his conclusions are followed here.

Plate 2   Cross-bedded Folkestone Beds. Weakly cemented medium- to coarse-grained sands in Rock Common Quarry, Washington [A13349]

Although the Lower Greensand of this district has yielded few ammonites, BGS cored boreholes at Thakeham, Washington, Nep Town and Streat, and materials from the Chichester district (Bristow and Morter, 1983; Bristow and Wyatt, 1983) have provided supplementary faunal evidence and the zonation of the local Lower Greensand may be attempted for the first time.

Of the non-cephalopod faunas, the bivalves are particularly useful for zonation purposes where well established faunal associations have been determined (Casey, 1961). For example: *Aptolinter aptiensis* is abundant in the *forbesi* Zone; *Plicatula carteroniana* is very common in the *transitoria* Subzone; *Aucellina* cf. *nassibianzi*, which in Germany occurs in the *nutfieldiensis* Zone (Kemper, 1982b), has recently been identified in boreholes in this district; the genus *Trapezicardita* appears to be diagnostic of the *nutfieldiensis* Zone; *Toucasia lonsdalii* characterises the *cunningtoni* Subzone; *Resatrix* (*Dosiniopsella*) is a good indicator for the *jacobi* Zone; *Birostrina salomoni* is especially characteristic of the *mammillatum* Zone. Gastropods prove less useful as stratigraphical guides, despite recent studies by a number of workers.

The belemnites in the Lower Greensand are mainly forms of *Neohibolites ewaldi* and these occur abundantly at two levels in the Weald (Casey, 1961), namely in the *bowerbanki* and *nutfieldiensis* zones. The successional subspecies *ewaldi*, *clava*, and *inflexus* have considerable stratigraphical value in Germany (Kemper, 1982a,b), but have not so far been identified in Britain.

Brachiopods are uncommon in the Lower Aptian, almost the only representatives being *Sellithyris sella* and *Sulcirhynchia hythensis* [= *Sulcirhynchia elegans*], apart from sparse *Cyrtothyris* and terebratellid genera such as *Oblongarcula*, *Tamarella* and *Vectella* in the *bowerbanki* Zone. The most abundant brachiopod faunas are found in the Upper Aptian *nutfieldiensis* Zone and above (see Middlemiss, 1962; Owen, 1962; 1965).

The earliest Aptian *bodei* Subzone is probably absent in this district. The presence of *Prodeshayesites* and ammonites of the *forbesi* Zone in nodule beds at Berwick [5250 0701], in the Lewes district (Casey, 1961, p.556), suggests that the relevant subzones are possibly present locally in the Brighton district. The oldest zone recognised (from indigenous faunas) in the Atherfield Clay of this district is that of *D. callidiscus* (Figure 8), in a comparable situation to that of East Kent (Casey, 1961, p.518). This demonstrates the non-sequential nature of the Weald Clay–Lower Greensand contact (p.26).

The *deshayesi* Zone and the *transitoria* Subzone of the *bowerbanki* Zone are represented in the Chichester district by the Hoes Farm Member (clayey sands and silts of the lower Hythe Beds), characterised by abundant *N. ewaldi* (Figure 8; Bristow and others, in press). The same fauna was also noted in markedly glauconitic beds in the Ripe Borehole [5059 1052] in the Lewes district, but not in the local boreholes at Washington, Nep Town and Streat, where beds of probable

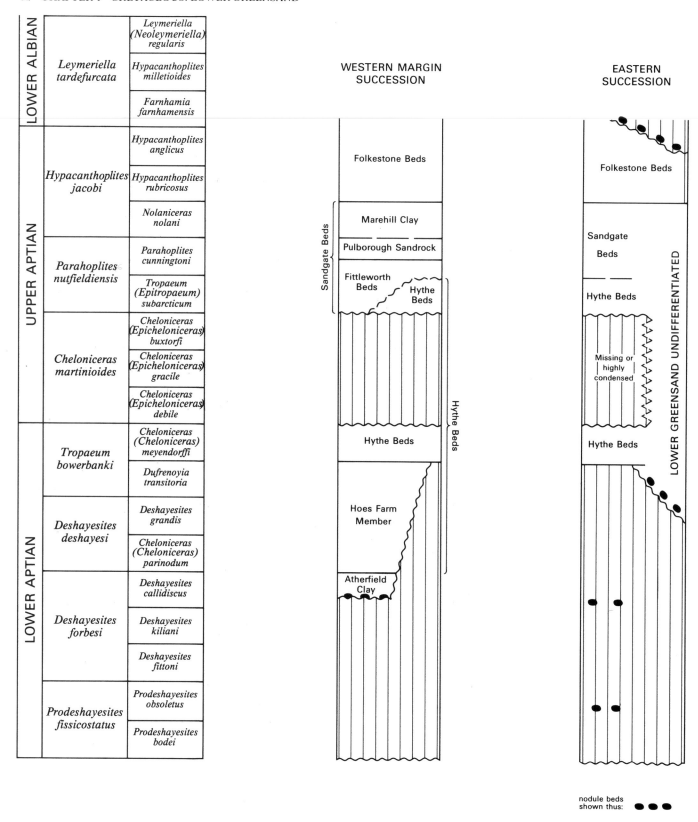

Figure 8 Zonal classification of the Lower Greensand of the Brighton district

Substage	Zone	Subzone
Lower (Early) Albian	*Douvilleiceras mammillatum* *	*Pseudosonneratia eodentata* *
		Otohoplites bulliensis
		Protohoplites puzosianus
		Otohoplites raulinianus
		Cleoniceras floridum
		Sonneratia kitchini *
	Leymeriella (L.) tardefurcata *	*Leymeriella (Neoleymeriella) regularis* *
		Hypacanthoplites milletioides
		Farnhamia farnhamensis *
Upper (Late) Aptian	*Hypacanthoplites jacobi* *	*Hypacanthoplites anglicus* *
		Hypacanthoplites rubricosus
		Nolaniceras nolani *
	Parahoplites nutfieldiensis *	*Parahoplites cunningtoni* *
		Tropaeum (Epitropaeum) subarcticum *
	Cheloniceras (Epicheloniceras) martinioides	*Cheloniceras (E.) buxtorffi*
		Cheloniceras (E.) gracile
		Cheloniceras (E.) debile
Lower (Early) Aptian	*Tropaeum (T.) bowerbanki* *	*Cheloniceras (C.) meyendorffi* *
		Dufrenoyia transitoria *
	Deshayesites deshayesi *	*Deshayesites grandis* *
		Cheloniceras (C.) parinodum *
	Deshayesites forbesi *	*Deshayesites callidiscus* *
		Deshayesites kiliani
		Deshayesites fittoni
	Prodeshayesites fissicostatus **	*Prodeshayesites obsoletus* **
		Prodeshayesites bodei

* recognised in the Brighton district and adjacent areas
** derived (remanié) fauna similarly recognised

meyendorffi Subzone age rest directly on the Weald Clay. A slight overstep is thus indicated.

The *martinioides* Zone has not been recognised in Sussex, in common with East Kent (Casey, 1961) and the Boulonnais (Amedro and Mania, 1976), where a marked non-sequence is apparent at this level.

The base of the Upper Aptian is marked by a sandstone surface encrusted by bryozoans and oysters and with *Sulcirhynchia* in the Washington Borehole at 70.92 m depth. In the Nep Town and Streat boreholes phosphatic nodules occur at this horizon but there is no lithological change (Figure 7). The correlative beds to the west in the Hoes Farm Borehole [SU 9808 1962] contain a fauna comparable with that of the Bargate Beds in Surrey of *nutfieldiensis* age (Casey, 1961, p.551).

The succeeding beds in the Washington, Nep Town and Streat boreholes contain an abundant shelly fauna dominated by *Entolium, Linotrigonia (Oistotrigonia) ornata,*

Mesolinga ?cornueliana, Nanonavis carinata and *Pseudolimea* cf. *gaultina*, together with the echinoid *Toxaster fittoni* and the belemnite *Neohibolites ewaldi*. The occurrence of the bivalve *Aucellina* cf. *nassibianzi* is recognised for the first time in Britain. *Aucellina* was recorded at 35.5 m depth in the Nep Town Borehole and at 49.3 m in the Streat Borehole. It was also noted at 11.5 m depth in the Hoes Farm Borehole (Figure 7). *A.* cf. *nassibianzi* is common in Germany in the *nutfieldiensis* Zone (Kemper, 1982a; 1982b), and these records in Britain reflect the same biostratigraphical event. Another possible *Aucellina* has been identified from the fuller's earths of Tilburstow Quarry [358 508] in Surrey, and this invites a biostratigraphical correlation between the Sandgate Beds of Surrey and lithologies of Hythe Beds type in Sussex.

The beds above 61 m in the Washington Borehole, 31 m in the Nep Town Borehole and 39 m in the Streat Borehole are silty loams of Sandgate Beds type and contain a characteristic shelly bivalve assemblage dominated by infaunal suspension feeders such as *Panopea* and *Pholadomya*, together with *Freiastarte praetypica, Mesosaccella woodsi, Mimachlamys aptiensis, Nucula (Leionucula) planata, N. (Pectinucula) arduennensis, Parmicorbula striatula* and *Resatrix (R.) parva*. This assemblage probably represents the *cunningtoni* Subzone.

The higher part of these beds (46 to 50 m in the Washington Borehole and 24 to 26 m in the Streat Borehole) contains abundant shelly faunas, locally preserved in ironstone nodules similar to those from near Mutton's Farm, Ashington (Kirkaldy, 1937) and at Thakeham Tileworks [1050 1495] (p.34). The fauna is similar to that of the Pulborough Sandrock of the Chichester district (Bristow and Morter, 1983; Bristow and Wyatt, 1983). The topmost beds of Sandgate Beds type in the Washington and Streat boreholes contain few fossils, but the presence of *Resatrix (Dosiniopsella)* in the Washington Borehole may indicate the *nolani* Subzone (see also Casey, 1961).

The Folkestone Beds of the Brighton district have provided little evidence of age, though the *farnhamensis* Subzone has been recognised at Storrington in the Chichester district (Casey, 1965, p.464) and the *anglicus, regularis* and *kitchini* subzones (in nodule beds in the basal Gault) in the Chalvington–Berwick area in the Lewes district (Casey, 1961, p.560).   AAM

DETAILS

Atherfield Clay

In the Thakeham Borehole [1084 1765] the Atherfield Clay was penetrated between 24.03 and 33.50 m. It comprised a succession of massive mudstones which were mainly pale yellowish brown, but were dominantly pale grey in the topmost 3.5 m. The highest 0.27 m of grey mudstone superficially resembled a fuller's earth, though mineralogical examination indicated that it was composed of quartz 40 per cent, montmorillonite 30 per cent, the remainder being mainly mica with traces of feldspar. Small pale fawn ironstone nodules were common and typically displayed open shrinkage cracks in which small tabular crystals of dark brown sphalerite were common; in addition, one nodule contained small colourless crystals of barite.

In this borehole the Atherfield Clay displayed a sharp base on the underlying Weald Clay mudstones. There was no basal nodule bed; a few glauconite grains were scattered through the lowest 0.15 m of the clay. A sharp and commonly burrowed lower contact was characteristic of the Atherfield Clay in boreholes several kilometres to the west in the Petworth area (Young and others, 1979). In contrast to the Petworth area, where the silty mudstones at the top of the Atherfield Clay pass imperceptibly upwards into the silty sands of the overlying Lower Greensand, the top of the Atherfield Clay at Thakeham was found to be sharp, possibly indicating an erosional surface.

The following fauna of the *forbesi* Zone was obtained from the Thakeham cores: *Sarcinella plexus*, *Ceratostreon sp.*, *Corbula spp.*, *Freiastarte subcostata*, *Parmicorbula elegantula*, *P. striatula*, *Pinna robinaldina*, *Pseudolimea* cf. *parallela*, *Resatrix sp.*, *R.* cf. *woodsi*, *Scaphula austeni*, *Vnigriella ?scapha* and *Toxaster sp.*. Beds at a depth of about 25 m, which contain *Drepanocheilus* cf. *kinclispira*, *P. striatula*, *Periplomya robinaldina* and *Pinna sp.*, may represent the Crackers horizon of the Isle of Wight sequence; crustacean fragments which were noted at a depth of 27.75 m may correlate with the Lower Lobster Bed.

The road-cuttings near Warminghurst [1170 1718; 1173 1670] and to the south of Park Barn [1190 1580] now show only poor exposures. The last locality was described by White (1924, p.18) as follows:

	Thickness m
HYTHE BEDS	[about 6.1]
ATHERFIELD CLAY	
Grey-brown and chocolate clays with nodules of clay-ironstone, becoming more numerous and smaller downward.	
Thin breccia [0.03 to 0.05 m] of small angular pieces of light yellow, fine-grained soft silty sandstone in light-brown sandy clay; base sharply defined and slightly uneven	in all about [6.1]
WEALD CLAY	
Lead-coloured shaly clay . . .	seen for [0.6]

The basal breccia was inferred to have been derived from the Weald Clay.

Medium grey clay is exposed in the bed of the stream [1246 1562] west of Ashington. The most easterly confirmed occurrence of Atherfield Clay was a temporary pit excavated at Upper Chancton Farm [1337 1442]; the spoil included stiff grey clays with many pale fawn ironstone nodules containing some sphalerite crystals. It was estimated that only 1 to 2 m of Atherfield Clay were present. The Atherfield Clay was absent in the Washington Borehole [1264 1345], approximately 1300 m south-west of Upper Chancton Farm.

The Sompting Borehole [1661 0636], drilled on the dip-slope of the South Downs north of Sompting, proved Atherfield Clay between the depths of 453.0 and 456.5 m. The junction with the Weald Clay appeared to be faulted and hence the thickness of 3.5 m for the Atherfield Clay was a minimum figure (Young and Monkhouse, 1980). The formation here consisted mainly of massive yellowish brown mudstones, which became greenish grey in the lowest 0.4 m. The Atherfield Clay yielded no macrofauna, except for a few indeterminate bone and wood fragments. The microfauna was similarly impoverished and only poorly preserved single specimens of the foraminifera *Gavelinella sp.* and *Epistomina sp.* were recovered. Messrs P. J. Bigg and I. P. Wilkinson, who studied the micropalaeontology of the Sompting specimens, have suggested (personal communication) that the striking dearth of fossils, together with the state of preservation of the foraminifera, indicate that post-depositional decalcification may have destroyed the original fauna.   BY, RDL, AAM

Hythe Beds

Lamplugh (*in* Reid, 1903, pp.9–10) described a section [101 164] by the side of the B2139 road south of Abingworth, where some 40 m of hassocky sandstone and clayey sands, with concretionary calcareous sandstones, were exposed. Only about 14 m of poorly bedded, fine-grained sandstone can now be seen; impersistent, hard, calcareously cemented beds are present and bioturbation and cross-bedding are prominent in places. Up to about 4 m of similar silty sandstone, also with some hard calcareous beds, are exposed in the sides of the same road west of Thakeham [1046 1737]. Deeply weathered, thinly bedded sandstones are poorly exposed in the sides of the lane near Thakeham church [1100 1732] and up to 2 m of mottled ochreous and medium grey sandstone with some hard calcareous beds may be seen at a spring [1120 1724] 200 m ESE of the church.

The Hythe Beds proved to a depth of 24.03 m in the Thakeham Borehole [1084 1765] consisted mainly of fawn to grey, silty, fine-grained sandstones. Fine sand-grade grains of glauconite were scattered throughout the beds in varying abundance. Hollow casts of sponge spicules were present in small numbers locally, and in places some foraminifera and finely comminuted shell debris were noted. Scattered grains of white mica were recorded at about 9.4 m. Patches of dark grey-brown phosphate, possibly associated with burrow-fills, occurred at a depth of 14.06 m. Wisps and discontinuous laminae of dark grey, silty clay were abundant and strongly bioturbated. Some discrete burrows up to 15 mm in diameter, with a concentric filling of sandy sediment, were also present. Although most of the beds possessed a weak to moderate calcareous cement, very hard, well cemented calcareous beds up to 0.5 m thick were common.

A bed of fuller's earth was present at a depth of 7.09 m. The poor condition of the core recovered from this depth did not allow an accurate measurement of the bed's thickness but it seemed unlikely to exceed 0.1 m. Mineralogical examination revealed a montmorillonite content of 60 to 65 per cent, with minor amounts of quartz, calcite and feldspar. Glauconite was abundant in the lowest 0.1 m of sandstone in the borehole. The lowest 50 mm of sandstone contained clasts of grey mudstone identical in appearance to the underlying top bed of the Atherfield Clay and the contact with the Atherfield Clay was sharp and possibly erosional.

The only macrofossil recovered from the cores was a specimen of the ammonite *Dufrenoyia sp.* at 14.1 m. The age of the Hythe Beds at Thakeham is uncertain.

The sunken lane to the north and south of Warminghurst exposes similar sandstones. One exposure here [1170 1672] shows 4 m of these beds, with irregular, hard, calcareous, concretionary masses up to 1 m across and thin siltier interbeds up to 0.3 m thick. The beds here dip north-west at about 3°. White (1924, p.19) mentioned dips of between 2° and 10° in this lane and G. W. Lamplugh (in manuscript) recorded the higher value at the southern end of the section: the dip appears therefore to steepen southwards.

On the southern side of the Greenhurst Anticline (Figure 24) a small pit [1076 1575] at Little Thakeham exposes 4 m of thickly bedded ochreous pale grey sandstone with bioturbated grey silty wisps. The beds here dip gently to the south.   BY, RDL, AAM, RAE

Sandgate Beds

Within the core of the Warminghurst Syncline (Figure 24) the Sandgate Beds comprise sandy or silty clays, clayey sands and glauconitic silts. A prominent break of slope marks the boundary with the Hythe Beds on the south side of this structure. On the south side of the Greenhurst Anticline, to the south-west of Little Thakeham, similar lithologies are present. Smooth pale grey clay was augered in Merrywood Lane [1076 1551] to the south of Little Thakeham. In the old Thakeham Tileworks pit [1050 1495], on the west side of Heath Common, some 3 m of well laminated buff silt and fine sand with a few burrows are exposed. Glauconitic clay with shells is said to have been found beneath the pit. A rich shelly fauna was collected by Mr S. J. McNicol in March 1963, from ironstone nodules in the beds then exposed, as follows: Brachiopoda (determined with the help of Dr E. F. Owen): *Cyclothyris deluci*, *Lamellaerhynchia* cf. *caseyi*, *Lingula truncata*; Bivalvia: *Anthonya cantiana*, *Ceratostreon sp.*, *Cucullaea (Ideonarca)* aff. *carinata*, *Entolium orbiculare*, *Gervillella* cf. *sublanceolata*, *Gervillia sp.*, *Mesolinga ?cornueliana*, *Mesosaccella woodsi*, *Mimachlamys aptiensis*, *Modiolus aequalis*, *Nucula meyeri*, *N. (Leionucula)* cf. *planata*, *Oxytoma pectinatum*, *Panopea plicata*, *Parmicorbula striatula*, *Phelopteria* cf. *rostrata*, '*Pleuriocardia*' cf. *ibbetsoni*, *Pleuriocardia* cf. *cottaldina*, *Pterotrigonia mantelli*, *Resatrix (R.) parva*, *?Senis sp.*, *Thetis minor*, *Venilicardia sowerbyi*, *Venilicardia sp.*; Gastropoda: *Anchura robinaldina*, *Avellana sp.*, *Nerineopsis* cf. *subattenuatum*, *Ooliticea sp.*; Nautiloidea: *Eutrephoceras sp.*   RDL, RAE, AAM

Hythe Beds and Sandgate Beds undivided

Heath Common – Wyckham Manor [190 134]

Up to 3 m of poorly bedded silty sandstone with some thin silt beds are exposed in a partially degraded pit [1253 1522] at Malthouse Farm, south-west of Ashington.

White (1924, p.21) noted 'brown loamy sand and sandy clay containing irregular concretions of ironstone with inclusions of loose glauconitic sand' in the banks of the lane west of Mutton's Farm [1187 1496]; casts of *Terebratula sp.* and *Trigonia sp.* were found in the ironstone nodules. Kirkaldy (1937, pp.117–119) recorded an extensive shelly fauna from this locality. White included these beds with the Sandgate Beds, and although the section cannot be located accurately it is clear from his description that it was close below the base of the Folkestone Beds.

Bright green, glauconitic, clayey, fine-grained sand and buff and green glauconitic sand were exposed in trenches [1257 1403; 1273 1393] north-east of Rock House.

In the Washington Borehole [1264 1345] the Lower Greensand sequence beneath the Folkestone Beds, between 38.41 and 95.63 m depth, consisted mainly of grey, silty, and in places clayey, fine-grained sandstones, with a few thin beds of sandy siltstone (Figure 7). Scattered glauconite of fine sand grade was almost invariably present and was locally abundant. White mica occurred in small amounts locally. Fairly intense bioturbation was a constant feature of the beds, and little original lamination was preserved. Dark grey silty clay wisps were usually prominent, and clay-lined burrows were common. Several beds of slightly clayey sand up to about 0.2 m thick were noted in the 12 m of beds immediately beneath the Folkestone Beds. Glauconite was particularly abundant in the 0.13 m of silt immediately beneath the Folkestone Beds and also in the beds between depths of 57.75 and 66.60 m. Below 62 m the sequence was almost entirely calcareous, and hard, well cemented, calcareous sandstone (ragstone) beds like those described at Thakeham were common below 69.68 m. The ragstones in the Washington Borehole were, however, rather more numerous and closely spaced than those in the Thakeham and Nep Town boreholes. A few phosphate nodules and phosphatised burrows were noted. Beds of fuller's earth, 0.07 and 0.17 m thick respectively, were recorded at depths of 87.51 and 91.55 m (Young and others, 1978). The upper bed had a montmorillonite content of 57 per cent, the lower one contained 91 per cent. The basal sandstone of the Lower Greensand rested directly on the Weald Clay, the top surface of which was penetrated to a depth of 40 mm by sand-filled burrows up to 10 mm in diameter.

The uppermost 4.5 m of strata beneath the Folkestone Beds in the Washington Borehole contain the bivalve cf. *Resatrix (Dosiniopsella) cantiana*, which may indicate a *Hypacanthoplites jacobi* Zone age (see Casey, 1961). The fauna obtained from the cores from 43 m down to 71 m suggests that these beds belong to the *Parahoplites nutfieldiensis* Zone. The beds from 43 to 61 m appear to be referable to the *P. cunningtoni* Subzone and have yielded the following forms: *Aetostreon latissimum*, *Freiastarte praetypica*, *F. sp.*, *Gervillia sp.*, *Nanonavis carinata*, *Panopea plicata* (in life position at depths of 55 m, 56 m and 56.50 m), *Parmicorbula striatula*, *Pholadomya martini*, *Resatrix sp.* and *Thetis sp.*, together with some wood and plant fragments at depths of 47.46 m and 60.41 m. The beds from 61 to 71 m are assumed to belong to the *Tropaeum subarcticum* Subzone and from them the following fauna has been collected: *Ceratostreon sp.*, cf. *Choristopetalum impar*, *Clisocolus* aff. *vectense*, *Entolium orbiculare*, *E. sp.*, *Linotrigonia (Oistotrigonia) ornata*, *Longinuculana sp.*, *Mesolinga ?cornueliana*, *Mimachlamys aptiensis*, *Resatrix (R.) parva*, *Neohibolites ewaldi*, *Toxaster fittoni* and *T. sp.* The beds below 71 m are of Lower Aptian age and have yielded a small shelly fauna as follows: *L. (O.) ornata*, *N. ewaldi* at 94.80 m, *Oxytoma pectinatum* at 84.50 m, *P. plicata*, *Pinna sp.*; *T. fittoni* and *Rotularia sp.*

Springs issue from near the junction with the Weald Clay at Buncton [1443 1392]. A bed of pale grey fuller's earth, estimated to be less than 0.2 m thick, was found by augering in the fields east of the Post Office [1447 1400]. The bed has not been traced laterally for more than a few metres but it appears to occur at a similar stratigraphical level to the lower fuller's earth beds of the Washington and Nep Town boreholes. About 1 m of firm, unbedded, yellow to grey, fine-grained sand is exposed in the northern side of a small pit [1525 1380] south-east of Upper Buncton House.

Firm ochreous brown sand with beds of hard sandstone were seen beneath an old barn [1585 1372] WNW of Wappingthorn. Flattened burrows, up to 9 mm long and 4 mm in diameter, were common, especially in the harder beds. The sides of the sunken lane [1688 1360] north of Wappingthorn expose 2 to 3 m of weathered pale fawn and brown clayey sand. South of Huddlestone Farm some 2 m of similar sands are exposed in another sunken lane [1798 1350]. Evenly bedded, uncemented, brown fine- to coarse-grained sands may be seen on the south side of the track [1855 1344] between Huddlestone Farm and Wyckham Manor.   BY, RDL, AAM, RAE

Ashurst – Henfield – Perching Sands Farm

A gulley [1751 1586] south of Sweethill Farm exposes 3 m of cross-bedded sandstones and silty sandstones dipping northwards. A similar thickness of poorly bedded, ochreous, pale grey, sandy silts, also dipping northwards, is exposed in the road bank [1796 1591] near Wellen's Farm. The latter name is said to be a corruption of 'wellings'—a reference to shallow, possibly artesian, wells in this vicinity.

Exposed in the river-cliff [1947 1620] south-west of Lashmars Hall are more than 12 m of fawn and grey fine-grained sandstone near the base of the Lower Greensand. This sandstone is only weakly cemented except in two hard beds near the base of the section. Clay-lined burrows up to 20 mm in diameter are common and these are typically more cemented than the surrounding sandstone. A notable feature of this exposure is the steep dip of 48° to the south. About 7 m of generally similar sandstones dipping south at 30° may be seen in the abandoned stone-pit [2009 1623] in Stonepit Lane, Henfield. Towards the base of the exposed section the beds are massive, but the topmost metre of sandstone is very weathered and friable. Burrows are common and stand proud on weathered faces. The disused railway-cutting [206 163] at Henfield is overgrown but Reeves (1947, p.83) noted a southward flattening of the dip in the sandstones formerly exposed.

The sequence of beds proved in the Nep Town Borehole [2110 1564] (Figure 7) had much in common with that found in the Washington Borehole (see above). The dominant lithology was intensely bioturbated, silty, fine-grained sandstone, with scattered glauconite and a little white mica. A few thin sandy siltstones and clayey sands were noted in the 25 m of beds beneath the base of the Folkestone Beds at 6.27 m depth, and glauconite was abundant in places. Below about 28 m depth the beds were generally calcareous, becoming very calcareous below 32.5 m. A bed of fuller's earth 0.23 m thick and with 96 per cent montmorillonite was recorded at a depth of 22.72 m (Young and others, 1978). The top 0.18 m of the bed was rather sandy and was penetrated by sand-filled burrows from the overlying sandstone; at the base burrows filled with fuller's earth penetrated the top 20 mm of the underlying sandstone. A massive, waxy textured, grey mudstone 1.04 m thick at 29.6 m depth, 23.33 m below the Folkestone Beds, is presumably equivalent to a 1.2-m bed recorded (White, 1924, p.21) as 'fuller's earth' from 25.3 m beneath the base of the Folkestone Beds in a well [2126 1564] at the Gardener's Arms, Henfield, approximately 150 m east of the Nep Town Borehole. Although the mudstone from the Nep Town Borehole superficially resembled a fuller's earth, mineralogical examination indicated a montmorillonite content of only 25 to 30 per cent, other minerals present being mica, kaolinite and quartz (Young and others, 1978, p.B94). Beds of hard, well cemented, calcareous sandstone (ragstone) were present below a depth of 36.20 m and this part of the sequence closely resembled the lower beds in the Washington Borehole, although the ragstone beds at Nep Town were more widely spaced. Traces of cross-lamination were observed at depths of 40.3 m and 41.0 m. Phosphatised burrow-fillings were common below 36.20 m. A second bed of fuller's earth encountered at 72.04 m was 0.34 m thick, with a montmorillonite content of 94 per cent (Young and others, 1978, p.B94). Like the higher bed at 22.72 m, this showed a sandy upper division, in this case 0.12 m thick, beneath which the bed consisted of massive, blocky, rather soapy, greenish grey mudstone. The presence of two similar fuller's earth beds at a closely comparable position in the Washington Borehole (p.35) suggest a possible correlation (Figure 7). The lowest 2.05 m of the Lower Greensand at Nep Town were rather finer grained than much of the overlying sand and contained a few phosphatic nodules. A sharp, burrowed junction with the Weald Clay was observed, with burrows up to 20 mm in diameter filled with Lower Greensand sediment penetrating up to 0.14 m into the Weald Clay.

Some 3 m of silty fine-grained sandstones are exposed on the west side of the A2037 road [2168 1527] near Barrowhill Farm. On the east side of the road [2165 1542] about 150 m farther north the junction with the overlying Folkestone Beds is exposed. The section seen in 1975 was as follows:

	Thickness m
FOLKESTONE BEDS	
Sandstone, medium-grained, dark brown, ferruginous (carstone)	0.2
HYTHE BEDS AND SANDGATE BEDS UNDIVIDED	
Silt, yellow, massive	0.1
Sand, fine-grained, orange-brown, with some horizontal clay wisps and burrow-fills	0.3
Sand, fine-grained, silty, purplish brown	0.6
Sand, fine- to medium-grained, purplish brown	0.6
Sand, fine-grained, silty, purplish brown, with some darker, slightly clay-rich laminae	0.7
Sand, yellow and purple, with some clay laminae and burrows	0.35
Sand, fine-grained, silty, purplish brown, with horizontal clay wisps	0.2
Sand, fine-grained, silty, grey and fawn, with bioturbated purplish brown silt laminae	seen to 2.0

The sides of Bramlands Lane [2349 1467], south of its junction with the A281 road, expose bioturbated, silty, fine-grained sandstones with ragstone bands up to 0.4 m thick.

A bed of fuller's earth up to 0.4 m thick immediately beneath the base of the Folkestone Beds north of Fulking village has been traced from Perching Sands Farm [2425 1261] to about 150 m east of Clappers Lane (Young and others, 1978). A field [2455 1255] between the farm and Clappers Lane is known as 'the fulling mills', suggesting that the clay may have been worked here and used for fulling wool, though no trace of any excavation survives. An excavation [2505 1272] in 1977 showed:

	Thickness m
FOLKESTONE BEDS	
Sand, medium- to coarse-grained, slightly clayey, brown; sharp ?bioturbated base	0.30
HYTHE BEDS AND SANDGATE BEDS UNDIVIDED	
Fuller's earth, massive, soft; purplish brown becoming ochreous yellow-brown downwards; sharp base	0.36
Sand, silty, micaceous, greenish grey, with scattered glauconite grains	seen to 0.10

Montmorillonite contents of around 93 per cent have been recorded from the fuller's earth.

BY, RDL

Albourne – Streat

A pale fawn silty clay at least 1.5 m thick in fields [2544 1591] south-east of Albourne Place consists of quartz and calcium montmorillonite, with minor amounts of mica and kaolinite: the montmorillonite content is between 20 and 30 per cent. This material is a mixed-assemblage clay resembling a bed of similar composition at a roughly comparable stratigraphical level in the Nep Town Borehole (see above).

Fawn and grey, soft, silty, fine-grained sandstones with at least one 0.3-m ragstone bed are exposed in the roadside [2642 1646] at Albourne Green. Kirkaldy (1937, pp.105, 107) described sections in road-cuttings at Albourne [2659 1667 to 2666 1596]. The Hythe Beds there consisted of 'snuff-coloured loamy sands with little glauconite and ... a few doggers of ragstone with a streaky appearance due to numerous lenticles of black clay and some seams of soft sandstone'. The Sandgate Beds were distinguished as '110 feet [33.5 m] of purplish, drab, mottled, and green-coloured loams and loamy clays containing much glauconite and rare concretions of marcasite and ironstone'. These sections cannot now be seen.

Silty fine-grained sands with numerous burrows were seen in the west bank of Langton Lane [2728 1676] a short distance south of a spring near the base of the Lower Greensand.

Strongly burrowed, generally poorly cemented, silty, fine-grained sandstones with some ragstone beds are exposed in the banks of the stream [3011 1627] in Reed Pond Shaw, north-west of Hassocks; individual beds are generally about 0.15 m thick. In the north bank of the stream [3067 1607] at the northern end of Woodsland Road, Hassocks, some 1.5 m of sandstones with distinct burrows up to more than 10 mm in diameter crop out. Near the southern end of Woodsland Road a temporary excavation [3054 1565] revealed ochreous fawn, glauconitic, clayey silt with numerous branching horizontal and inclined burrows.

At Ockley Manor [3155 1626] blocks of pale fawn and grey, bioturbated, silty, fine-grained sandstone may be seen in the north-eastern bank of the road. Kirkaldy (1937, p.107) mentioned this locality as one at which the Hythe Beds were exposed and commented that an exposure in the nearby cart track [3217 1625] at Oldland Windmill was the most easterly locality that displayed 'hard stone' at this level.

The brief log of a well [3205 1523] at Ditchling Pumping Station records that sands and sandstones with some sandy clay were present between the base of the Folkestone Beds at a depth of 2.7 m and the top of the Weald Clay at 70.6 m. The log suggests that cemented sandstones were present in the lower part of the sequence.

The Streat Borehole [3492 1485] proved a succession of beds similar to those seen in the Washington and Nep Town boreholes (Figure 7). A few thin beds of very sandy siltstone were present in fine-grained sandstones down to about 39 m depth. A band of massive pyrite nodules with many casts of indeterminate bivalves and gastropods occurred at 26.21 m. Below 30 m the beds were almost invariably calcareous; ragstone beds were common below 42.20 m to the base of the Lower Greensand at 69.65 m. Glauconite was abundant in places, particularly in the lowest 2 m of the sequence. Black phosphatic nodules were present near the base. The top 70 mm of the Weald Clay was penetrated by burrows up to 20 mm in diameter filled with glauconitic sand.

Most of the undivided Hythe Beds and Sandgate Beds sequence of the Streat Borehole belonged to the *Parahoplites nutfieldiensis* Zone, but the lowest few metres were provisionally referred to the *Cheloniceras meyendorffi* Subzone of the Lower Aptian. Beds down to about 39 m yielded the following fauna indicative of the *Parahoplites cunningtoni* Subzone: *Arenaciarcula sp.*, *Barbatia* cf. *marullensis*, *Corbula sp.*, *Cryptochasma sp.*, *Freiastarte praetypica*, *Merklinia aptiensis*, *Mesosaccella woodsi*, *Nanonavis carinata*, *Nucula (Leionucula) planata*, *N. (Pectinucula) arduennensis*, *Panopea mandibula*, *P. plicata* (in life position at 38.91 m), *Parmicorbula striatula*, *Pholadomya martini*, *Plicatula sp.* and *?Resatrix sp.*

Between 39 and 58 m the beds referred to the *Tropaeum subarcticum* Subzone provided the following forms: *?Ageria*, *Aucellina* cf. *major*, *Entolium sp.*, *Freiastarte praetypica* (in burrow at about 39 m), *Linotrigonia (Oistotrigonia) sp.* cf. *ornata*, *Merklinia sp.*, *Mesolinga cornueliana*, *Nanonavis carinata*, *Nucula (Leionucula)* cf. *planata*, *Oxytoma pectinatum*, *Parmicorbula striatula*, *Pholadomya* cf. *martini*, *Pseudolimea* cf. *gaultina*, *Resatrix parva* and *Sanmartinoceras* (or *Aconeceras*) *sp.* *Nanonavis carinata* was particularly common in a group of beds between about 43 and 46 m and *Pseudolimea* cf. *gaultina* was abundant between about 46 and 48 m, with *M. cornueliana* common just above 48 m.

The position of the base of the *T. subarcticum* Subzone, and hence the boundary between the *nutfieldiensis* Zone and the *C. meyendorffi* Subzone of the *bowerbanki* Zone, has not been fixed precisely in this borehole but may lie at a phosphatic bed near 58 m. The beds between 58 and 64.70 m yielded the following bivalves: *Clisocolus vectense*, *Nucula (Leionucula) sp.*, *Pholadomya martini* and *Pinna sp.* The Lower Greensand between 64.70 and 69.50 m yielded *Vectella morrisi*, *Aptolinter aptiensis*, *C. vectense*, *M. cornueliana* and *Pinna sp.* and is tentatively ascribed to the last subzone. The presence of *Pinna sp.* at 61.00 m and 64.70 m provides a local correlation with the Nep Town Borehole (Figure 7).

The east bank of the road [3514 1516] east of Streat church exposes about 1.5 m of ochreous brown and fawn clayey silts, which, though very weathered, retain traces of lamination and clay-lined burrows.

White (1924, p.20) described a section in an artificial channel [3630 1475] 'Between Plumpton Mill (near East Chiltington) and Upper Mill a quarter of a mile [0.4 km] southward' as follows: 'A dark-grey, fine-grained loamy sand, seen for a few feet at the shallow northern end of the channel, is succeeded southward by a higher light grey-brown, speckled, glauconitic sand, and this in turn by yellow sand without glauconite. Though lacking hard bands, these sands probably all belong to the Hythe Beds. They appear to be at least 30 feet [9.1 m] thick. By the sluice at its upper end the channel opens into a small round pool, the steep sides of which show a clear but hardly accessible section of 15 to 20 feet [4.6 to 6.1 m] of dark bluish to greenish-grey sandy clay, loaded with fine-grained glauconite, and containing layers of ferruginous concretions; evidently a member of the argillaceous series identified with the Sandgate Beds.' BY, AAM

Sompting Borehole

In the Sompting Borehole [1661 0636] 13.9 m of strata between the base of the Folkestone Beds and the top of the Atherfield Clay were classified as Undivided Lower Greensand by Young and Monkhouse (1980). The beds consisted mainly of strong, bioturbated, glauconitic, clayey, silty, very fine-grained sandstones and they closely resembled those at a similar stratigraphical level at outcrop and in the Washington Borehole (p.35). The bivalves *Pseudolimea cottaldina*, '*Mesosaccella*' *?scapha* and a fragment of *?Pterotrigonia* were collected from silty mudstones between 440.46 and 440.88 m. A Lower Aptian zonal position no higher than the *Deshayesites forbesi* Zone was suggested by Morter (*in* Young and Monkhouse, 1980, p.308); however, a *Deshayesites deshayesi* zonal age may be more appropriate. Some indeterminate fish scales and vertebrae and pyritised sponge spicules were found. BY

Folkestone Beds

Heath Common – Buncton

A pit [1100 1505] on the north side of Heath Common shows 8 m of red and ochreous, cross-bedded, medium- to coarse-grained sand. Some impersistent clay partings are present, especially towards the bottom of the exposure. The northern face of an abandoned sand-pit [1130 1483] on Heath Common exposes about 4 m of similar sands with a few fine-grained pebbly layers beneath 1 to 1.5 m of sandy, flinty Head.

In the Sandgate Pit, a section [1049 1407] showed 10 m of Folkestone Beds, consisting of deep pink to rusty-brown coarse-grained sands. Several rather darker-coloured, coarser-grained bands up to 40 mm in thickness were present, within which pebbles of vein-quartz, tabular fragments of siltstone up to 10 mm across, and one fragment of oolitic limestone were noted. Near the bottom of the face there was a massive bed of silty sand about 0.3 m thick, with wisps and discontinuous laminae of pale grey clay up to about 3 mm in thickness. Patchy dark brown iron-staining was common throughout and weak hematite cement occurred locally. In this section cross-sets were between 3 and 4 m thick, whereas in a working face approximately 100 m to the west cross-sets were mainly less than 0.5 m thick in the topmost 4 m of the face and impersistent pale grey clay beds were common at around 2.5 m from the top. A largely inaccessible face farther west in the pit [1019 1403] was more than 18 m high and showed very well developed cross-bedding. The cross-sets varied in thickness from 0.3 m to more than 2 m and faced mainly to the south-east. Some wavy lamination was noted in the topmost 2 m of beds. Carstone with a reticulate pattern of dark brown secondary iron-cement was widespread across the face.

Between 8 and 9 m of cross-bedded, coarse-grained sands are exposed in a sand-pit [1065 1388] 450 m east of Abbots Leigh. Clay drapes less than 10 mm thick are present on foresets in the basal part of the sequence.

Extensive sections through the Folkestone Beds are exposed in the Rock Common Quarry [1250 1350] (Plates 1 and 2). The beds exposed in the southern face are within a few metres of the base of the Gault. In this face up to 13 m of reddish brown, cross-bedded, medium- to coarse-grained sands with some subangular to subrounded quartz gravel partings, are exposed. Scattered lenses of fine-grained sand occur near the top of the section. The cross-sets are generally less than 1 m thick. An irregular network of carstone covers much of the face and is associated in places with red staining of the adjacent sands. In the eastern face of the pit up to 20 m of similar sands are exposed; in the lower part of the face the cross-sets are up to 3 m thick, with foresets facing due south. Higher in the face the cross-sets are only 1 m in thickness and the foresets face approximately south-east.

The Washington Borehole [1264 1345] was drilled in the southern part of the Rock Common Quarry. It proved 38.41 m of

Folkestone Beds beneath the pit floor, which was estimated to be 13 m below the base of the Gault. Water borings [1218 1339; 1222 1339] west of Green Farm, proved 53.3 m and 55.8 m of Folkestone Beds; both boreholes commenced at about 5 m below the base of the Gault.

A quarry extending almost 1 km eastwards along the strike from near the old windmill at Rock Common [1281 1369] exposes up to 15 m of cross-bedded and finely laminated brown to red, fine- to coarse-grained sands with some fine pebbly layers. Concentric patches of purplish brown secondary iron-staining are common and there are also lenses of carstone up to 30 mm thick and 2 m in length conformable with the bedding. At one place in the bottom of the pit [1380 1349] a bed was noted consisting of greenish brown, glauconitic, rather pebbly, coarse-grained sand, with pale grey clay wisps and numerous burrows up to 5 mm in diameter.　　BY, RAE

Small Dole – Woodmancote

In the area immediately surrounding the Horton Clay Pit, Small Dole [2100 1240], several boreholes have been drilled through the base of the Gault and have continued for up to 25 m into the Lower Greensand. The sequence proved at the base of the Gault is complex and varies from one borehole to another. However, it appears that the relatively well sorted sands of the Folkestone Beds seen at outcrop approximately 500 m to the north-east near Small Dole are absent. The succession here was described by Casey (1961, p.558), who quoted the log of one borehole (number 9a) located on the eastern edge of Horton Wood [211 126] as typical of the sequences encountered. The following description is based on that of Casey with additional faunal information provided by Mr A. A. Morter:

	Thickness m	Depth m
GAULT (p.47)	[17.2]	[17.2]
FOLKESTONE BEDS [equivalent]		
? mammillatum Zone		
Band of dark, gritty phosphatic nodules and small pebbles in glauconitic loam	[0.2]	[17.4]
tardefurcata Zone (*regularis* Subzone)		
Horton Wood Clay: non-calcareous, dark grey, with hard, flat, whitish nodules, especially at top, a few pyritic nodules and numerous algal filaments; some threads of glauconitic sand; washed residue full of glauconite and mica, a few foraminifera. *Mesosaccella woodsi*, *Aconeceras* cf. *neonisoides*, *A. spp.* and *Leymeriella* cf. *tardefurcata*, *L. (Neoleymeriella) regularis*, *Sanmartinoceras (Sinzovia) sp.*; crustacean limbs fairly common	[3.8]	[21.0]
? tardefurcata Zone (*milletioides* Subzone)		
Sandy clay, bright green, glauconitic with phosphatic nodules, some gritty	[0.9]	[21.9]
jacobi Zone		
Silt, grey with threads of white sand, becoming clayey downwards and passing into	[3.7]	[25.6]
Sandy clay, bright green, glauconitic with pink powdery traces of fossils, passing into	[0.3]	[25.9]
Sand, clayey, glauconitic, weathering white	[2.3]	[28.2]
Loam, dark green, glauconitic with sandy pockets; line of small pebbles and crushed fossils at base	[0.9]	[29.1]
SANDGATE BEDS		
Sandy clay, grey-green	[3.2]	[32.3]
Loam, bright green, glauconitic with rotted fossils, mostly *Exogyra* (*? = Aetostreon*)	[2.7]	[35.0]
Clayey sand and sandy clay, grey-green, passing into	[6.5]	[41.5]
Loam, glauconitic, bright green, with traces of fossils	[0.3]	[41.8]

In his 1961 paper Casey took the bed at 17.4 m to be the *mammillatum* nodule bed. He regarded the underlying clay with a *regularis* Subzone fauna as distinct from the Gault and mis-spelt the name as 'Hopton Wood Clay'. The development of the *regularis* Subzone in a clay facies is unusual in this country, the nearest comparable occurrence being in Hanover, north Germany (Casey, 1961, p.559).

Very similar sequences have been proved in a number of subsequent boreholes in the area of the clay-pit. In particular, it has been possible to identify the Horton Wood Clay. However, there is little to justify considering the beds between 17.2 and 29.1 m in borehole 9a as an anomalous development of the Folkestone Beds. On lithological grounds, the Horton Wood Clay can better be included with the Gault, the underlying glauconitic sandy clay with phosphatic nodules being regarded as the basal bed of this formation. The beds beneath 21.9 m can all be assigned to the undivided Hythe Beds and Sandgate Beds. Under this interpretation, the base of the Gault here lies within, or close to, the *tardefurcata* Zone, in contrast to Danny [2908 1548] where the base is of *eodentata* age (p.48), and to the Lewes district where at Chalvington the base is within the *anglicus* Subzone of the *jacobi* Zone (Casey, 1961, p.560). This transition may have been the result of irregular overstep by the Gault.

At outcrop in the Tottington Sands area [2225 1280], approximately 1 km ENE of the Horton Clay Pit, hand auger evidence suggests that the junction of the Folkestone Beds and Gault is also complex and exhibits some similarities to the sequence proved in the Horton Clay Pit boreholes. At one place [2212 1278] near Truleigh Sands, cross-bedded, coarse-grained sands of typical Folkestone Beds aspect were succeeded by grey plastic clay, which in turn was overlain by dark greenish grey glauconitic sandy clay near the base of the Gault. This grey plastic clay may be the Horton Wood Clay, here underlain by undoubted Folkestone Beds.

Between Poynings Grange [2581 1311] and Holmbush Farm [2475 1415] the Folkestone Beds outcrop narrows strikingly. There is no evidence of faulting here and even allowing for relatively high dips in the axial region of the Pyecombe Anticline it is clear that there is a considerable reduction .in thickness of the formation (Young, 1977, p.20). In places, notably near the A281 road [2530 1403] west of Poynings Crossways, the Folkestone Beds can only be a few metres thick. The continuity of the Folkestone Beds outcrop is disrupted by strike faulting between Holmbush Farm and Woodmancote [2326 1493].

Henfield

The Folkestone Beds have been worked in a disused sand-pit [2110 1563] at Nep Town, Henfield. Approximately 5.6 m of sands are exposed in the eastern face beneath up to 0.4 m of sandy, flinty Head. The beds here mainly comprise buff, uncemented, medium- to coarse-grained sands. Scattered grains of dark brown limonite are common and may represent oxidised glauconite. There are some laminae of coarser sand up to 10 mm thick, composed of quartz grains up to 5 mm in diameter: a grain of black chert was observed in one of these laminae. Cross-lamination is common, with foresets dipping towards the south or south-east. A 40 mm bed of pale grey, faintly laminated clay, with several sand laminae, occurs 3.6 m from the top of the face. Patchy brown ferruginous staining of the sands is common and a 1 m-thick zone, about 1.5 m from the top of the face, exhibits a reticulate network of dark brown, hard, ferruginous carstone veins. The small trough faults mentioned at this locality by White (1926, p.22) are no longer visible. The Nep Town Borehole [2112 1562] was drilled in this pit. It started at the level of the base of the exposed section and the base of the Folkestone Beds was proved at a depth of 6.27 m. At least 11.87 m of Folkestone Beds are therefore present at Nep Town, though the thickness of the unexposed highest beds is unknown.

Other wells in the Henfield area, at the Gardener's Arms public house [2126 1564] and at Henfield Common [2183 1548], proved 17.4 m and 17 m of Folkestone Beds respectively, but again these are minimum thicknesses. The total thickness of the Folkestone Beds in the Henfield area is estimated to be about 23 m. Subangular and subrounded chert pebbles, up to 10 mm in diameter, occur in yellow coarse-grained sand in a small section [2277 1522] at the side of a track near Limekiln Cottages, 1.5 km south-east of Henfield.

BY, TEL

Albourne – East Chiltington

The Folkestone Beds have been dug from small pits [2663 1540; 2697 1535] on either side of the A23 London to Brighton road, about 1 km south of Albourne. About 2 m of brown medium- to coarse-grained sand are exposed at the top of the north-western face [2680 1535] of the pit on the eastern side of the road. Kirkaldy (1937, p.99) recorded a total thickness of 21.3 m for the Folkestone Beds in the road-cutting immediately north of these pits.

The Danny Sand Pit at Hurstpierpoint has long been known for the sections it provided in the Folkestone Beds and the basal beds of the Gault (White, 1924, p.29; Kirkaldy, 1935, p.526; Casey, 1961, p.560). At the time of the field survey (1975) the following section was measured in the southern face of the pit [2908 1548]:

	Thickness m
GAULT	
Mudstone, grey, with glauconitic sandy clays in lowest 1.75 m (see p.48)	3.25
FOLKESTONE BEDS	
Sandstone, coarse-grained, brown to yellowish brown, limonite-cemented. Scattered quartz pebbles up to 3 mm in diameter. Some crude wavy lamination. Sharp uneven lower contact with large lobate masses resembling load casts penetrating underlying sand for up to 90 mm	0.15
Sand, medium- to coarse-grained, pale pinkish fawn to dull red, strongly cross-bedded. A few burrows up to 20 mm in diameter in top 0.3 m and a few quartz pebbles up to 5 mm in diameter in top 50 mm	5.00

At the base about 2 m of vertical section were concealed by debris; beneath this a further 2 m of sand, like that described above, was seen in the lowest part of the pit. Thus a total of approximately 9 m of Folkestone Beds was probably present.

Casey (1961, p.559) considered the 0.15 m of ferruginous sandstone to be equivalent to the 'Iron Grit' which forms a basement bed to the Gault farther west in Sussex (see p.41). Owen (1971, p.41) also included this bed with the Gault, but both White (1924, p.29) and Kirkaldy (1935, p.526) regarded it as part of the Folkestone Beds. Kirkaldy considered that the iron cementation here was of relatively recent origin and this view is accepted.

The medium- to coarse-grained sands exposed in the pit exhibited well marked cross-bedding with planar foresets, many of which were accentuated by brown ferruginous staining and were inclined to the south-east. Some of the cross-laminae were notably

coarser grained, with quartz grains up to 3 mm in diameter and scattered small clay flakes were noted. In common with the Folkestone Beds elsewhere in the district a pronounced patchy red or pink staining of the sands was present here. This reddening was seen to cut across primary sedimentary structures and was clearly a secondary feature. In a section on the north-western side of the pit [2898 1554] the reddening was mainly confined to the lowest 2 m of sand; the overlying 2 m were very pale fawn to white in colour and gave the appearance of having been leached.

Up to 2 m of pale fawn, uncemented, very fine-grained sands, with some very slightly clayey wisps, are exposed in the sides of the lane [2890 1579] north-west of the Danny Sand Pit. These sands are close to the base of the Folkestone Beds. Overgrown and degraded sand workings extend for over 500 m from the eastern end of the Danny Sand Pit to near the B2036 Burgess Hill to Brighton road.

A temporary excavation in former sand-pits [3012 1535] west of the railway at Hassocks exposed approximately 2.5 m of brown, medium- to coarse-grained sand and soft sandstone. Cross-bedding was well developed with tabular foresets dipping eastwards. Cross-sets up to about 1 m thick were noted. Purplish red staining was prominent in places and hard, ferruginous, carstone bands up to 20 mm thick were observed, generally cutting across sedimentary structures, though one conspicuous 0.1 m-thick carstone near the base of the section followed the cross-lamination. Foundation excavations in Keymer Road, Hassocks [3053 1549] exposed fawn, fine-grained sand near the base of the Folkestone Beds, overlain by 0.6 m of medium- to coarse-grained sand.

A well [3127 1383] at Whitelands proved 30.8 m of 'sand' (Robertson and others, 1964, p.17), presumed to be Folkestone Beds, between the Gault and grey sandy clays of the Sandgate Beds-equivalent.

An old pit [3252 1527] immediately west of Ditchling church exposes almost 2 m of pale fawn, massive, friable sandstone, which displays some reddish brown mottling.

South of Streat the Folkestone Beds have been worked from sand-pits on either side of Streat Lane. The pit west of the road is still worked on a small scale and its western face [3483 1482] exposes approximately 7 m of slightly micaceous fine- to medium-grained sand. Much of the sand is pale fawn to yellow and it shows only faint traces of small-scale cross-bedding with northward dipping foresets; dewatering structures also occur. Two continuous bands of relatively homogeneous reddening are seen in the face, separated by up to 2 m of yellowish fawn sand in which occur traces of cross-bedding and irregular brown ferruginous bands; the lower band is about 1.5 m thick; the upper band is about 1 m thick and 1 m below the top of the section.

Although parts of the south-western face [3489 1477] of the pit were graded and somewhat obscured, it provided the following section through the junction of the Folkestone Beds and Gault:

	Thickness m
GAULT	
11 Clay, dark green, glauconitic, with many burrows; passing down to	0.75
10 Clay, sandy, dark green, very glauconitic; many burrows filled with pale fawn sand similar to the underlying bed; becoming sandier downwards. (Some sandy limonite nodules presumably derived from this bed lying on surface of slope)	about 0.30
FOLKESTONE BEDS	
9 Sand, fine- to medium-grained, pale fawn to white, slightly micaceous; top penetrated by burrows from bed above; colour becoming darker downwards, with some grey wisps and pyrite nodules; passing down to	about 2.00

8 Sand, fine-grained, silty, pale grey and fawn, compact, micaceous; strongly bioturbated; becoming dark grey downwards, with scattered grains and pellets of glauconite in lowest 0.5 m; passing down to   about 2.00
7 Sand, silty, clayey, dark grey weathering white; intensely burrowed; some coarse-grained glauconite in about lowest 0.15 m; sharp base   about 0.50
6 Sand, medium-grained, clayey, orange-brown, with scattered quartz grains up to 2 to 3 mm in diameter; becoming less clayey downwards and showing crude lamination and strong bioturbation; some scattered coarse-grained glauconite   0.60
5 Sand, medium-grained, limonitic, reddish brown, with a few grains up to 2 mm in diameter   0.01
4 Sand, coarse-grained, yellowish brown with grains up to 4 mm in diameter; some crude lamination; becoming finer grained downwards and passing down into   about 0.75
3 Sand, medium- to coarse-grained, yellowish brown, with traces of lamination; occasional patchy reddening; passing down to   about 0.50
2 Sand, medium- to coarse-grained, reddish brown; passing down to   about 1.00
1 Sand, medium- to coarse-grained, fawn   about 0.50

Some difficulty is experienced here in fixing the level of the boundary between the Lower Greensand and the Gault. Beds 1 to 4 are obviously of Folkestone Beds character, and the glauconitic clays (beds 10 and 11) resemble the beds seen at the base of the Gault elsewhere, for example at the Danny Sand Pit. However, beds 5 to 9 exhibit intermediate characteristics and could perhaps be taken as a group of passage beds between the Folkestone Beds and the Gault. Gossling (1929, p.248) described broadly similar, though thinner, passage beds at the base of the Gault in Surrey, and Kirkaldy (1935, p.527) suggested that thin sands at the base of the Gault at Copyhold Wood, south of Buncton, were of like character (see p.45). The thin ferruginous sand (bed 5) suggests a feeble development of the 'Iron Grit' lithology found at the base of the Gault in the extreme west of the district (p.41). The overlying sands and clayey sands (beds 6 to 8) contain glauconite and appear to be intermediate in lithology between topmost Folkestone Beds and basal Gault. However, beds 1 to 9 are predominantly sandy and in poorly exposed ground are difficult to distinguish from the typical sands of the Folkestone Beds. They are grouped here with the Folkestone Beds and the base of the Gault is placed at the base of the glauconitic clay (bed 10). No fauna has been recorded from any of these beds. The Streat Borehole was drilled in the floor of this pit and penetrated 3 m of Folkestone Beds before passing into the silty sandstones of the undivided Hythe Beds and Sandgate Beds. The Folkestone Beds at Streat appear to have a total thickness of between 15 and 20 m.

In a flooded sand-pit [3670 1460] north of Novington Manor up to 2 m of yellowish brown, medium-grained sand are exposed in the south-eastern corner. The sand, which contains a little interstitial clay, is uncemented and generally structureless, with a few quartz, chert and lignite grains up to 3 mm in diameter. Field evidence in the neighbourhood suggests that the Folkestone Beds are appreciably thinner here than at Streat Sand Pit, and may be less than 10 m in thickness.

Sompting Borehole and Warren Farm Well

In the Sompting Borehole [1661 0636] the Folkestone Beds were present between the depths of 404 and 439.1 m (Young and Monkhouse, 1980). Only the lowest 7.1 m were cored and much of the formation was seen as rock cuttings; these consisted mainly of yellowish brown to greyish red, moderately well sorted, uncemented to poorly cemented, medium- to coarse-grained sands. Many grains exhibited a pink ferruginous staining and scattered grains of glauconite were common. Cores from below 432 m consisted mainly of similar medium- to coarse-grained sands, with some quartz and chert grains up to 3 mm in diameter. Between 432 and 437 m the sand was calcareous and between 438.5 and 438.9 m glauconite was abundant. Below 438.9 m the sands were rather poorly sorted and well cemented though non-calcareous. Chert and limonite pebbles up to 7 mm in diameter were found in the lowest 0.1 m of the formation.

The Folkestone Beds were reached at the bottom of a deep well [3517 0565] at Warren Farm, Woodingdean (Whitaker and Reid, 1899, p.83; Edmunds, 1928, pp.194–195; see also p.49). After passing through 95.09 m of Gault clays the well was completed at a depth of 391.67 m in 1.5 m of 'Greensand with seams of white sand, mixed with pebbles', which is assumed to have been the basal bed of the Gault. Red sand, which was proved beneath this bed with a hand auger, is considered to have been the top part of the Folkestone Beds. An inrush of water flooded the excavation before further observations could be made.   BY

CHAPTER 5

Cretaceous: Gault and Upper Greensand

The marine transgressions during Aptian times which led to the deposition of the predominantly arenaceous sediments of the Lower Greensand were followed early in the Middle Albian by a more extensive transgression across the whole of southern England and the Anglo-Paris Basin. This transgression was marked by a rapid change in sedimentation, the well sorted sands of the Folkestone Beds being replaced by the compact, grey, marine mudstones of the Gault. In much of the Weald the Gault becomes silty in its higher beds and passes both upwards and laterally into the Upper Greensand (Figure 9). The Gault and Upper Greensand are therefore two separate facies within the beds between the Lower Greensand and the Lower Chalk. Structural lines, perhaps a series of submerged ridges and troughs, established in the Anglo-Paris Basin during Aptian and Lower Albian times continued to influence sedimentation in the Middle Albian, as evidenced by thickness variations in the Gault throughout the basin (Owen, 1971). Within the present district the Gault thickens eastwards from 60 m in the Washington area to more than 90 m near Plumpton. If, however, the Upper Greensand is taken into account the total thickness of Middle and Upper Albian sediments at outcrop is fairly constant across the district. Little is known about these beds where they are concealed beneath the Chalk, save for the Sompting Borehole [1661 0636], in which the combined thickness of Gault and Upper Greensand was 79 m. Of this thickness, the 25 m of Upper Greensand is similar to that at outcrop to the north, though some thinning of the Gault is apparent.

GAULT

The Gault outcrop is characteristically marked by a belt of heavy clay land, usually given over to permanent pasture. Exposures are few, though the basal beds may be seen at a number of places and the clay-pits at Small Dole (p.47) provide excellent sections.

The nature of the contact between the Folkestone Beds and the Gault in the southern Weald was reviewed in Kirkaldy (1935). Although the change in sedimentary conditions from the Folkestone Beds to the Gault was very marked, the precise position of the junction is difficult to place in certain sections. The basal beds vary across the district and in places the sequence appears to exhibit a small thickness of 'passage beds'. In the west the basement bed consists of deep red ferruginous sandstone, known as the Iron Grit (Anderson, 1986). Farther east the bottom metre or so of the Gault is typically sandy, with abundant glauconite and, in places, phosphatic nodules.

Above the basement bed the main body of the Gault consists largely of compact grey mudstones and silty mudstones most of which appear to be calcareous; the lower part of the sequence is richly fossiliferous. Beds of phosphatic nodules probably indicate non-sequences; certain of these are stratigraphically significant and enable correlations to be made with the Gault of other areas.

Throughout the district the mudstones become progressively siltier upwards. East of Westmeston, where the Upper Greensand is absent, the upper silty beds of the Gault are succeeded sharply by the Glauconitic Marl at the base of the Lower Chalk. West of Westmeston there is a gradual passage into the Upper Greensand. In the Chanctonbury Borehole [1445 1215], the one continuously cored borehole to have penetrated this part of the succession, the position of the boundary between the Gault and the Upper Greensand was chosen arbitrarily.

UPPER GREENSAND

West of Westmeston the silty upper beds of the Gault pass upwards into the Upper Greensand (Figure 9). In the present district the Upper Greensand comprises a distinctive, striped, strongly bioturbated, calcareous, fine-grained siltstone, generally known as 'malmstone' (Plate 3). At outcrop the rock is usually pale fawn with grey streaks, though unweathered material from boreholes is grey. Although the precise boundary between the Gault and the Upper Greensand is difficult to place in borehole cores the line can be readily mapped in the field. The junction of the Upper Greensand and the Lower Chalk is sharp and distinctly burrowed, as is the junction of the Gault and Lower Chalk where the Upper Greensand is absent. Over much of its outcrop the Upper Greensand forms a well marked low scarp feature at the foot of the main Chalk escarpment; this feature is particularly prominent in the Washington [120 127] and Edburton areas [234 114]. Fragments of malmstone commonly form an abundant soil brash and exposures of the beds are relatively common in the sides of lanes.

East of Westmeston the Upper Greensand is absent along the whole of the South Downs in the adjacent Lewes district (Lake and others, 1987), but it reappears farther south in the Eastbourne district, where, at Beachy Head, a rather different Upper Greensand sequence is exposed (Young, 1978). There, a series of glauconitic, micaceous, fine-grained sandstones rests with a sharp bioturbated base on typical Gault mudstones, and the upper boundary with the Lower Chalk is much less clear than in the Brighton district.

A bivalve and ammonite fauna indicative of the Upper Albian *Stoliczkaia dispar* Zone (see below) has been obtained from the Upper Greensand malmstones at several localities in the Brighton district. The Upper Greensand at Eastbourne has generally been regarded as being of Late Albian age, though Hart (1969) has suggested that on micropalaeontological grounds much of the sequence may be of early Cenomanian age. If so, much of the Upper Greensand of the Brighton district and that of Eastbourne are of dif-

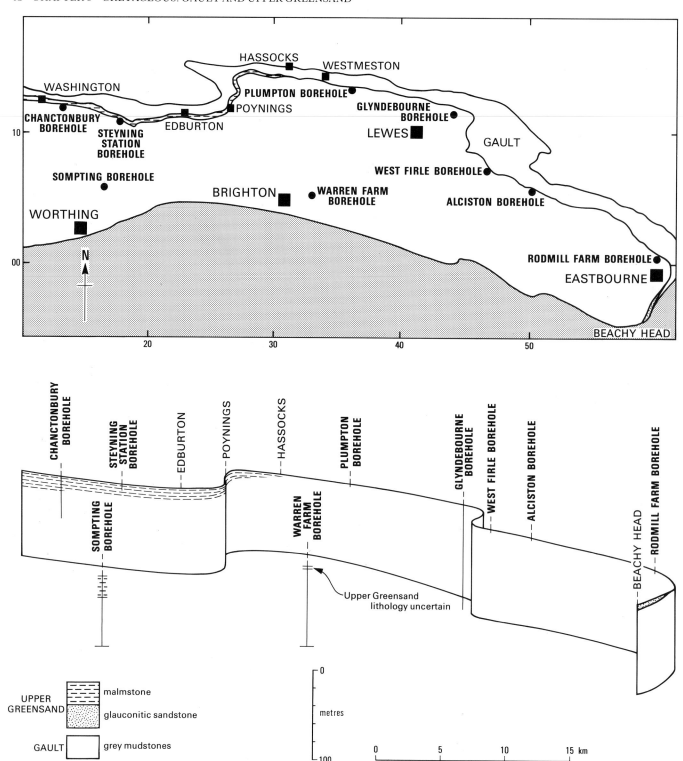

Figure 9   Lithological variations in the Gault and Upper Greensand between Chanctonbury and Eastbourne

Plate 3   Upper Greensand. Calcareous siltstones (malmstone) exposed in a garden at Fulking [A13371]

ferent ages, and the Eastbourne sequence may correlate with the Glauconitic Marl of the Brighton district.   BY

STRATIGRAPHICAL PALAEONTOLOGY

The Gault of this district ranges in age from the *Pseudosonneratia eodentata* Subzone, now placed by Owen (1984) in the topmost Lower Albian *Douvilleiceras mammillatum* Zone, through to the Upper Albian *Mortoniceras (M.) rostratum* Subzone of the *Stoliczkaia dispar* Zone. The Upper Greensand, where present, ranges from the *rostratum* Subzone into the *Durnovarites perinflatum* Subzone and possibly into the earliest Cenomanian.

The modern zonation of the Middle and Upper Albian is based on ammonite zones largely derived from the Gault sections at Folkestone, Kent. Spath (1923a; 1923b; 1926; 1941) set up the zonal scheme which was based on the earlier detailed work of Price (1874; 1876; 1879). The zonation was modified in later studies, notably by Casey (1961; 1966), Milbourne (1955; 1961; 1962; 1963) and Owen (1958; 1960; 1963), which were subsequently reviewed in Hancock

(1965). Owen made extensive reviews of the Middle Albian (1971) and of the Middle and Late Albian (1975; 1979; 1984), which led to the zonation of the Albian tabulated below (see also Figure 10).

Substage	Zone	Subzone
Upper (Late) Albian	*Stoliczkaia dispar*	*Durnovarites perinflatum*
		Mortoniceras (M.) rostratum
	Mortoniceras (M.) inflatum	*Callihoplites auritus* (upper part)
		Callihoplites auritus (lower part)
		Hysteroceras varicosum (upper part)
		Hysteroceras varicosum (lower part)
		Hysteroceras orbignyi
		Dipoloceras cristatum

Middle Albian	*Euhoplites lautus*	*Anahoplites daviesi*
		Euhoplites nitidus
	Euhoplites loricatus	*Euhoplites meandrinus*
		Mojsisovicsia subdelaruei
		Dimorphoplites niobe
		Anahoplites intermedius
	Hoplites (H.) dentatus	*Hoplites spathi* (upper part)
		Hoplites spathi (lower part)
		Lyelliceras lyelli
Lower (Early) Albian (topmost)	*Douvilleiceras mammillatum*	*Pseudosonneratia eodentata*

Kennedy and Hancock (1979) reviewed and listed Albian faunas and published zonal and subzonal assemblages of ammonites. Unfortunately, owing to errors in earlier published work, the *varicosum*, *auritus* and *rostratum* subzonal faunas were misunderstood (Owen, 1984). Faunal lists for the *Mortoniceras aequatoriale* and *M. alstonense* subzones now relate in part to the *auritus* and *rostratum* subzones, though the upper part of the *auritus* Subzone is still poorly known in respect of ammonite faunas (Gallois and Morter, 1982). Also, following earlier authors, the *auritus* Subzone was regarded as synonymous with Bed XI at Folkestone; however, the latter includes the top part of the *varicosum* Subzone near its base (Owen, 1975).

The ammonite faunas

The zonation above relates to the European or Hoplitinid province of Owen (1975), made up of the endemic hoplitid genera *Anahoplites*, *Dimorphoplites*, *Euhoplites* and *Hoplites* which dominate the Middle Albian, and *Callihoplites* and *Epihoplites* which dominate the Upper Albian, together with the rarer *Discohoplites*, *Lepthoplites* and *Pleurohoplites*. The hoplitinid zones and subzones are interspersed with sub-zones containing ammonites of warmer-water Tethyan origins, which represent southern derived incursions (Owen, 1975; 1979). In the Middle Albian these Tethyan forms are represented by *Lyelliceras* and *Mojsisovicsia*, and other genera such as *Brancoceras*, *Eubrancoceras* and *Oxytropidoceras*. In the Upper Albian there was a major invasion of the Hoplitinid province by *Dipoloceras* and the brancoceratid ammonites *Hysteroceras* and *Prohysteroceras*, accompanied by large mortoniceratid ammonites. This expansion of the faunal province was part of a widespread event which allows international correlation. The *auritus* Subzone saw a decline in the brancoceratids and a relative increase in hoplitid numbers with *Callihoplites* and *Lepthoplites*, but a renewed Tethyan influence is seen with the entry of *Stoliczkaia* in the *dispar* Zone.

Many of these Tethyan ammonites are limited to southern Britain and are absent in areas such as East Anglia (Gallois and Morter, 1982) and northern Germany (Owen, 1979), which have a 'Boreal' aspect to their faunas. In the *dispar* Zone, however, the distribution of these ammonites is more widespread and this reflects the enhanced effect of the transgression in the latest Albian.

Inoceramids and other faunas

Work in East Anglia (Gallois and Morter, 1982) has shown that the ammonite zones can often be determined by the use of other associated faunas. The inoceramid bivalves, which are the most common fossils of the Gault (Casey, 1966; Kauffman 1977; 1979; Owen, 1975; 1979; 1984), are especially useful.

The Middle Albian inoceramids are dominated by *Birostrina concentrica* and its subspecies, together with the rarer '*Inoceramus*' of the *anglicus* group. The lower part of the Upper Albian, *cristatum* and *orbignyi* subzones, contains abundant *Birostrina sulcata* especially in the higher part of the latter subzone. This species is accompanied by the 'transition form' derived from *B. concentrica*, *B. subsulcata*, which occurs mainly at the base of the *cristatum* Subzone (Casey, 1966; Owen, 1975; 1979). These are accompanied by less common forms such as '*Inoceramus*' *anglicus*, '*Inoceramus*' of the *crippsi* group ('*I.*' cf. *bellevuensis*), '*Inoceramus*' of the *anglicus–commancheanus* group and a small thin-shelled *Birostrina concentrica gryphaeoides* (Gallois and Morter, 1982).

Above the *varicosum* Subzone most authors, especially Casey (1966) and Kauffman (1979), could not determine the true succession of inoceramid faunas because of the confusion over ammonite zonation mentioned above. The early part of the *varicosum* Subzone contains abundant inoceramids dominated by forms of *B. concentrica* subspecies C and D of Kauffman which occur together in this subzone. The latter has sometimes been identified as '*I.*' *tenuis*. These are accompanied by '*Inoceramus*' of the *anglicus* and *crippsi* groups. The upper part of the *varicosum* Subzone shows a decline in numbers of all these forms and these are progressively replaced by the thick, smooth-shelled '*Inoceramus*' *lissa* (Gallois and Morter, 1982), which reaches its acme in the lower part of the *auritus* Subzone. *B. concentrica* and its subspecies appear to be extinct by the end of the *varicosum* Subzone.

The upper part of the *auritus* Subzone marks the extinction of '*I.*' *lissa*, and a virtual inoceramid 'hiatus' existed until the Cenomanian. Apart from a few very rare thin-shelled forms of the *crippsi* group, inoceramids are replaced by the bivalve *Aucellina*, which is uncommon in the *auritus* Subzone but becomes abundant in the *dispar* Zone (Morter and Wood, 1983).

Other shelly fossils are locally useful and their distributions, which have been plotted by Price (1874; 1879) and Casey (1966) at Folkestone, can also be used in the Gault over most of southern England; for example the bivalve *Anomia carregozica* is nearly always well represented at the top of the *intermedius* Subzone (Bed II) at Folkestone. Gallois and Morter (1982) in East Anglia have termed this the 'Anomia-rich band', which probably represents an unusual, possibly slightly euxinic environment which spread through the Gault sea at the end of *intermedius* times.

The gastropod *Anchura* (*Perissoptera*) *carinata* described from Sussex (Mantell, 1822) is probably characteristic and common in the *nitidus* Subzone.

The belemnite *Neohibolites minimus* is common in the Lower Gault (Middle Albian) and the lower part of the Upper Albian, but it is especially abundant in the topmost part of the *intermedius* Subzone and in the lower part of the *orbignyi* Subzone (Milbourne *in* Hancock, 1965; Gallois and Morter, 1982).

Microfossils

In recent years a large amount of work has been carried out on Middle and Upper Albian microfossils, notably the foraminifera (Carter and Hart, 1977; Price, 1977; Frieg and Price, 1981; Hart and others, 1981) and ostracods (Hart, 1974; Wilkinson and Morter, 1981). Much of this work has been related to the ammonite zonation of Owen (1975), though problems still exist over the delimitation of the *Callihoplites auritus* Subzone owing to lack of exposure and the absence of suitable sections.

The foraminifera and ostracoda of the Glyndebourne Borehole [4220 1141] to the east of this district were studied in detail by Harris (1982), who established a succession of twelve subzones spanning the Middle Albian and most of the Upper Albian. Many of these are closely tied to the macro-fossil zonation and reflect the transgressive and regressive events of Middle and Late Albian time. A series of eight 'biohorizons' or events were recognised which can be directly related to macrofossil zonation, lithology and fundamental changes in the palaeoecological environment.

For example, Biohorizon 8, which marks the entry of abundant *Globigerinelloides bentonensis*, coincides with the abundant occurrence of the bivalve *Aucellina* at the base of the *dispar* Zone (Morter and Wood, 1983) and the influx of possible cooler waters into the area (Price, 1976).

Nannofossil studies (Taylor, 1981) lack some precision in their relationship with macrofossil zonation. Much of the work so far has been done in eastern England (Black, 1972; 1973; 1975) and northern France (Zeighampour, 1981).

Work on microfloras has so far achieved no detailed zonal scheme. Kemp (1970), working on British pollen and spores, recognised only three first appearances within the Albian, though no satisfactory sections have been studied above the *Hysteroceras varicosum* Subzone.

The study of phytoplankton (dinoflagellate cysts) in Britain has progressed little beyond the work of Cookson and Hughes (1964). The main work on these fossils was carried out in northern France (Davey and Verdier, 1971; 1973), but the distribution of floras is somewhat provincial and probably subject to facies changes and palaeoclimatology (Châteauneuf and Fauconnier, 1979).

The local succession

The top of the Lower Albian (*Pseudosonneratia eodentata* Sub-zone) is represented by glauconitic loams at the base of the Gault at Danny [2908 1548]. In the Horton Clay Pit [2100 1240] at Small Dole the zonal age of the basal Gault is in doubt but the Middle Albian is well represented by a thick succession which contains rich faunas of the *lyelli*, *spathi*, *intermedius* and *meandrinus* subzones (Figure 10; Owen, 1971). The *subdelaruei* Subzone is, however, very thin and the *daviesi* Subzone is probably absent (Owen, 1975; 1984). The clay-pit also exposes Upper Albian sediments of the *cristatum* Sub-zone and lower part of the *orbignyi* Subzone with the *Euhoplites inornatus* Band. The beds above this are poorly exposed.

The higher part of the *auritus* Subzone and the *dispar* Zone were cored in the Chanctonbury Borehole [1445 1215]. The top part of the Gault (84.00 to 89.84 m) contained a *rostratum* Subzone (basal *dispar* Zone) fauna and the Upper Greensand

above also contained a possible *rostratum* Subzone fauna. The Upper Greensand to the west of the River Adur has yielded limited faunas which may indicate that the *Durnovarites perinflatum* Subzone is represented there.   AAM

DETAILS

Gault

Area west of the River Adur

Sections at the top of the south-eastern face [0954 1389] of the disused Marley Brick and Tile Company pit east of Chantry Mill, Storrington, 500 m west of the Brighton district, showed cross-bedded and locally reddened medium- to coarse-grained sands of the Folkestone Beds, overlain with a sharp base by the Iron Grit (p.41); this was succeeded, also with a sharp contact, by up to 2.5 m of grey clays with scattered coarse sand grains in their lowest 0.3 m. The Iron Grit was 0.12 m thick and consisted of a very hard, deep red, ferruginous pebbly sandstone with subrounded quartz pebbles up to 5 mm in diameter. Kirkaldy (1935, p.528) described a similar section in this pit, noting glauconite grains and carbonised wood in the lowest 0.23 m of the clay. In a discussion of the sections in the pit, Owen (1963, p.45) recorded *Inoceramus concentricus* and *Hoplites (H.) spp.* with *dentatus*-like ribbing from between approximately 1 and 2 m above the base of the Iron Grit, together with a poorly preserved and partly phosphatised specimen of *Hoplites* cf. *dentatus* from roughly 2 m above the Iron Grit; he considered the beds yielding these fossils to belong to the *spathi* Subzone.

There are no exposures of the Gault between Storrington and Steyning, though White (1924, p.26) described and figured a section in the sides of Barns Farm Lane [1058 1370], east of Storrington, showing Folkestone Beds overlain by the basal Gault with Iron Grit dipping southwards at 5°, as follows:

	Thickness m
[GAULT]	
Dark grey micaceous sandy glauconitic clay, stained red in lowest 3 in [0.08 m]	seen [0.9]
Blood-red grit: a compact, heavy, argillaceous iron-sandstone with small polished pebbles of quartz and dark siliceous rocks. Nests of glauconite grains in places	[0.04 to 0.1]
[FOLKESTONE BEDS]	
Dark yellowish to light brown coarse, slightly loamy sand with small pebbles (as in bed above) and friable ill-defined white phosphatic concretions: the topmost inch or so stained bright red	seen [0.9]

Kirkaldy (1935, p.528) recorded a similar section in sand-pits [1200 1342] now covered by the Washington By-pass at the junction of the A24 London to Worthing road with the A283 road to Storrington.

The Iron Grit appears to die out a short distance east of Washington. The following section [approximately 1416 1313] in Copyhold Wood, near Weppons Farm, was recorded by Kirkaldy (1935, p.527):

	Thickness m
GAULT	
7 Brown clay	[0.46]
6 Greenish sandy clay	[0.08]
5 Irregular layer of white nodules set in greenish sandy clay with small lydite and quartz pebbles up	

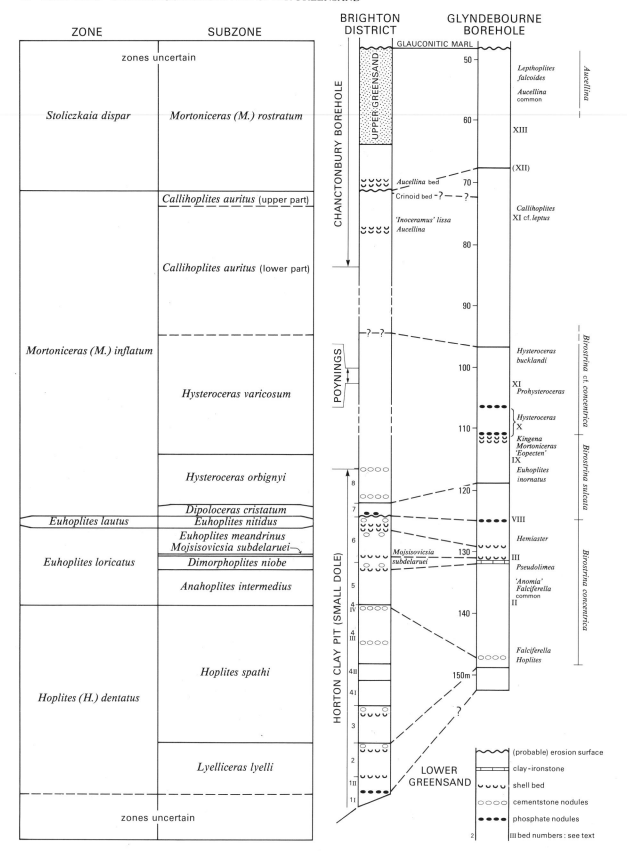

Figure 10 Zonal classification of the Gault of the Brighton district compared with that of the Glyndebourne Borehole, near Lewes

to two inches [50 mm] in diameter	[0.05]
4 Black sandy clay	[0.03]
3 Continuous layer of nodules, many with a ferruginous centre. The nodules are hard and up to three inches [76 mm] in length	[0.05]
2 Red-brown coloured, medium sand streaked with black clay. Passing down into	[0.3]
[FOLKESTONE BEDS]	
1 Brown coarse sand	seen [0.9]

The Iron Grit was not present here but Kirkaldy observed that the incoming of ferruginous conditions was indicated in the lowest beds of the Gault. He further noted that the bed taken here as the basal bed of the Gault constitutes a passage between the sands of the Folkestone Beds and the overlying Gault clays.

Old sand-pits on either side of the Steyning to Ashurst road [1739 1305] are now degraded and overgrown; Kirkaldy (1935, pp.526–527) described the basal beds of the Gault here as consisting of glauconitic sandy clay with soft, phosphatic nodules up to 30 mm across, composed of quartz, lydite and glauconite grains set in a white matrix. Specimens of *Douvilleiceras* aff. *mammillatum*, *Beudanticeras sp.* and *Lima (Mantellum)* cf. *gaultina* have been obtained from these pits.

The topmost 18.21 m of the Gault, consisting essentially of monotonous grey silty mudstones, were cored between the depths of 83.0 and 101.21 m in the Chanctonbury Borehole [1445 1215]. The zonal positions of the Gault and Upper Greensand penetrated here are shown in Figure 10. There is a gradual passage from the siltstones of the Upper Greensand (see p.49) to the silty mudstones of the Gault. The uppermost Gault between 83 and 89.84 m, belongs to the *Mortoniceras rostratum* Subzone; the base of this division is taken at an erosion surface which has been recognised widely in this country; the plentiful macrofauna includes *Pharetrospongia strahani*, *Aucellina spp.*, *Entolium orbiculare*, *Plicatula radiola gurgitis*, *Pycnodonte (Phygraea)* aff. *vesicularis*, *Syncyclonema sp.*, *Gyrodes sp.*, *Callihoplites seeleyi crenata*, *Lepthoplites* cf. *pseudoplanus*. Beds between 88.90 and 89.94 m are probably equivalent to Bed XII at Folkestone (Casey *in* Smart and others, 1966; Owen, 1975), which is now regarded as the base of the *Stoliczkaia dispar* Zone (Dr H. G. Owen, Dr R. J. Price and Dr C. S. Harris, personal communications); this basal fauna with common *Aucellina* can also be matched with Bed 17 (Gallois and Morter, 1982) of the East Anglian Gault sequence in which *Aucellina spp.* are abundant. The basal part of the beds, with numerous examples of *Pharetrospongia*, resembles the Chert Beds sequence of south-west England, where beds of calcareous sponges occur near the base. From the beds between 89.84 and 92.60 m the following macrofauna has been identified: *Smilotrochus sp.* indet., *Entolium orbiculare*, *Gryphaeostrea canaliculata*, *Plicatula radiola gurgitis*, *Spondylus gibbosus*, indeterminate scaphopod, *Isocrinus ?legeri* and echinoid and fish remains; this limited fauna is typical of the upper part of the *auritus* Subzone and is well seen in Bed 16 of the Gault in East Anglia (Gallois and Morter, 1982). Between 89.84 and 90.00 m columnals of the crinoid *Isocrinus ?legeri* were common, together with the bivalve *Spondylus gibbosus*; this bed probably correlates with the Milton Crinoid Bed at the top of the *auritus* Subzone in East Anglia and possibly also with certain beds at the base of the Chert Beds near Beer, Devon. Between 92.60 and 96.08 m a limited but diagnostic *auritus* Subzone fauna was present, dominated in the lower part by *Aucellina sp.* and fragments of *Inoceramus*; this division represents the '*Inoceramus*' lissa Beds of East Anglia and forms part of a Europe-wide belt in which small fragments of '*I.*' *lissa* are common. Below 96.08 m the mudstones contained the bivalves *Entolium orbiculare* and *Pycnodonte (Phygraea)* aff. *vesicularis*, together with indeterminate oysters and sponge fragments; the nannofossils 'proto-*Eiffellithus*' *sp.* and *Eiffellithus turriseiffeli* were obtained from these beds and indicated a position within the *Callihoplites auritus* Subzone (Dr A. W. Medd, personal communication).

Area east of the River Adur

The Horton Clay Pit [2100 1240] at Small Dole has provided the most extensive exposures of the Gault in this country (Figure 10), though owing to the method of working, clean faces are uncommon and the exposures available change rapidly. It has attracted the attention of a number of workers, including White (1924, pp.27–28), Casey (1961, p.558), Milbourne, (1961, pp.135–137), and Owen (1963, p.46; 1971, pp.34–41). The following account has been compiled from the work of Dr H. G. Owen and of Mr R. A. Milbourne. The previous published account by Dr Owen (1971) only encompassed the Lower Gault; small parts of the section have been revised following his later field observations and he has provided sections for the Upper Gault succession. Mr Milbourne has also supplied further manuscript material.

The following section and enumeration of divisions are based on Dr Owen's work:

	Thickness m
UPPER GAULT	
Hysteroceras orbignyi Subzone (Division 8)	
Clay, pale grey, weathered	seen to 1.73
Cementstone band, grey, hard and persistent	0.18
Clay, grey	0.15
Impersistent lenticles of reddish grey mudstone and phosphatic nodules	0.03
Dipoloceras cristatum Subzone	
Clay, dark grey, with scattered phosphatic nodules; the clay becomes very dark grey, drab coloured in lower part; thin seam of brown nodules at base (Division 7)	2.47
LOWER GAULT	
Euhoplites nitidus Subzone	
Clay, marly, fawn-grey, with cementstone nodules showing cone-in-cone structure (Division 6 vii)	0.53
Clay, dark grey, with scattered phosphatic nodules (Divison 6 vi)	0.36
Clay, fawn-grey, shelly, with scattered phosphatic nodules and part-phosphatised, part-pyritised fossils (Division 6 v)	0.41
Euhoplites meandrinus Subzone	
Clay, dark grey, with paler bands some of which contain very scattered cementstone nodules; shell seams occur throughout (Divison 6 iv)	4.90
Mojsisovicsia subdelaruei Subzone	
Clay, fawn, with sporadic phosphatic nodules and part-phosphatised fossils (Division 6 iii)	0.03
Dimorphoplites niobe Subzone	
Clay, marly, fawn-grey, shelly, with a few cementstones (Division 6 ii); passing down into	0.56
Clay, mid-grey with scattered shells (Division 6 i)	0.66
Clay, marly, fawn-grey, shelly, with large cementstone nodules showing cone-in-cone structure (Division 5 iv)	1.22
Anahoplites intermedius Subzone	
Clay, dark grey, slightly micaceous, shelly, with scattered phosphatic nodules, and a more concentrated band, 0.53 m thick, commencing 0.76 m from the base; crushed fossils occur throughout (Division 5 iii)	3.66
Clay, marly, fawn, weathering ferruginous (Division 5 ii)	0.30

Clay, dark grey, slightly micaceous, shelly, with
numerous shell seams (Division 5 i)   2.44

Hoplites (Hoplites) spathi Subzone

Marl, fawn-grey, tough, blocky, with cementstone
nodules in the lower part (Division 4 iv)   0.60

Clay, fawn-grey and dark grey, slightly
micaceous, shelly, with scattered shell seams;
slightly paler bands alternate and contain part-
phosphatised fossils (Division 4 iii)   8.99

Two clay bands, fawn-grey, shelly, and with
small nodules of cementstone, are separated by a
darker grey clay seam containing many crushed
shells; part-phosphatised fossils occur in both
fawn-grey bands (Division 4 ii)   2.54

Alternating bands of dark grey shelly clay with
crushed fossils and fawn-grey shelly clays with
occasional partly phosphatised ammonites
(Division 4 i)   3.86

Clay, fawn, shelly, with cementstone concretions
and some partly phosphatised fossils (Division 3
iv)   0.61

Clay, dark grey, shelly, with a few partly
phosphatised fossils (Division 3 iii)   0.69

Clay, fawn, shelly, with a shell seam at base
containing cementstone nodules and partly
phosphatised fossils (Division 3 ii)   0.46

Clay, dark grey, shelly, with many crushed shells
and a few scattered phosphatic nodules (Division
3 i)   4.11

Lyelliceras lyelli Subzone

Clay, fawn-grey, shelly, with some large partly
phosphatised ammonites in soft marly
concretions (Division 2 vi)   0.30

Clay, mid-grey to fawn-grey, shelly(Division 2 v)   0.20

Clay, fawn-grey, shelly with some large part-
phosphatised ammonites; a shell-seam 0.1 m
above the base, washed out in places, yields
beautifully preserved part-pyritised, part-
phosphatised fossils (Division 2 iv); passing
down into   1.12

Clay, dark grey, shelly, (Division 2 iii); passing
down into   0.36

Clay, fawn-grey, more shelly than bed above
(Division 2 ii); passing down into   0.30

Clay, mid-grey, blocky, darkening upwards with
phosphate nodules scattered throughout; shelly,
particularly at the base, which is marked by a
shell seam; the bed becomes less fossiliferous
0.3 m above the base (Division 2 i)   2.31

Clay, dark grey, glauconitic, with patches of
glauconite on bedding planes; the uppermost
0.3 m is shelly; below this glauconite increases
and pyrite-infilled worm burrows occur (Division
1 ii)   2.44

Pseudosonneratia eodentata Subzone

Loam, dark green, glauconitic, hard, with rafts
of clay and pockets and channels of coarse sand;
sandy phosphatic nodules and small pebbles;
pyritic nodules at top; hard pebbly band, 0.15 m
thick, 0.61 m from base (Division 1 i)   0 to 2.44

LOWER GREENSAND (see p.38)   —

The lowest 4 m of beds are beneath the exposed workings in the pit
and are known only from boreholes.

Owen (1971, p.35) recognised sedimentary rhythms within the
clays here, each rhythm beginning with relatively rapid

sedimentation characterised by marly beds and bands of
cementstone nodules. Individual rhythms are up to 9.5 m thick.
Owen also observed that the fawn-grey clay beds contained a varied
benthonic fauna.

In the Upper Gault, Milbourne (1961, p.135) recorded some
35 ft [10.67 m] of *orbignyi* Subzone strata which, added to the
cristatum Subzone (7 ft 2 in) [2.18 m], made a total thickness of 42 ft
2 in [12.85 m] for the Upper Gault, compared to the 4.56 m of
Upper Gault described by Owen (in MS). However, Milbourne
undoubtedly saw some beds higher than those seen by either
Templeman in 1922 (*in* White, 1924) or Owen in 1962. The details
of the faunas are retained on file at the BGS office at Keyworth.

Excavations for an electricity pylon [2510 1465] at Holmbush
Plantation, near Poynings Crossways revealed grey clays from
which the following upper *Hysteroceras varicosum* Subzone fauna was
collected: *Cyclocyathus fittoni*, *Cirsocerithium subspinosum*, *Dentalium
(Fissidentalium) sp.*, *Pycnodonte (Phygraea)* aff. *vesicularis*, *Anahoplites* cf.
picteti, *Euhoplites alphalautus*, *Epihoplites sp.* (cf. *denarius* gr.),
Hysteroceras cf. *andinum*, *H. carinatum*, *H. carinatum* aff. *robustecostatum*,
H. cf. *choffati*, *H.* aff. *subbinum*, *Mortoniceras (Deiradoceras)* cf. *cunningtoni*, *Neohibolites sp.* A small exposure [2535 1253] in the south
bank of an unnamed stream east of Clapper's Lane, Poynings,
showed about 0.3 m of dark grey, glauconite-free clay within the
basal beds of the Gault beneath 1.5 m of very glauconitic clay. The
contact with the Folkestone Beds was probably close beneath the
base of the exposed sequence.

The south face of the Danny Sand Pit [2908 1548] exposed
Folkestone Beds overlain by the basal beds of the Gault (White,
1926; Kirkaldy,1935). The following section was measured in 1975.

	Thickness m
GAULT	
Clay, grey, uniform; occasional patches of yellow powdery ?phosphatic material; scattered glauconite grains near base; passing down to	1.0
Clay, greenish grey, rather waxy-textured, glauconitic; numerous patches of yellow powdery material (?jarosite) as above; passing down to	0.5
Clay, greenish grey to greenish black; glauconite appears to be concentrated in 2 to 3 mm-wide branching burrows; becoming sandy near base and passing down to	1.0
Clay, very sandy, ochreous fawn and dark greenish grey, glauconitic; strongly bioturbated; becoming more sandy towards sharp base	0.75
FOLKESTONE BEDS (see p.39)	seen to 5.15

Casey (1961, p.560) noted the presence of *Lyelliceras* and
Beudanticeras laevigatum at about 2 m above the base of the Gault and
Owen (1971, p.41) indicated that the *eodentata* Subzone was
represented in these lowest beds.

The south-western face [3489 1477] of the Streat Sand Pit provides a good section through the upper part of the Folkestone Beds
and the base of the Gault (see p.39).

In the Plumpton Borehole [3545 1350] some 0.06 m of pale fawn-
grey silty clay of typical Gault aspect (p.66) was proved beneath the
base of the Glauconitic Marl at a depth of 29.24 m.

Deep boreholes and wells

The most recent borehole to penetrate the Gault in this district was
the Sompting Borehole [1661 0636], drilled in 1978. No cores were
taken from this formation but cuttings indicated that the Gault here
is 54 m thick, consisting predominantly of grey silty mudstone.
Coarse-grained glauconitic sand was recorded at the base and the

junction with the overlying Upper Greensand appeared to be transitional, probably resembling that proved in the Chanctonbury Borehole [1445 1215].

The record of a deep well [2272 0507] at Shoreham shows that it terminated in Gault at a depth of 400.81 m, though the level of the top of the Gault is uncertain. Edmunds (1928, p.187) recorded the Lower Chalk overlying Gault at a depth of 1300 ft [396.24 m], but added that G. W. Lamplugh 'was of the opinion that the Gault was reached somewhere between 1260 ft and 1315 ft [384.05 m and 400.81 m]'. It is not clear whether any Upper Greensand was present.

A hand-dug well at Warren Farm, Woodingdean [3517 0565] provided the following section through the Gault (Whitaker and Reid, 1899, p.83; Edmunds, 1928, pp.194–195:

	Thickness m	Depth m
UPPER GREENSAND (?part)		
6 'Firestone' (p.50)	3.05	295.05
GAULT		
5 Clay, varying from ash-brown to black and bluish black	85.95	381.00
4 Clay, with seams of green sand, much vegetable matter, wood and pyrites	7.62	388.62
3 Clay, brown, non-calcareous, with hard white nodules (?phosphatic)	1.52	390.14
?LOWER GREENSAND or GAULT		
2 'Greensand' with seams of white sand, mixed with pebbles (?phosphatic nodules)	1.53	391.67
LOWER GREENSAND		
1 Sand, red, touched by a small auger	—	—

The description given of bed 2 of this sequence closely resembles the sandy, glauconitic, basal beds of the Gault seen at outcrop elsewhere in the district. Casey (1961, p.559) suggested that bed 3 might be a correlative of his Horton Wood Clay at Small Dole (p.38) and classified it as part of the Lower Greensand. However, in this Memoir the Horton Wood Clay is included with the Gault and bed 2 is considered to be the basal bed of this formation; on this basis the total thickness of Gault present in the Woodingdean well is 96.62 m.

Upper Greensand

Area west of the River Adur

Over much of its outcrop between the western edge of the district and Steyning [177 111] the Upper Greensand forms a prominent north-facing scarp feature rising up to 15 m above the Gault country to the north.

Excavations at the Rectory, Washington [1192 1281], showed typical malmstone in which were found fragments of Aucellina sp. A loose block of malmstone collected near an old pit [1424 1269] south of Weppons Farm contained a specimen of Plicatula radiola gurgitis. Both of these bivalves are common in the Stoliczkaia dispar Zone, though the former also occurs in the underlying Callihoplites auritus Subzone.

In the Chanctonbury Borehole [1445 1215] Upper Greensand was penetrated between the depths of 67.32 and 83.0 m (Figure 10). Much of the formation consisted of the typical striped, bioturbated, calcareous, silty malmstone seen at outcrop. The junction of the Upper Greensand and the Glauconitic Marl was a sharp erosion surface. A very hard, compact, silty limestone bed, 0.2 m thick, was penetrated at 70.40 m. Beds of very hard malmstone occurred between 73.64 and 73.96 m and between 74.38 and 74.94 m. A few phosphatic nodules were recorded in places and these were most common between depths of 79 and 80 m. The very highest Upper Greensand beds, between the base of the Chalk at 67.32 m and 70.4 m, provided only a limited macrofauna, including Plicatula sp. and the oyster Pycnodonte (Phygraea) sp. The zonal position of beds between 70.4 and 78.3 m is uncertain. The restricted macrofauna found comprises Entolium orbiculare, Plicatula radiola gurgitis, together with indeterminate ostreids, a trochid gastropod, echinoid and fish fragments, and is not diagnostic of age, though the presence of the Plicatula suggests an Albian rather than a Cenomanian age. The following dispar Zone macrofauna was obtained from between 78.3 and and 84.0 m: Anticonulus sp., Aucellina sp., Entolium sp., Ludbrookia tenuicosta, Neithea sp., Plicatula sp., Glenotremites sp., together with echinoid, crinoid and fish debris. It seems probable that these beds are of rostratum Subzone age, though a perinflatum Subzone age cannot be ruled out. Sediments of perinflatum Subzone age commonly mark the beginning of the Upper Greensand facies in eastern England and it is thought that a similar situation obtains at Chanctonbury.

Mouse Lane [1717 1163], immediately west of Steyning, provides a number of good exposures through the top part of the Upper Greensand. In the north banks of the lane up to 2.5 m of fawn and grey malmstone are exposed, overlain in places by the Glauconitic Marl. The malmstone is typically strongly bioturbated, with distinct burrows up to 8 mm in diameter, and locally shows alternations of hard and softer beds.

The eastern side of the A283 Steyning to Washington road just west of Steyning [1737 1163] exposes up to 2.5 m of poorly cemented pale fawn and grey malmstone. Hard compact malmstone crops out on the western side of the road at this place. Pale fawn and grey to ochreous brown malmstone near the top of the Upper Greensand is seen in a 1.5 m exposure [1771 1144] near St Andrew's Parish Church, Steyning.

The Upper Greensand was proved in two boreholes at Steyning Station. The first of these [1816 1133], drilled in 1927, proved 14.3 m of Upper Greensand without reaching the Gault. The second, the BGS Steyning Station Borehole [1818 1130], was drilled in 1973; it penetrated a minimum of 1.04 m of Glauconitic Marl and continued in fawn and grey wispy-bedded Upper Greensand malmstone to a depth of 10.66 m.

Area east of the River Adur

Between Horton Hall [2095 1160] and Poynings [262 120] the Upper Greensand outcrop is marked by a prominent low scarp feature with much malmstone soil brash. A well at Edburton [2313 1145], starting near the top of the Upper Greensand, proved 2.4 m of Head overlying Upper Greensand, which passed into Gault at a depth of 12.8 m. The road-cutting [2323 1142] near Edburton church exposes up to 4.0 m of poorly cemented to well cemented malmstone, with occasional Chondrites burrows and clay-lined burrows up to 5 mm in diameter, high in the Upper Greensand.

Approximately 0.8 m of grey and fawn malmstone is seen in the east bank of the track [2343 1157] at Aburton Farm, Edburton. Excavations nearby [2342 1151] exposed similar beds which yielded the following fauna of bivalves and ammonites indicative of the Stoliczkaia dispar Zone: Aucellina sp., Plagiostoma globosa, Plicatula gurgitis, Callihoplites cf. pseudoglaber and C. cf. tetragonus. Aburton farmhouse [2343 1145] is one of the few buildings in the district in which Upper Greensand malmstone has been used to any extent as a building stone.

A partially overgrown section [2448 1140] in the roadside near Perching Manor Farm shows 3.0 m of poorly cemented to well cemented, medium grey malmstone with sporadic Chondrites and some concentrically filled burrows up to 15 mm in diameter.

Good sections in Upper Greensand malmstones may be seen in the road-cuttings near the Shepherd and Dog public house, Fulking. White (1924, p.30) noted that, in all, approximately 7.6 m of beds were exposed here. The following section [2467 1139] is typical:

	Thickness m
Malmstone, mottled pale grey and fawn, bioturbated, massive	about 0.7
Malmstone, pale grey, friable, structureless	0 to 0.14
Malmstone, clayey, dark olive-grey; strongly bioturbated; some relict lamination; fissile appearance on weathering	0.6
Malmstone, clayey, pale fawn, with irregular patches of orange staining; very shattered	0.2
Malmstone, pale olive-grey, with olive-black and pale fawn wisps; intensely bioturbated; possibly some relict lamination; some olive-black, clay-lined burrows from 2 to 4 mm in diameter	0.35
Malmstone, medium grey, well cemented; weathers into rounded blocks; strongly bioturbated; burrows from 1 to 6 mm in diameter; locally burrows are less pronounced, giving the rock a more homogeneous appearance; passes laterally into pale fawn and orange-brown friable, shattered malmstone	seen to 1.2

Numerous subvertical NE–SW-trending joints cut the beds in this section, though some fail to reach the uppermost massive malmstone bed. Generally similar malmstones are exposed in the bed of the stream [2465 1133] nearby. The strong spring [2471 1126] that feeds the stream rises from just above the Glauconitic Marl.

Large blocks of hard malmstone in the soil [2582 1170] south-west of Dyke Farm, Poynings, have yielded an indeterminate nautiloid and *Callihoplites* cf. *pulcher*, indicative of the *dispar* Zone.

In Poynings village up to 1.0 m of typical pale grey and fawn malmstone is exposed beneath the foundations of buildings at Dyke Farm [2607 1195], and the road banks immediately east of the Royal Oak public house [2625 1200] expose up to 1.0 m of rather flaggy-weathering malmstone.

The eastern face of an old pit [2930 1446] south-west of Coldharbour Farm shows the following beds:

	Thickness m
Malmstone, pale fawn-grey and pale grey, relatively hard, wispy-laminated; 'flaggy'-weathering; passing down to	about 3.0
Malmstone, fawn-grey, friable, wispy-laminated with *Aucellina sp.*, *Entolium sp.*, *Mimachlamys hispidus* [= *M. robinaldina*], *Neithea sp.*, *Spondylus* cf. *gibbosus*, and some indeterminate fish fragments; weathering into rounded blocks; becoming softer and rather clayey towards the base	seen to 1.75

The lowest beds in this section were exposed by digging and showed evidence of a downward passage into the silty clays at the top of the Gault. Augering in the degraded southern face of the pit showed the base of the Glauconitic Marl at about 1.5 m above the level of the top of the section described and hence the Upper Greensand here is about 7 m thick.

Topley (1875, p.158) commented that in the railway-cutting [2987 1416] at the northern entrance to Clayton Tunnel (now obscured) the Upper Greensand consisted of darkish sandy marl and marly sand with no hard beds; White (1924, p.30) suggested that in this description Topley's 'marl' should be read as 'malm'.

A pit [3140 1396] near Whitelands provides the most easterly exposure of the malmstone facies and displays 2.5 m of pale grey and fawn, rubbly-weathering malmstone overlain by the Glauconitic Marl (p.66). The Gault – Upper Greensand junction probably occurs at 2 to 3 m below the exposed section. The top 50 mm of the Upper Greensand is penetrated by burrows filled with glauconite-rich sediment from the overlying bed. Bivalves collected from the Upper Greensand at this locality include *Entolium orbiculare*, *Neithea sp.*, *?Pycnodonte (Phygraea) sp.* (cap valve) and *?small Plicatula sp.*; all are long-ranging forms and provide no evidence of zonal age.

Deep boreholes and wells

In the Sompting Borehole [1661 0636] cuttings from beneath the base of the Chalk at 325 m indicated that grey calcareous fine-grained siltstones, similar to the malmstones of the outcrop, were present and, like the beds at outcrop, passed down into the mudstones of the Gault. The Gault – Upper Greensand junction occurred at about 350 m depth. The formational thickness of 25 m is greater than that proved in the Chanctonbury Borehole (p.49), and may be an overestimate.

Considerable uncertainty surrounds the nature of the beds immediately beneath the Chalk in the well at Warren Farm, Woodingdean [3517 0565] (see p.49). In the published log Whitaker and Reid (1899, p. 83) assigned 3.05 m of 'Firestone without water' overlying the Gault to the Upper Greensand. Above this level the log recorded 99.97 m of 'Lower Chalk and partly Upper Greensand' with inadequate supporting descriptions.   BY, AAM, DM

CHAPTER 6

Cretaceous: Chalk

INTRODUCTION

The Chalk comprises a sequence of microporous limestones up to 425 m thick. These limestone are coccolith biomicrites with a varying content of larger shell fragments. Flint occurs as nodular courses, tabular beds and linings to fractures, and characterises the upper parts of the sequence. Concentrations of phosphate, glauconite and pyrite are present locally.

Traces of clay-grade detritus (mainly quartz) occur throughout the Chalk, but overall comprise less then one per cent of the rock. At various levels the clay material occurs as marl seams and partings, locally as part of a rhythmic sequence of marls and argillaceous chalks, and elsewhere resting on minor erosion surfaces. Such surfaces reflect different degrees of reworking of the underlying chalk and are marked variously by intense burrowing, by the presence of borings and encrustations associated with subsequent phosphatisation and glauconitisation, or by the erosion of the chalk to form pebbles. In areas of shallow-water deposition the upper surface of the sediment may have been secondarily cemented by aragonite, the degree of secondary lithification ranging from patchy hardening to complete induration. Nodular chalks are the first stage in this sequence of progressive synsedimentary cementation, leading to the formation of a lithified surface known as a hardground (Bromley, 1978), which caps a chalkstone (Bromley and Gale, 1982).

A further distinction may be made between lithologies which in the past would have been grouped together under the general description 'nodular chalks', and in particular between griotte chalks and nodular chalks, in a restricted sense (Mortimore, 1979). Griotte chalks have a structure comprising 'augen' of chalk enveloped by marl. This fabric, which resulted from processes of bioturbation, has been extensively modified by early diagenesis and compaction. Two types of griotte can be recognised: nodular griottes, where the augen are markedly flattened, have angular forms and are crossed by stylolites; and soft-sediment or 'smooth' griottes, where the augen have subrounded surfaces and do not project in weathered faces. The term 'griotte marl' has been applied to the more marly chalks which possess this structure. Nodular chalks, in the restricted sense, may superficially resemble nodular griottes, but marl envelopes are lacking in the fabric.

Previous descriptions of the Chalk of this district have used the traditional three-fold division into Lower, Middle and Upper Chalk. The present survey has shown that, in common with the Lewes district to the east (Lake and others, 1987), this classification is impracticable for mapping purposes. Consequently, the Chalk is here divided into only two parts, namely the Lower Chalk and the undivided Upper and Middle Chalk (the Sussex White Chalk Formation of Mortimore, 1983).

The subdivision of the Lower Chalk into Glauconitic Marl, Chalk Marl, Grey Chalk and Plenus Marls follows a long-established convention (Jukes-Browne and Hill, 1903). In the Upper and Middle Chalk, the members distinguished by Mortimore (1986) and used for descriptive purposes in the Lewes district (Lake and others, 1987), have also been recognised, but not mapped, in this district (Figure 11). These are, in descending order, as follows:

Culver Soft Chalk Member
Newhaven Griotte Marl Chalk Member
Seaford Soft Chalk Member
Lewes Nodular Chalk Member
Ranscombe Griotte Chalk Member

The boundaries between these members are taken at lithological marker horizons, generally marl seams. Using geophysical borehole logs, in conjunction with core material, it has been possible to classify wells and boreholes in the Upper and Middle Chalk and to provide further information on the succession at depth in this district.

The Chalk is currently zoned on the basis of macrofaunal assemblages, using ammonoids, crinoids, brachiopods and bivalves as zonal indices (Figure 11), although in recent years complementary zonal schemes have been erected using dominantly benthonic forms of foraminifera for the Cenomanian (zones 7 to 14 of Carter and Hart, 1977) and for the Coniacian to Maastrichtian stages (Bailey and others, 1983). Modern research has also demonstrated the utility of faunal marker bands which reflect biostratigraphical 'events' for correlation purposes.

In this description the biostratigraphy of the Lower Chalk is related to the sequences near Lewes and Dover. The lower members of the succeeding sequence are poorly exposed and the reader is referred to the description of the Lewes district (Lake and others, 1987) for detailed palaeontological information. The faunas of the Newhaven and Culver members are described below (pp.58 – 64).   RDL, RNM, CJW.

LOWER CHALK

The Lower Chalk is present at outcrop in the lower part of the main escarpment and in the adjacent ground to the north. It rests everywhere with a sharp base on the underlying formation: across much of the outcrop this is the Upper Greensand, but from Westmeston eastwards the Lower Chalk overlies silty clays of the Gault. The top of the Lower Chalk is taken at the base of the Melbourn Rock, which locally has given rise to a prominent feature on the Chalk escarpment. The Lower Chalk ranges in thickness from 78 m to over 90 m, much of the variation being attributable to the Chalk Marl (see below).

The Glauconitic Marl, or 'Chloritic Marl' of early authors, forms the basal bed of the Lower Chalk and comprises sandy marl with an abundance of sand-grade glauconite grains which give the rock a dark green colour.

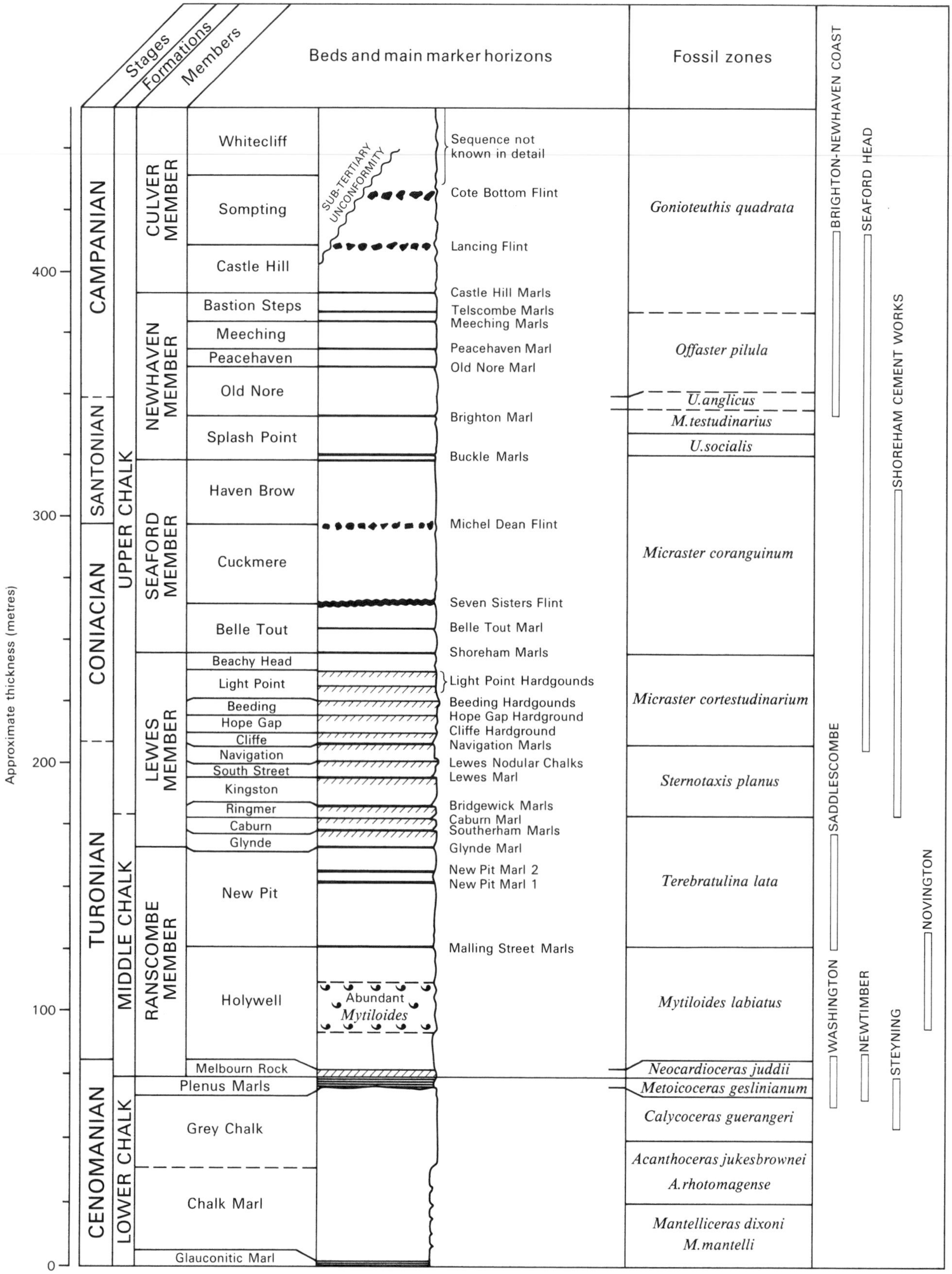

Figure 11 The subdivisions of the Chalk and the stratigraphical range of some important sections

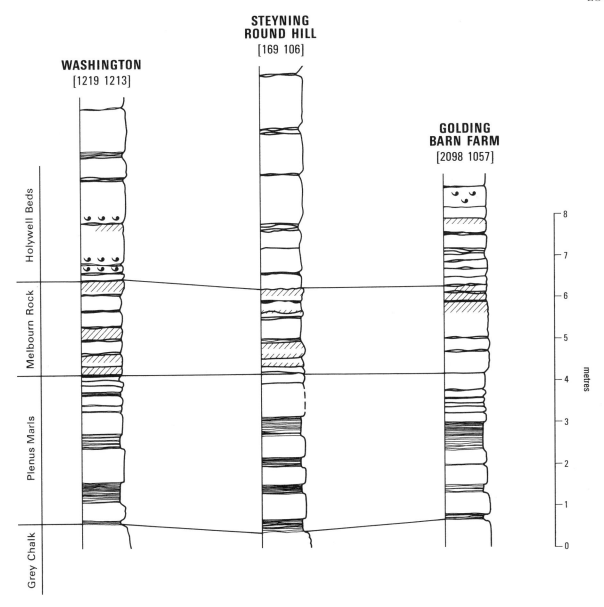

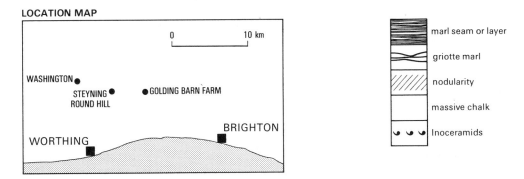

Figure 12   The Plenus Marls and Melbourn Rock of the Brighton district

Dark grey phosphatic nodules are common and the bed is extensively bioturbated. Thin beds of hard sponge-bearing limestone are present locally. The contact with the underlying beds is sharp and intensely burrowed, whereas the upper limit is gradational with the progressive reduction in glauconite content. This bed is typically about 1 m thick.

The Chalk Marl, 35 to 45 m thick, comprises a rhythmic sequence of grey marls and hard marly limestones which are commonly sponge-bearing in the lower part of the unit. The limestones are locally truncated by erosion surfaces. These hard beds contain well preserved and uncrushed ammonites, bivalves, brachiopods and sponges, whereas the fossils in the marls are generally crushed. Nodules of pyrite are common in places, particularly in the marls. The middle part of the Chalk Marl tends to be more marly than the underlying strata, and this lithology passes upwards into beds with less clay material. The highest 6 to 10 m of silty limestones mark a transitional passage to the Grey Chalk above.

The Grey Chalk consists of pale grey marly chalk with a few thin marls, about 40 m thick, which is more massively bedded than the Chalk Marl. The topmost unit of the Lower Chalk comprises dominantly greenish grey marly beds which are termed the Plenus Marls after the characteristic belemnite *Actinocamax plenus*. These beds, which are widespread over much of the Anglo-Paris Basin, also contain several beds of harder chalk. Important erosion surfaces occur at the base and within the sequence (Jefferies, 1961; 1963). The Plenus Marls are consistently 3 to 4 m thick in this district (Figure 12), whereas to the east, around Lewes and Eastbourne, marked variations in thickness and marl content occur (Lake and others, 1987).

There are no complete sections of Lower Chalk in the Brighton and Worthing district and only the Sompting Borehole [1661 0636] has traversed this sequence in recent years. The Lower Chalk of this borehole was not cored, but chippings indicated the depths of the major lithological changes (Young and Monkhouse, 1980). A second, fully-cored borehole at Chanctonbury [1445 1215] started in the middle part of the Lower Chalk, above the change from Grey Chalk to Chalk Marl (Figure 13). Geophysical logs, particularly resistivity and gamma, enable correlation between these two boreholes and the Victoria Gardens and St Peter's Church boreholes [3138 0449; 3146 0497] near the Old Steine, Brighton. Observed thicknesses of the Lower Chalk are: Amberley Pits Borehole [027 116] about 95 m, Sompting Borehole about 78 m, the former Rodmell Pit, Lewes [440 064] at least 85 m.

Fossils are typically few and poorly preserved in the Glauconitic Marl; those recovered are characterised by an assemblage of small *Aucellina* including *A. gryphaeoides* and *A. uerpmanni*. At Dover (Figure 13) this assemblage also occurs in the overlying beds and the combined succession probably belongs to the *Neostlingoceras* [*Hypoturrilites*] *carcitanense* Subzone of the *Mantelliceras mantelli* Zone.

Within the Chalk Marl several key macrofossil bands have been recognised (Wood *in* Lake and others, 1987) which are useful for correlation. These are as follows (see also Figure 13):

1 The total range of the brachiopod *Monticlarella? rectifrons*.

2 A band characterised by an assemblage of thick-shelled, inflated, relatively weakly sculptured inoceramids of the group of *Inoceramus virgatus*.
3 The lower *Orbirhynchia mantelliana* band. This band coincides with the first appearance of *Acanthoceras*.
4 A band of highly fossiliferous chalk with a diverse fauna of small brachiopods comprising *Grasirhynchia martini*, *Kingena concinna*, *Modestella geinitzi* and *Platythyris squamosa*.
5 The upper *Orbirhynchia mantelliana* band. The upper limit of this band is thought to coincide with the so-called 'mid-Cenomanian non-sequence' (Carter and Hart, 1977), at which level there is a marked change in the foraminiferal assemblages from predominantly benthonic below to predominantly planktonic above.

A tentative correlation between the successions of the Chanctonbury Borehole, Southerham (Lewes) and Aycliff (Dover), using a combination of lithostratigraphical marker horizons (primarily prominent limestones) and biostratigraphical marker bands, is shown in Figure 13.

The detailed biostratigraphy of the Grey Chalk is imperfectly known in this district, although the incoming of acanthoceratid ammonites referred to the *A. jukesbrownei* group is an important marker in the transition beds at the base of the Grey Chalk.

In the Plenus Marls, faunal changes have been noted at erosion surfaces above Beds 1, 3 and 5 of Jefferies (1961; 1963) (see also Figure 14). The surface above Bed 3 marks a major change in both the macrofossil and planktonic foraminiferal assemblages, and the extinction datum of *Rotalipora cushmani*. The overlying beds have a fauna believed by Jefferies (1961) to represent a period of lowered sea temperatures.

CJW, RNM

UPPER AND MIDDLE CHALK

In the Brighton and Worthing district the Upper and Middle Chalk comprises up to 335 m of dominantly white chalky limestones. This succession has been subdivided by Mortimore (1986) into members (p.51), each of which has a distinctive chalk lithology and a typical geophysical signature. The traditional boundary between the Middle Chalk and the Upper Chalk (as variously defined by earlier authors) lies within the Lewes Member (Figure 11). The Ranscombe Member, at the base of the sequence, is characterised by both nodular and smooth griotte chalks, with layers of true nodular chalks in the highest beds; the upper part of the sequence contains numerous discrete marl seams. The Ranscombe Member has sparse nodular flints, but is essentially flintless, in contrast to the remainder of the succession, which is flinty throughout. The Lewes Member comprises nodular and incipient hardground chalks. The Seaford Member represents a marked change in the depositional environment, and is characterised by soft white chalks with abundant courses of nodular flint (some very large), and numerous iron-stained spongiferous horizons representing minor sedimentary breaks. Marly griotte chalk, with discrete marl seams, is again present in the Newhaven Member, and the overlying essentially marl-free Culver Member is typified by soft chalks with nodular flints.

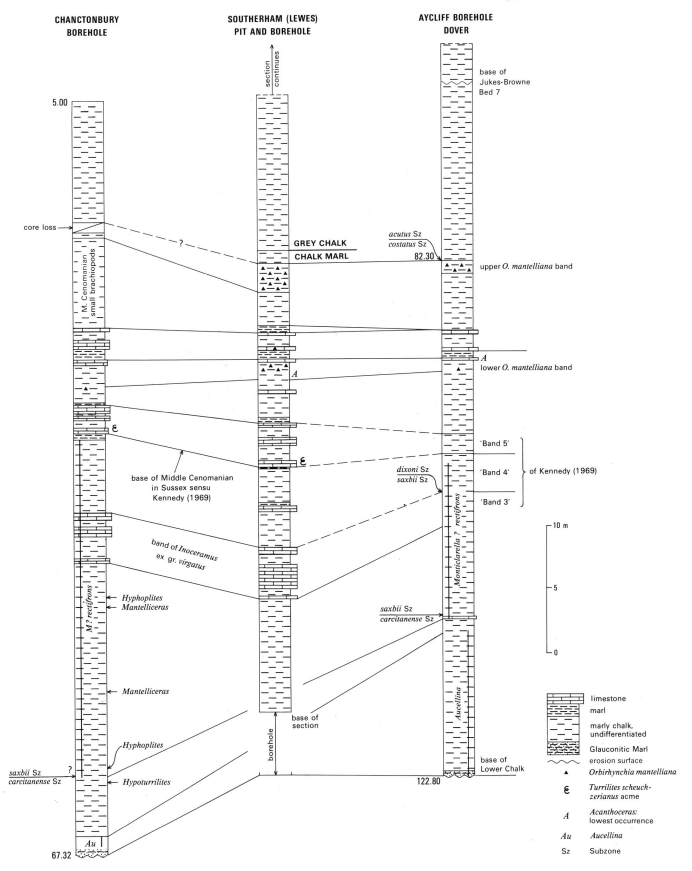

Figure 13   Outline correlation of the Lower Chalk of the Chanctonbury Borehole, the Southerham Pit, Lewes, and of the Aycliff Borehole, Dover

Figure 14 Section of the Plenus Marls at Steyning Limeworks, showing the faunas of the individual beds (after Jefferies, 1963)

Within these members various markers have been recognised (Figure 11), which are important for correlation purposes both at outcrop and where identified in geophysical borehole logs. These markers have been grouped informally into beds for descriptive purposes.

Parts of the Chalk sequence of the Brighton and Worthing district, particularly the Ranscombe and Lewes members, are appreciably more indurated than their equivalents near Lewes. The important marker horizons, the marl seams and flint nodules, are more persistent in this district than in the latter area.

The outcrops of the Ranscombe Member and the lower part of the Lewes Member are largely confined to the main escarpment of the South Downs (Frontispiece), but they also form inliers in Moulsecoomb valley [326 066] (Figure 15). The Seaford Member tends to occupy the ground between the primary and secondary escarpments of the Downs, whereas the Newhaven Member forms much of the secondary escarpment, which is particularly well developed west of the River Adur along Lychpole Hill [153 073]. The latter member also makes up the major part of the cliffs between Black Rock, Brighton, [335 033], and Newhaven, in the Eastbourne district. The Culver Member occupies some of the higher ground on the dip-slope of the secondary escarpment and caps the sea-cliffs between Telscombe Cliffs and Newhaven.

The various members correspond approximately to biostratigraphical zones as follows: the Ranscombe Member to the *Neocardioceras juddii* to mid-*Terebratulina lata* zones; the Lewes Member to the mid-*T. lata* to uppermost *Micraster cortestudinarium* zones; the Seaford Member to the *Micraster coranguinum* Zone; the Newhaven Member to the *Uintacrinus socialis* to basal *Gonioteuthis quadrata* zones; and the Culver Member to the higher part of the *G. quadrata* Zone (Figure 11).

Ranscombe Griotte Chalk Member

The Ranscombe Member is characterised by pale greenish grey relatively massively bedded chalks with layers of interwoven thin marls (griotte texture) and some thicker, distinct marl beds. The base of the Ranscombe Member is taken at the base of the Melbourn Rock, and the upper boundary at the erosion surface beneath the Glynde Marl (Figure 11). This member varies from about 45 m to over 90 m in thickness.

The Melbourn Rock comprises up to 5 m of hard nodular griotte chalks with thin marl intercalations (Figure 12). Glauconite is commonly present as coatings to the nodules. The lower part of the member above the Melbourn Rock (the Holywell Beds) is locally nodular, with smooth griotte chalks and, in parts, gritty with the debris of inoceramids

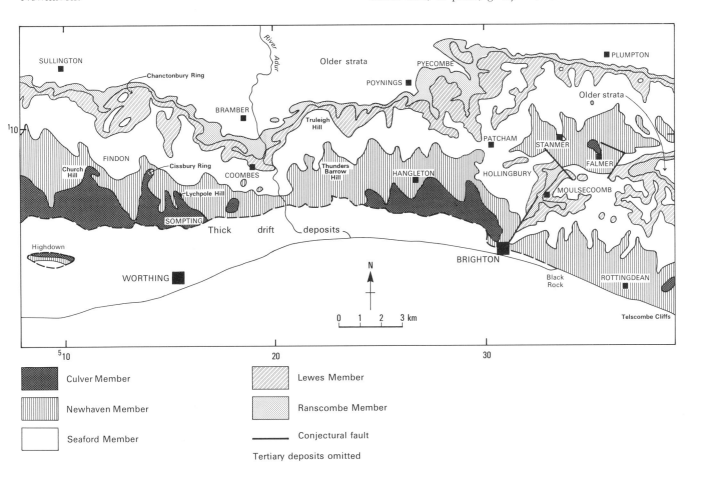

Figure 15   The distribution of the members of the Upper and Middle Chalk; derived from Gaster (1937; 1951)

belonging to the genus *Mytiloides*. Above this the chalk in the New Pit Beds is more massive, and distinct marl seams occur; of these the New Pit Marls (Figure 11) are readily identified and have been recognised on the geophysical logs of boreholes.

Lewes Nodular Chalk Member

The Lewes Member, which is 49 to 95 m in thickness, comprises a rhythmic sequence of soft chalks, nodular chalks and hardground chalks with thin marls, and in it regular courses of flints appear in the succession for the first time. The hardgrounds tend to occur towards the tops of the various subdivisions of this member (Figure 11). The base of the member occurs at the erosion surface beneath the Glynde Marl. The upper limit is placed at the top of the upper of the paired Shoreham Marls.

In the lower part of the succession, the beds between the hardgrounds show a griotte texture similar to that of the Ranscombe Member, whereas in the higher beds this texture is replaced by Bänderkreide or *Zoophycos* chalk. *Zoophycos* is a helical trace fossil which appears in section as discrete sub-parallel slivers of darker chalk within a paler matrix. The various nodular chalks up to the Navigation Hardground(s) (below the Navigation Marls) are indurated and locally cap the primary escarpment. The marl seams in the lower part of this member are persistent in Sussex and are reflected on the geophysical logs of boreholes.

The Kingston Beds (Figure 11) have yielded sparse elements (including ammonites and gastropods) of the aragonitic 'reussianum fauna', which characterises the top-most hardground of the Chalk Rock in the Chilterns and adjacent areas. The base of this rock bed defines the conventional boundary between the Middle Chalk and Upper Chalk of earlier authors.

The best section in the Lewes Member is in the Shoreham Cement Works quarry at Upper Beeding [203 088] (p.68), which, in conjunction with a small quarry [2133 1031] north of Beeding Hill, provides a complete sequence. Here, the member is attenuated compared with its development around Lewes, particularly in the lower part. The marl seams are more clearly defined and the nodular character of the chalk is more pronounced than elsewhere in Sussex. The three Navigation Hardgrounds recognised at Lewes have coalesced to form one massive rock bed and this is the most readily recognised feature of the section. The cement works quarry is taken as the type locality for the contact between the Lewes Member and the overlying Seaford Member.

Seaford Soft Chalk Member

The Seaford Member generally comprises about 80 m of homogeneous white chalk with regularly spaced courses of large nodular flints, some of which provide stratigraphical markers; of these the Seven Sisters Flint Band is the most pronounced and marks the base of the Cuckmere Beds (Figure 11). The Haven Brow Beds contain the other more conspicuous flint courses. Iron-stained sponge-beds are present, particularly in the lowest 10 m, at one level in the middle part of the succession, and in the highest 20 m. This member lacks nodular beds but two horizons, the Cuckmere

Sponge Bed at Birling Gap and the upper of a pair of sponge beds on the Race Hill, Brighton [342 058], are glauconitised and/or phosphatised. The base of the member is taken above the upper Shoreham Marl and the top at the base of the lowest of the Buckle Marls (Figure 11).

Newhaven Griotte Marl Chalk Member

The Newhaven Member is characterised by white flinty griotte chalks with persistent marl seams and sequences of flintless chalk with hard beds. The flints are less conspicuous than in the Seaford Member. Where the marl content is low, the flint content is appreciably less and the hardgrounds are typically well developed and are locally mineralised.

The base of the member is taken below the lowest Buckle Marl and the top above the upper Castle Hill Marl (Figure 16). Its thickness ranges from 53 to 75 m. Whereas thick marly sequences have been proved from Mill Hill [212 065] to Hangleton and in boreholes at Hove and in the centre of Brighton, attenuated successions with few marls have been observed between Red Hill [285 082], Brighton railway station and Falmer (Mortimore, 1985).

Brydone (1915) recognised the utility of marl seams in this part of the Chalk for correlation purposes. His stratigraphy has been largely confirmed by Mortimore (1985; 1986), who has named the various marker horizons (Figures 16, 17, 18). Some marls cause pronounced peaks on the geophysical borehole logs, and can be traced from Sussex to Dorset. The marls between the Brighton Marl and the paired Meeching Marls are commonly particularly pronounced. Above the Meeching Marls, marls are less common, and soft, white, flinty chalks predominate.

Culver Soft Chalk Member

The Culver Member, the highest member preserved in the district, is poorly exposed, although at least 60 m are present to the north of Worthing. Here Gaster (1924), in an extensive study, first recognised beds containing the crinoid *Applinocrinus cretaceus* [*Saccocoma cretacea*] and the few pits expose previously unrelated sequences of soft homogeneous white chalks with nodular flint courses, similar to the Seaford Member.

A key marker flint sequence in the Castle Hill Beds, best seen on the coast at Newhaven (Figures 16, 20), is present in the pits near Lancing described by Gaster (1924). His pits 1 and 4 show the marls typical of the Newhaven Member; pit 4 also exposes the Telscombe Marls and it has yielded abundant large *Offaster pilula planata*. The adjacent pit 3 shows the base of the *Applinocrinus* [*Saccocoma*] *cretaceus* Subzone marked by the Lancing Flint. Other key fossils, such as forms of the bryozoan *Bicavea*, have also been found here, thus confirming Gaster's original observations.   RNM, CJW, RDL

BIOSTRATIGRAPHY OF THE NEWHAVEN AND CULVER MEMBERS

The sequence in the Newhaven and Culver members exposed at Seaford Head [492 977], some 11 km outside the district, is the most complete one available and the zonal thicknesses given in this account were measured there.

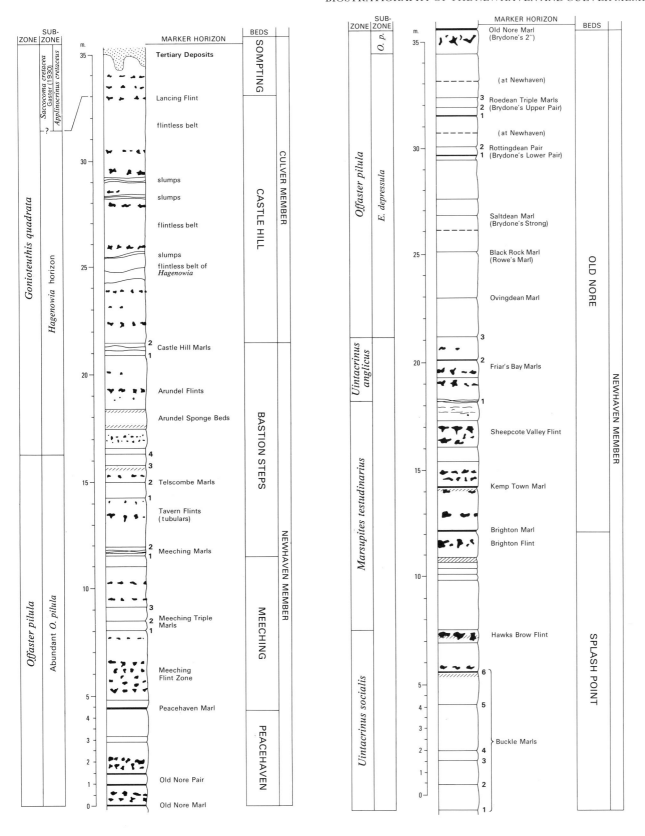

Figure 16 The simplified sequence of the Newhaven and Culver members at the coast between Brighton and Seaford

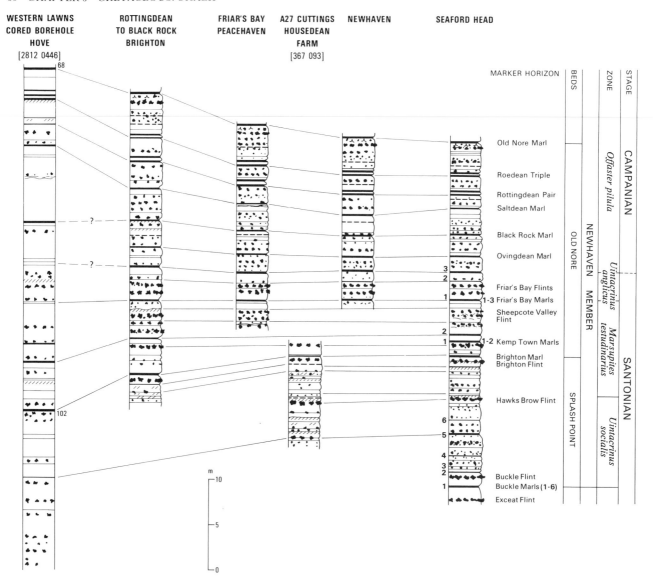

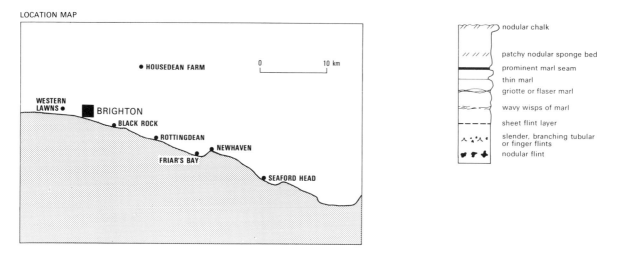

Figure 17 The correlation of the lower part of the Newhaven Member between Hove and Seaford Head

Uintacrinus socialis Zone (8 m thick at Seaford Head)

Uintacrinus socialis enters at the base of the Newhaven Member and occurs abundantly in and above the Buckle Marl 3 (Figure 18), in the Buckle Marls 4 to 6 interval, and in the sponge-bed associated with the Hawks Brow Flint. The beds above the Buckle Marl 3 are characterised by *Porosphaera* of large size. Other fossils present are the large rhynchonellid brachiopod *Cretirhynchia plicatilis*, *Terebratulina rowei*, *Actinocamax verus*, *Bourgueticrinus granulosus*, *Echinocorys sp.*, *Micraster coranguinum* and *M. rostratus*. The giant ammon-

ite *Parapuzosia leptophylla* occurs at several levels.

Marsupites testudinarius Zone (10.6 m thick at Seaford Head)

Marsupites testudinarius enters about 1.5 m above the Hawks Brow Flint, and ranges up to the lowest of the three Friar's Bay marls (Figures 16 and 18), with acme occurrences in the two sponge beds 0.5 m above the Brighton Marl and just beneath the Kemp Town Marl respectively. The calyx plates are small and unornamented in the beds below the Brighton Marl, reach their maximum size and degree of ornament in

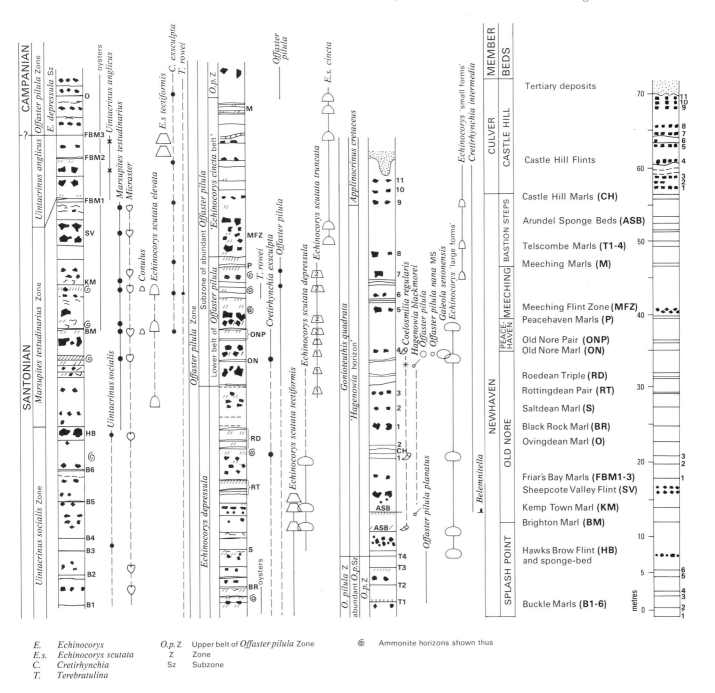

E.   *Echinocorys*
E.s. *Echinocorys scutata*
C.   *Cretirhynchia*
T.   *Terebratulina*

O.p.Z Upper belt of *Offaster pilula* Zone
Z   Zone
Sz   Subzone

Ⓖ Ammonite horizons shown thus

Figure 18 The biostratigraphy and lithostratigraphy of the Newhaven and Culver members at Seaford Head

the first of the two sponge beds, retain their large size but lose their ornament in the second sponge-bed, and then become progressively smaller to the top of the zone; the highest plates noted have been ornamented forms. The zone is characterised by the distinctive large pyramidate *Echinocorys scutata elevata*, its frequency of occurrence approximately paralleling that of *Marsupites*; the higher beds of the zone yield transitional forms between *E. scutata elevata* and the *E. s. tectiformis* of the overlying *anglicus* and basal *pilula* zones. The two sponge-beds contain additionally *Cretirhynchia exsculpta*, *Terebratulina rowei*, *Actinocamax verus*, *Parapuzosia leptophylla*, small *Conulus sp.* and *Micraster rostratus*. The abundance of *C. exsculpta* and the extreme rarity or absence of the belemnite *Gonioteuthis granulata* in the Sussex *testudinarius* Zone contrasts with the situation in the equivalent beds in Kent, where *C. exsculpta* has not been recorded and *G. granulata* is relatively common at the single *Marsupites* acme level. The higher part of the Sussex *testudinarius* Zone, above the Brighton Marl, is rich in the oyster *Pseudoperna boucheroni*, which typically occurs in clumps. This richness in oyster (and also inoceramid) debris continues into the lower part of the *pilula* Zone, and corresponds to the 'Grobkreide' or coarse-grained shelly chalk lithofacies found at this level in Northern Ireland, northern England and northern Germany (Fletcher and Wood, 1978). Inoceramid debris, probably *Sphenoceramus spp.*, is abundant in the top 0.5 m of the zone, immediately beneath the Friar's Bay Marl 1.

Uintacrinus anglicus ZONE (3 M THICK AT SEAFORD HEAD)

Uintacrinus anglicus occurs sparingly between the Friar's Bay Marls 1 and 3. Brydone (1914) recorded common small and dwarf brachials and sporadic small *Marsupites*-like (calyx) plates from the Friar's Bay Marl 1 to 2 interval, where they were associated with abundant *Terebratulina rowei*, and he noted that only rare brachials and no *T. rowei* were present above this level. Bailey and others (1983; 1984) proposed that the *anglicus* Zone should be taken to mark the top of the Santonian Stage in chalk facies, rather than the extinction level of *Marsupites* as is customary. The *anglicus* Zone has so far been proved unequivocally only in Sussex and Kent, although it is probable (cf. Brydone, 1915) that it is present in the Isle of Wight and inland Hampshire as well. The fauna of the *anglicus* Zone includes *Cretirhynchia exsculpta*, *Echinocorys scutata tectiformis* (particularly between Friar's Bay Marls 2 and 3) and *Micraster sp.*

Offaster pilula ZONE (30.6 M THICK AT SEAFORD HEAD)

The present investigation has confirmed the biostratigraphical subdivisions established by Brydone (1914), namely a lower succession (*Echinocorys depressula* Subzone) in which *Offaster pilula* is rare and *Echinocorys scutata tectiformis* is replaced upwards by *E. s. depressula*[1]; and a higher sequence (abundant *Offaster pilula* Subzone) comprising two discrete belts of abundant *Offaster pilula* (the lower with *E. scutata truncata* and the higher terminating with *Offaster* of exceptionally large size), separated by an *Offaster*-free belt characterised by

---

1 *Echinocorys (scutata) depressula* is a replacement name introduced by Brydone (1939) for the pre-occupied name *E. depressus* of his earlier papers.

Echinocorys s. cincta. The relationship between these subdivisions and the detailed lithostratigraphy based on the section at Seaford Head (Mortimore, 1985, table A) is shown in Figure 18. Figure 19 shows Brydone's subdivisions alongside Rowe's (1900) zonation and the modifications to the *pilula* Zone proposed by Gaster (1924).

Echinocorys depressula SUBZONE

The lower part of the *depressula* Subzone up to the Black Rock Marl is characterised by *Pseudoperna boucheroni*, continuing the oyster-rich facies that began at the Brighton Marl within the *testudinarius* Zone; Brydone (1914) noted *Bourgueticrinus utriculatus* (*Bourgueticrinus* Form 6) in these beds. The lowest *Offaster pilula* was recorded by Brydone in the Ovingdean– Black Rock Marl interval, although it is uncertain whether this refers to *O. pilula* s. s. The Black Rock Marl is the marl that Rowe (1900) took to mark the junction between his *Marsupites* and *Actinocamax quadratus* zones; fossils in museum collections labelled '*A. quadratus* Zone, Brighton' are more likely to have been collected in the *pilula* Zone, rather than in the succeeding *Gonioteuthis* [*Actinocamax*] *quadrata* Zone as presently interpreted, and care has to be exercised in this respect.

The replacement of the trapezoidal *Echinocorys s. tectiformis* by the depressed and rounded *E. s. depressula* occurs between the Saltdean and Rottingdean marls, just below the conspicuous tabular flint seam present at Seaford Head. This level also marks the highest occurrence of the belemnite *Actinocamax verus*. A possible non-sequence at the Saltdean Marl is suggested by the presence of glauconitised pebbles and moulds of originally aragonite-shelled bivalves. The beds with *Echinocorys s. depressula* were said by Brydone to be characterised by *Bourgueticrinus papilliformis* (*Bourgueticrinus* Form 5), a species which characterises the crinoid zones up to a level within the *testudinarius* Zone, and then is absent up to the *depressula* beds. Brydone (1914) took the junction between the *depressula* and abundant *pilula* subzones at the base of the Old Nore paired marls but the boundary is here placed at the thin marl 1 m beneath the Old Nore Marl, that is at a level corresponding to the base of the uppermost 3 m of the *depressula* Subzone as originally defined. The highest beds of the redefined *depressula* Subzone are characterised by innominate forms of *Echinocorys*, including variants anticipating *E. scutata truncata*.

ABUNDANT *Offaster pilula* SUBZONE

Revising the lower boundary of the Abundant *Offaster pilula* Subzone downwards has the effect of making the belt of *E. s. truncata* more or less co-extensive with the lower of the two *Offaster pilula* belts, since *O. pilula* occurs regularly with *E. s. truncata* in the 1 m bed beneath the Old Nore Marl and also in the interval between the Old Nore Marl and the Old Nore paired marls. Two forms of *E. s. truncata* are present. The form that is found up to the Old Nore paired marls is larger and with a less well defined apical disc than the typical small *E. s. truncata* with exaggerated apical disc of the beds from the Old Nore paired marls to the Peacehaven Marls. These are shown as *truncata* 1 and *truncata* 2 on Figure 18. As Brydone noted, *Offaster pilula* does not become abundant until above the lower of the paired marls. It tends to be associated with *E. s. truncata*. The lower *Offaster pilula* belt

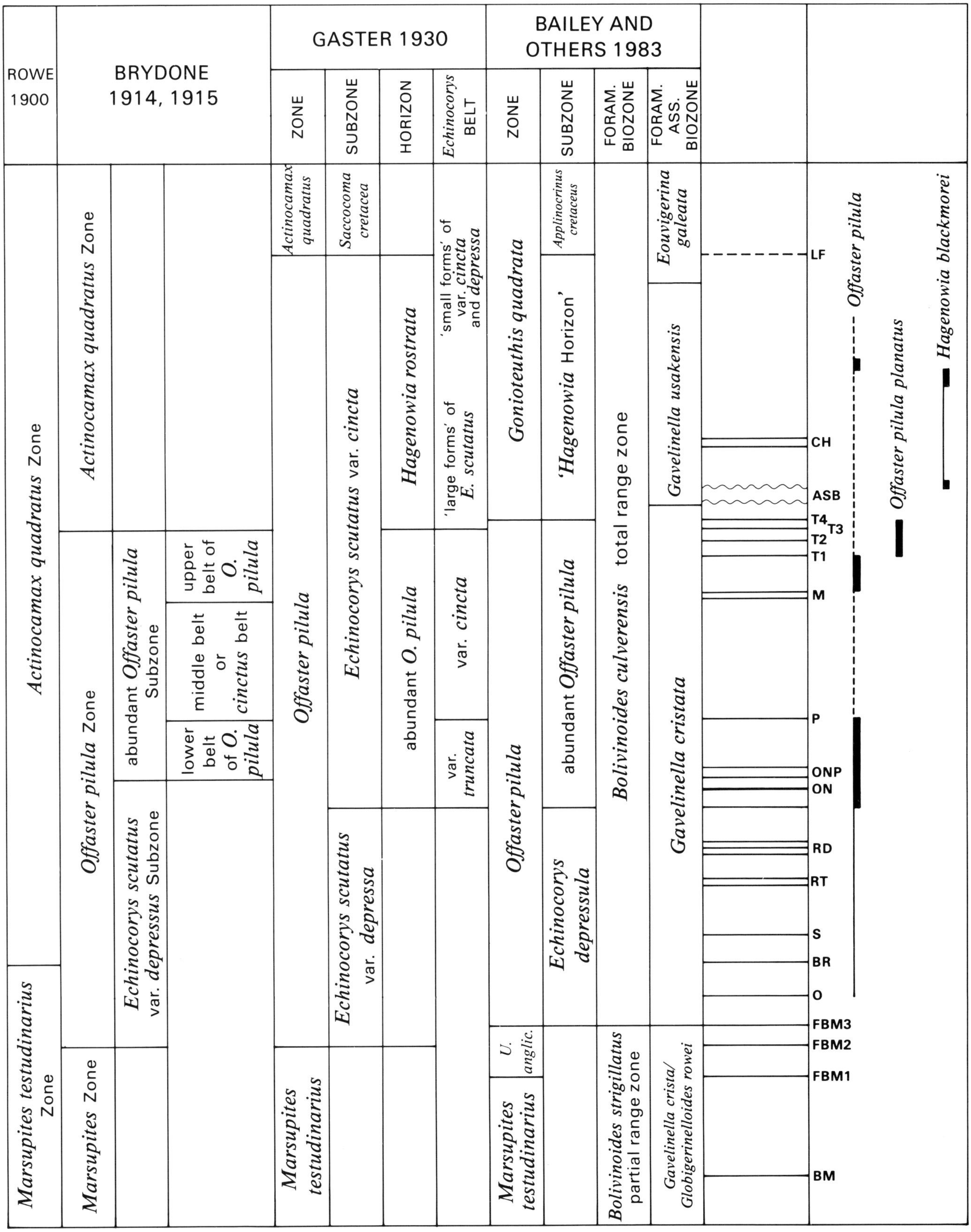

ROWE 1900	BRYDONE 1914, 1915			GASTER 1930				BAILEY AND OTHERS 1983					
				ZONE	SUBZONE	HORIZON	Echinocorys BELT	ZONE	SUBZONE	FORAM. BIOZONE	FORAM. ASS. BIOZONE		

Abbreviations for lithological markers are shown in Fig 18; LF = Lancing Flint

Figure 19   The development of the biostratigraphical subdivisions of the Newhaven and Culver members

marks the top of the range of *Cretirhynchia exsculpta*, and is characterised by a diverse fauna including *Terebratulina rowei* (which reappears at this level after disappearing within the *anglicus* Zone), *Inoceramus balticus pteroides*, large ammonites (*Hauericeras* and *Parapuzosia*), *Bourgueticrinus elegans* and *Micraster* cf. *coravium*.

The belt of *Echinocorys s. cincta* is virtually devoid of *Offaster pilula*. *E. s. cincta* occurs regularly in the Meeching Flint Zone above the Peacehaven Marl, but does not become abundant until just below and in the lower of the paired Meeching Marls. The only other common macrofossils are *Gryphaeostrea canaliculata striata* and *Bourgueticrinus elegans*.

Offaster pilula reappears just above the Meeching Marls and ranges up to the lowest of the four Telscombe Marls. Within the interval bounded by Telscombe Marls 1 and 4, *O. pilula* exhibits a sudden and dramatic increase in size, culminating in the giant forms named by Brydone (1939) var. *planatus* and var. *convexus*, and grouped by Ernst (1971) as the subspecies *O. pilula planatus*. The Telscombe Marls thus delimit Brydone's so-called '*planoconvexus*' bed, which marks the top of his *Offaster pilula* Zone and is an important marker that can be traced throughout southern England. Large forms of *Echinocorys s. cincta* and other large innominate *Echinocorys* also occur at this level.

Gonioteuthis quadrata ZONE (18.6 M THICK AT SEAFORD HEAD)

On the basis of work by Gaster (1924; 1929), that part of the *Gonioteuthis quadrata* Zone exposed in the hinterland of Worthing is divided into a lower 'Horizon of *Hagenowia rostrata*' (15 to 18 m) and an upper Subzone of *Saccocoma cretacea* [now, following Peck (1973), *Applinocrinus cretaceus*] comprising the remaining 38 m. Gaster attempted to expand Brydone's concept of the *pilula* Zone to take in the '*Hagenowia* horizon' in view of the occurrence of small *Echinocorys* reminiscent of *E. s. depressula* and *E. s. cincta* in the upper beds of the latter unit, but this view has not found acceptance. The name 'Horizon of *Hagenowia rostrata*' or '*Hagenowia* horizon' is unfortunately chosen, since the species of echinoid in question is *H. blackmorei* and, although it is said to range throughout and characterise the unit, it is common and conspicuous only at one level where it occurs in flood abundance. In the absence of a modern subzonal subdivision of the *quadrata* Zone, the terms '*Hagenowia* horizon' and '*cretaceus* Subzone' are retained, although they are both inherently unsatisfactory.

Hagenowia HORIZON (16.6 M THICK AT SEAFORD HEAD)

The *Hagenowia* horizon marks a great increase in faunal diversity compared with the underlying *pilula* Zone, and is particularly characterised by the diminutive thimble-shaped calcisponge *Retispinopora lancingensis*, *Coelosmilia regularis*, large *Isocrania* ex gr. *egnabergensis*, *Kingena blackmorei*, *Orbirhynchia bella*, *Inoceramus sarumensis*, *I. subsarumensis* and asteroid marginals of exceptionally large size (*Metopaster* and *Pycinaster*). There is a significant microfaunal and macrofaunal change at or about the level of the Arundel Sponge Beds, the entry of *Gavelinella usakensis* coinciding with the entry of the *Cretirhynchia intermedia–norvicensis* lineage (represented by *C. intermedia*) and *Belemnitella* ex gr. *praecursor*. The only *Belemnitella* known from the area is a fragment collected by Dr A. S. Gale from the Arundel Sponge Beds at

Newhaven, although the genus was reported to occur relatively commonly in the *Hagenowia* horizon around Salisbury (Bailey and others, 1983). *Gonioteuthis* also occurs regularly from the *Hagenowia* horizon upwards, following its rarity in the Abundant *Offaster pilula* Subzone. *Hagenowia blackmorei* occurs sparsely in the higher Arundel Sponge Bed, and abundantly in the laminated slumped beds between the Castle Hill Flints 3 and 4. Beneath the Castle Hill Flint 4 is the thin seam of *Offaster pilula* noted by both Brydone (1914) and Gaster (1924); this bed also yields the dwarf variant *O. pilula* var. *nana* and *Galeola senonensis*. The lower two-thirds of the *Hagenowia* horizon is characterised by large *Echinocorys* (Gaster's innominate 'large forms'), whereas the beds above the *Offaster* level, constituting Gaster's so-called '*cinctus* belt', yield predominantly small forms, including some superficially resembling small *E. s. cincta* and *E. s. depressula*.

Applinocrinus cretaceus SUBZONE (BASAL 2 M ONLY EXPOSED AT SEAFORD HEAD; ESTIMATED TO BE 38 M THICK NEAR WORTHING)

The *Applinocrinus cretaceus* Subzone provides a marked contrast with the macrofossil-rich *Hagenowia* horizon, in that these chalks are rich in microfossils, and larger fossils are relatively uncommon, with the exception of *Echinocorys*, which are for the most part distorted. Most of the rich fauna recorded by Gaster (1924) was obtained by washing and sieving bulk samples of chalk, or else was collected from air-weathered faces. The zonal index, in particular, is an extremely small fossil that is easily overlooked. Characteristic fossils of this subzone include *Retispinopora arbusculum*, small *Glomerula gordialis*, *Bicavea radiata*, *B. striata*, *Lunulites cretaceus*, '*Rhynchonella limbata*' sensu Gaster, *Bourgueticrinus* Form 7 of Brydone and '*Cidaris subvesiculosa*' sensu Gaster. Bryozoans are so abundant at some levels that the rock could be described as a bryozoan chalk. Figure 20 is based on Mortimore's work (1985, fig.5e), and shows the stratigraphical relationship of Gaster's Worthing pits to the highest parts of the successions exposed in the sea-cliffs east of Brighton. Key marker horizons or bioevents within the *cretaceus* Subzone are provided by the Charmandean Flint (Gaster's pits 7, 8 and 10), below which there is an horizon with *Offaster pilula* var. *nana* and the other characteristic fossils of the subzone; and a bed below the Cote Bottom Flint (Gaster's pit 17), which has yielded *Galeola papillosa*. The upper limit of the subzone is not known, but the subzonal assemblage (including *Applinocrinus*) extends up to Gaster's pit 24 at Warningcamp in the Chichester district; this locality, which has also yielded *Galeola papillosa*, is believed to lie stratigraphically immediately above Gaster's pit 17 and to be the level at which *Gonioteuthis* first becomes relatively common.   CJW, RNM

DETAILS

Lower Chalk

GLAUCONITIC MARL

Area west of the River Adur

In the Chanctonbury Borehole [1445 1215] the Glauconitic Marl was 1.02 m thick and comprised alternating soft marls and hard limestones. Poorly preserved sponges were found in the highest hard bed.

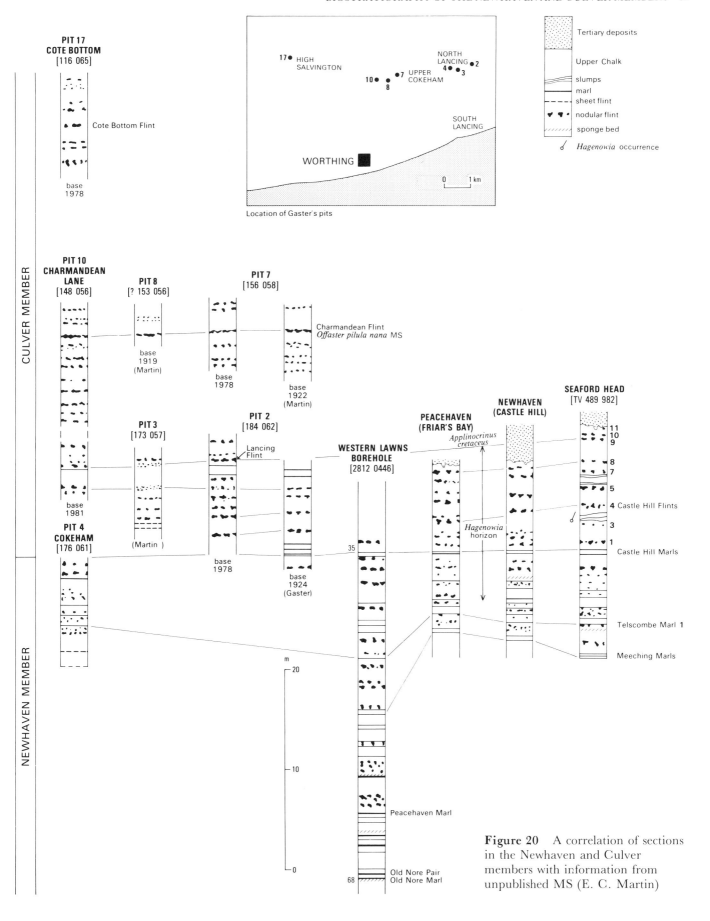

Figure 20   A correlation of sections in the Newhaven and Culver members with information from unpublished MS (E. C. Martin)

Up to 1.8 m of typical Glauconitic Marl overlying Upper Greensand were noted in the banks of Mouse Lane, Steyning [1716 1162]; within the lowest 0.8 m of the marl, burrow-fillings had a higher glauconite content than the surrounding sediment; the Upper Greensand was penetrated by burrows which extended up to 50 mm down from the sharp base of the Glauconitic Marl. The marl is also exposed in the side of the road [1782 1140] west of St Andrew's Parish Church, Steyning. In the BGS Steyning Station Borehole [1818 1130] the Glauconitic Marl was at least 1.04 m thick; greyish black phosphatic nodules were common in the lowest 0.07 m.

The base of the Chalk was not cored in the Sompting Borehole [1661 0636] but abundant glauconite-rich cuttings were recovered from this level. The evidence from the cuttings and the gamma log indicated that Glauconitic Marl was present within the depth-range of 321 to 325 m. The base of the Chalk was, therefore, taken at 325 m, but the thickness of the Glauconitic Marl probably does not exceed one or two metres.

Area east of the River Adur

About 1 m of slightly glauconitic, marly chalk is exposed in the western bank [2368 1135] of the road at Edburton.

The junction between the Upper Greensand and Glauconitic Marl occurs in an old pit [3140 1396] north of Whitelands Pumping Station. In this section 0.85 m of strongly burrowed glauconitic chalk was exposed. The glauconite tended to be concentrated in burrow-fillings. Numerous black phosphatic nodules, up to 20 mm in diameter, were seen near the base, and a hard bed, 0.15 m thick, with uncrushed sponges and black phosphatic nodules was 0.2 m above this.

Some 0.5 m of Glauconitic Marl was proved in the Plumpton Borehole [3545 1350] at Wales Farm. The bed here rests with a sharp base on silty mudstones of the Gault (p.48).

CHALK MARL

Area west of the River Adur

The Chanctonbury Borehole [1445 1215] provided the only complete cored section through the Chalk Marl within the district. It showed the typical rhythmic alternations of dark-coloured, soft, marly chalk and paler, hard, commonly sponge-bearing limestones.

An abundant fauna was collected from the Chanctonbury cores. The succession was essentially similar to that of the Southerham Grey Pit at Lewes (Lake and others, 1987, fig. 16), but there was a marked expansion in the beds below the *I.* ex gr. *virgatus* band, reflected in the increased range of *Monticlarella? rectifrons* (p.54). As with the Glyndebourne Borehole, *Aucellina* was restricted to the Glauconitic Marl and was apparently absent in the basal part of the Chalk Marl below the entry of *M.? rectifrons*. The major limestones in the Chanctonbury Borehole between the bed with *Orbirhynchia mantelliana* (corresponding to the lower *O. mantelliana* band) and the band of diverse small brachiopods appeared to correlate well with the three prominent limestones in the Southerham Grey Pit, and with the equivalent limestones in the Folkestone-Dover succession (Lake and others, 1987). Compared with their occurrence in sections in eastern Sussex, the brachiopods in the band of diverse small brachiopods were sparse and of small size. There was no evidence for the upper *O. mantelliana* band, but this may have resulted from core loss at the level in question; however, unpublished data from the cored Amberley Borehole [027 118] in the Chichester district suggest that the corresponding succession there is relatively unfossiliferous. There were insufficient biostratigraphical data to interpret the uppermost part of the Chanctonbury Borehole.

Small exposures of pale grey soft marly chalk at a low level in the Chalk Marl occur in the road banks [1690 1170] at the western end of Mouse Lane, Steyning, near the exposure of Glauconitic Marl

already noted above. Kennedy (1969, p.496) recorded the following *Neostlingoceras carcitanense* Subzone fauna from a concretion, 2 m above the Glauconitic Marl, on the north side of the lane: *Anisoceras plicatile, Idiohamites ellipticus, Lechites sp.* and *Sciponoceras sp.*, together with the bivalves '*Inoceramus*' *crippsi* and *Plagiostoma globosa.*

Beneath the road-bridge at Castle Lane [1828 1089] about 1.5 m of cream to pale grey bioturbated marly chalk with some hard, massive beds up to 0.2 m thick were exposed on the east side of the abandoned railway-cutting. On the west side of the cutting, 120 m south of the bridge, up to 4 m of similar chalk was exposed beneath river terrace deposits.

In the Sompting Borehole [1661 0636] no cores were taken from this division but the rock cuttings and the geophysical logs suggest a thickness of about 45 m for the Chalk Marl.

Area east of the River Adur

There are no permanent sections in the Chalk Marl between the River Adur and Pyecombe. Kennedy (1969, p.496) recorded a rich fauna from a 'band of hard calcareous concretions about 3 m above the base of the Chalk' in a temporary section [2108 1135] on the east side of the A2037 road near Horton Farm, Upper Beeding. The ammonites recorded by Kennedy included *Hyphoplites curvatus arausionensis, H. pseudofalcatus, H. falcatus interpolatus, H.* cf. *falcatus, Hypoturrilites gravesianus, H. tuberculatus, Mantelliceras cantianum, Sciponoceras sp.* (undescribed) and *Schloenbachia varians.* The remaining fauna comprised *Aporrhais sp., Avellana sp., Turritella (Torquesia) sp., Anomia sp., Barbatia galliennei, Cardita sp.,* '*Inoceramus*' cf. *crippsi* and '*I.*' cf. *crippsi reachensis,* in addition to abundant hexactinellids, many epifaunal bivalves, serpulids and bryozoa. Many of the ammonites collected here are notable for their good preservation. All retain growth striae, apertures are preserved on some *Schloenbachia* and specimens of *Hypoturrilites* retain their spines. The species of *Mantelliceras* present suggest this to be an *N. carcitanense* Subzone fauna.

Cuttings [2745 1358] on the east side of the A23 road near the entrance to Newtimber Limeworks, Pyecombe, exposed beds in the upper part of the Chalk Marl, from which specimens of *Orbirhynchia mantelliana* have been obtained. Similar beds of soft marly chalk and hard chalk were seen in degraded cuttings [2790 1292] on either side of the A281 road at The Dale, Pyecombe; White (1924, p.36) recorded *Holaster subglobosus, Ostrea vesiculosa?, Inoceramus crippsi* and *Acanthoceras rhotomagense* from this locality and noted that the beds dip ENE at about 15°.

Many species of fish and other fossils were obtained from the Chalk Marl in the railway-cutting [2985 1410] immediately north of Clayton Tunnel and from the same beds in the lower workings of the adjacent limeworks [2970 1393] during the middle of last century. A number of fine specimens from here are included in the Willett Collection of Chalk fossils in the Booth Museum, Brighton.

An incomplete cored Chalk Marl sequence, 28.8 m thick, was penetrated by the Plumpton Borehole [3545 1350]. The sequence was characterised by common *Monticlarella? rectifrons* and '*Inoceramus*' *crippsi,* suggesting that the borehole began in the *Mantelliceras saxbii* Subzone, below the beds with abundant *Inoceramus virgatus.* Hard limestones towards the base contained sponges and *Schloenbachia varians.* Up to 2.5 m of fractured marly chalk with a few oxidised pyrite nodules were exposed in a small pit [3640 1341] on the east side of Plumpton Lane, north of the Half Moon public house. Up to 2 m of hard chalk and soft marly chalk in alternating beds about 0.3 m thick crop out in the sides of the B2116 road [3639 1316] immediately south-east of the Half Moon.

The Chalk Marl was poorly exposed over a distance of about 350 m in a ditch on the east side of Novington Lande [3724 1341 to 3721 1308] and characteristic alternations of hard chalk and marly chalk were noted. Kennedy (1969, p.447) estimated that some 25 m of chalk were represented here. The hard beds provided a large fauna (Kennedy, 1969, pp. 497, 537), in which representatives of both *N. carcitanense* and *Mantelliceras saxbii* subzonal assemblages are present. Ammonites recorded here include *Hyphoplites campichei, H. curvatus, H.* cf. *falcatus, Idiohamites alternatus, I.* cf. *ellipticus, Mantelliceras* cf. *cantianum, M.* cf. *mantelli, M. picteti, M. saxbii, Neostlingoceras carcitanense, Scaphites obliquus, Schloenbachia varians* and *Sciponoceras sp.* The associated fauna comprised *Concinnithyris? sp., Grasirhynchia? sp., Dentalium sp., Angaria? sp., Avellana sp., Emarginula sp., Leptomaria wilmingtonensis, Barbatia galliennei, Cucullaea sp., Entolium orbiculare, 'Inoceramus' crippsi, 'I.' crippsi reachensis, Isoarca obesa, Oxytoma sp., Plagiostoma globosa, Pseudolimea* cf. *elongata, Pycnodonte vesicularis, Tellina sp., Unicardium ringmeriense* and *Cymatoceras elegans.*

GREY CHALK

In the abandoned pit of the Steyning Limeworks [1755 1040], about 20 m of alternating thick, massive, hard chalks and soft grey marls were exposed in the northern and eastern parts of the quarry. These beds were overlain in the south-western face by the Plenus Marls (see below).

Rock cuttings and geophysical logs indicate that the Grey Chalk was some 43 m thick in the Sompting Borehole [1661 0636].

An old pit [2249 1128] south of Truleigh Manor Farm exposed up to 5 m of rather blocky, off-white, marly chalk with some thin marls. A subhorizontal shear zone, 0.3 m thick, was noted 2 m above the base of the section.

The Newtimber Limeworks Quarry [2782 1374], north-west of Pyecombe, exposed roughly the top 24 m of the Grey Chalk, the Plenus Marls, and the complete thickness of the Melbourn Rock. The section at the eastern end of the main face was as follows:

	Thickness m
MIDDLE CHALK (Ranscombe Member)	
Chalk, hard, white to off-white, rubbly-weathering, nodular; some very thin marl partings	about 3.5
Melbourn Rock: chalk, hard cream to pale fawn, markedly nodular; in beds up to 1.5 m thick separated by marls up to 80 mm thick	3.0
LOWER CHALK	
Plenus Marls: chalk, very marly, pale fawn to greyish fawn, commonly with a slight greenish tinge; some paler harder beds up to 0.5 m thick	about 4.0
Grey Chalk: chalk, off-white, in beds up to 1.5 m thick, interbedded with more marly beds up to 0.2 m thick; a few pyrite nodules; unexposed interval of 3 m above 3.5 m from base	23.5

A similar sequence was described here by White (1924, p.35), who observed that much of the chalk was relatively unfossiliferous, though he recorded *Inoceramus crippsi* and *Ostrea sp.* from the Grey Chalk. Kennedy (1969, p.497) found a specimen of *Calycoceras naviculare* loose in the quarry. The Grey Chalk dips at about 6° slightly north of east and has joints trending between W–E and WNW–ESE.

PLENUS MARLS

The sections at Washington Chalk Pit [1219 1213], Steyning Round Hill [169 106] and Golding Barn Farm bostall [2098 1057] are shown in Figure 12. Jefferies (1963) has described the fauna from the Plenus Marls in Steyning Limeworks pit [1748 1036] (Figure 14).

Although no cores were taken from this level in the Sompting Borehole [1661 0636], the gamma log suggests that the Plenus

Marls were present between depths of 225 and 231 m. Rock cuttings of pale grey, marly chalk recovered from these levels support this interpretation.

A chalk-pit [2672 1207] on the east side of the Poynings to Devil's Dyke road, east of Poynings church, showed a degraded section through the top few metres of the Lower Chalk, in which some 2.5 m of Plenus Marls were overlain by 0.75 m of Melbourn Rock.

A small exposure in the north bank of Cowden Lane [2821 1265], Pyecombe, showed 1.6 m of Plenus Marls beneath about 0.2 m of Melbourn Rock. The contact was sharp and channel-like in form and appeared to have been subsequently sheared.

The Plenus Marls present in the top of the cutting [2922 1204] near the southern portal of Clayton Tunnel dip gently southwards and reach the base of the cutting approximately 320 m farther south.

In Newtimber Limeworks Quarry [2782 1374] the Plenus Marls are well exposed, about 4.0 m thick, though many parts of the section are rather inaccessible (see above). White (1924, p.35) noted that *Actinocamax plenus* and *Ostrea sp.* occur within the marls here.

About 0.75 m of Plenus Marls, overlain by the Melbourn Rock, are exposed near the top of a degraded chalk-pit [3480 1316] at the foot of the escarpment north of the Jubilee Plantation, Plumpton. Here White (1924, p.35) recorded about 2 m of Plenus Marls underlain by some 6 m of Grey Chalk. Jukes-Browne and Hill (1903, p.68) also described the section in this pit.

Upper and Middle Chalk

MELBOURN ROCK

The sections at Washington Chalk Pit [1219 1213], Steyning Round Hill [169 106] and Golding Barn Farm bostall [2098 1057] are shown graphically in Figure 12. Other exposures of the Melbourn Rock include those at the side of the farm road [1742 0988] at Soper's Bottom, north of Annington Hill; in the roadside chalk-pit [2672 1207] on the east side of the Devil's Dyke road; in the north side [2821 1265] of Cowden Lane, south-west of Pyecombe; and in the railway-cutting [2922 1204] at the southern end of Clayton Tunnel. Newtimber Limeworks Quarry [2782 1374] showed excellent sections through the Melbourn Rock and a few metres of the succeeding beds (see above).

An exposure of the Melbourn Rock was provided in the old chalk-pit [3480 1316] at the foot of the escarpment north of the Jubilee Plantation, Plumpton. In the rather inaccessible part of the face, the topmost beds of the Plenus Marls (see above) were overlain by about 5 m of hard nodular chalk. Several marl beds up to 15 mm thick were interbedded with the nodular chalk in the lower part of the sequence.

STRATA ABOVE THE MELBOURN ROCK

Area west of the River Adur

A specimen of *Romaniceras deverianum* was collected from chalk of mid to high-*lata* Zone age in a degraded pit [117 120] on Highden Hill.

The Ranscombe Member (Holywell Beds) was exposed in two abandoned pits on the north-eastern slopes of Steyning Round Hill. In the more northerly of these [1687 1055] some 20 m of strata consisted of massive and nodular white chalk in beds up to 1.5 m thick alternating with pale grey marls, markedly variable in thickness, up to 0.3 m. The other pit [1679 1027] exposed about 11 m of massive chalk with marl partings up to 0.21 m thick in the Glynde Beds; the uppermost beds included the Southerham Flints and iron-stained nodular beds overlain by the Southerham Marl 1; excavations revealed the Glynde Marl beneath the scree below. The fauna collected included *Terebratulina lata, Inoceramus* cf. *cuvierii* and less common *Sternotaxis planus.*

A pit [1795 0871] on the west side of Winding Bottom showed 5.8 m of chalk of the Caburn and Bridgewick beds; a griotte texture was noted in the uppermost 3.8 m of beds.

The Neolithic flint mines at Church Hill [1145 0823] and Cissbury Ring [1365 0795] exploited flint courses in the Newhaven Member. At the former site flints in the lower part of the *Offaster pilula* Zone were worked (Mortimore, 1986). Sections in the Newhaven Member at North Lancing were described by Gaster (1924).

The Culver Member was exposed in an old pit [1275 0620] north-west of Durrington and in the Charmandean Pit (Gaster's pit 10) [1485 0575]. In the latter pit, 10 m of moderately well bedded chalk with five prominent courses of flint nodules were seen: the Charmandean Flint was the highest of these (Figure 20). Up to 7.6 m of white massive chalk dipping slightly west of south at 5°, with several bands of flint nodules, were exposed in an abandoned pit (Lambley's Lane pit, Gaster's pit 7) [1563 0590] WNW of Sompting Abbotts. Many of the flints were burrow-fills: one bed, up to 0.2 m thick and about 5 m from the top of the face, consisted of partly coalescing nodules up to about 0.75 m across, the Charmandean Flint. *Offaster pilula* var. *nana* occurred in a thin band immediately beneath this flint band (see p.64).

Area east of the River Adur

The Shoreham Cement Works, Upper Beeding [203 088], exposes beds which range from the lower part of the Lewes Member to the upper part of the Seaford Member (Figure 21). Examples of the '*reussianum* fauna', including *Lewesiceras sp.*, have been obtained from the beds above and below the Lewes Marl. Abundant *Cladoceramus* of early Santonian age, occur in association with the Michel Dean and Flat Hill flint bands.

The nodular beds of the lower part of the Lewes Member, between the Glynde Marl and the Lewes Marl, including those not exposed in the previous quarry, were formerly exposed in a pit [2090 1055] south-east of Golding Barn Farm. The Southerham, Caburn, Bridgewick and Lewes marls were recognised in the main face.

The largely degraded Saddlescombe Quarry [2700 1162] in the upper Ranscombe and lower Lewes members showed the Southerham Marls and flints in the highest part of the section. These beds were crossed by a normal fault with strong slickensiding. On the grassy scree slopes below the top crags, it was possible to identify the Malling Street, New Pit and Glynde marls; at about the level of the Malling Street Marls a well preserved specimen of *Collignoniceras woolgari* was collected.

Hard, rubbly-weathering chalk was exposed locally in degraded pits [2895 1390] on the eastern shoulder of Wolstonbury Hill. White (1924, p.38) noted that this pit gave a section through some 10 m of nodular chalk in the *M. labiatus* Zone; he recorded 'a well-marked iron-stained conglomeratic band, dipping 5° to 6° south-east' on the north side of the pit about 6 m above the base of the section.

A specimen of *Micraster corbovis* of *lata* Zone type was obtained from the upper Glynde Beds at Westmeston Bostall [338 131]. This is the earliest recorded *Micraster* in this district.

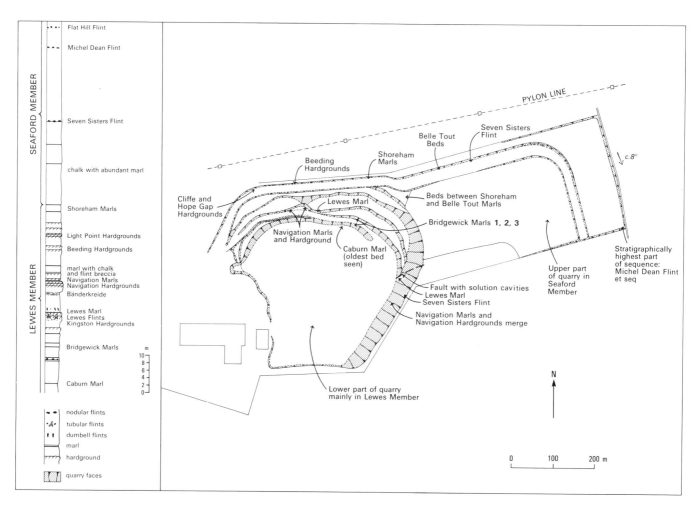

Figure 21   The distribution of lithologies at Shoreham Cement Works, Upper Beeding

The disused Novington Chalk Pits [3686 1288], south-east of Plumpton, provided one of the best exposures of the Ranscombe Member within the district. Approximately 30 m of beds were seen here, comprising thickly bedded, rather nodular, off-white chalk, with many marl wisps and exhibiting a griotte texture (Holywell Beds and New Pit Beds). Some marl beds up to 0.15 m thick were present, particularly in the lowest 3 m; these middle Holywell Beds contain abundant *Mytiloides spp.* In the higher part of the face the Malling Street Marl occurs between two nodular chalk horizons; the higher nodular bed (in the New Pit Beds) yielded *Terebratulina lata*, *Collignoniceras sp.*, *Lewesiceras sp.* and *Conulus subrotundus.*

A small pit [3764 1280] to the south-east of Warningore Bostall exposed up to 3 m of hard, rather nodular, rubbly chalk of the Ranscombe Member at the top of the face. A softer, marly bed, 0.15 m thick, occurred about 1.5 m below the top of the section.

Further small exposures of the Lewes Member were noted in degraded pits and laneside sections on the escarpment. To the south, the Lewes Member crops out in the Moulescoomb inlier and temporary exposures have shown sections in the Bridgewick and Lewes marls downslope from Moulsecoomb Station. The Navigation Marls were exposed in the western excavations for this station. Gaster (1951, plate 3), on the basis of zonal mapping, inferred the presence of oblique faults in the Moulsecoomb–Falmer area (Figure 15) but he may have been misled by thickness variations in the beds concerned.

Boreholes and trial pits for the Brighton By-pass road north-west and north of Brighton have shown that parts of the Newhaven Member are attenuated, with little marl, in the Red Hill [2859 0828], Old Boat Corner [3250 0947] and Stanmer [3338 0882] areas. At Old Boat Corner the *truncata* hardgrounds above the Old Nore Marl and Peacehaven Marl are strongly glauconitised and phosphatised.

During the construction of the A27 Falmer By-pass [354 089] the Newhaven and Culver members were exposed beneath a cover of disturbed Tertiary beds (p.73). The sections lay mainly in the Castle Hill Beds and yielded small *Echinocorys* forms of Gaster (1924).

A trench section [3712 0923] near Long Hill exposed the Haven Brow Beds with abundant small *Conulus albogalerus*. An unusual bed, containing abundant large *Cretirhynchia plicatilis* corroded *Bourguetticrinus granulosus* and glauconitised chalk pebbles, was found in the chalk of the topmost *Uintacrinus socialis* Zone in Housedean Farm road-cutting [367 093]. These constituents were scattered through 0.4 m of sediment, suggesting that currents were strong.

A sharply pyramidate form of *Echinocorys* was found to be abundant in beds near the top of the *socialis* Zone in a former quarry [340 048] in Sheepcote Valley.

Coast section

The foreshore between Goring and Lancing is largely covered by sand, flint shingle, and banks of chalk cobbles. At intervals, however, patches of chalk are exposed which appear to be in situ. Martin (1932) concluded that the zones represented on the foreshore were as follows:

T. lata: eastwards from the Sea Barn, Goring, to midway between Grand Avenue and Wallace Avenue [132 020]
S. planus: eastwards from Wallace Avenue to Ham Road, Worthing [162 028]
M. cortestudinarium: eastwards from Ham Road to 'a point south of Pearson's Retreat' (presumably near Brougham Road) [169 030]
M. coranguinum: eastwards from south of Pearson's Retreat to at least the line of sewage outfall at East Worthing [173 032]
Higher zones were not exposed

The *T. lata* Zone beds noted above form the core of the Littlehampton Anticline (Martin, 1932, fig. 17). Martin (1938) also recorded the faunal zonation of nearby temporary sections inland. He recognised the boundary between the *T. lata* and *S. planus* zones near the junction of Mulberry Lane and Limbrick Lane, Goring [1115 0292] and farther north the chalk of the *M. cortestudinarium* Zone was reached at a place [1107 0328] 90 m north of the railway-crossing.

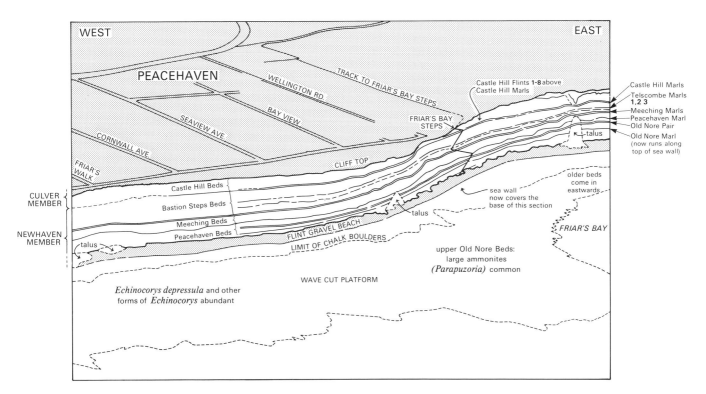

Figure 22   The cliff section at the eastern end of Peacehaven

In contrast to its inland outcrop, the Newhaven Member is well exposed in the coastal cliffs east of Brighton Marina [340 032]. At the marina a group of five thin marls occurs beneath the Brighton Marl (Figure 26). They dip eastwards and reach the modern wave-cut platform to the east of the marina; an abundance of *C. plicatilis* and fragmentary silicified inoceramids is present in the pebbly material on this surface.

The path to the cliff-top at the eastern end of the marina provides a section between the Brighton Marl at the base and the Rotting-dean paired marls at the top (Figure 17). The eastward dip brings in higher beds including the Old Nore Marl, which is the most promi-nent marl in the sequence and is at the mid-point in the cliff eastwards at Rottingdean. Between Rottingdean and Saltdean,

Echinocorys scutata tectiformis is common in and above the Friar's Bay Marls on the wave-cut platform.

Near Peacehaven the cliff exposes beds between the Old Nore Marl and the Castle Hill Flints (Figure 22). The beds containing the latter are the highest preserved beneath the Tertiary deposits of the district. The Old Nore Marl is present on the wave-cut platform to the west of Bastion Steps [412 007] and at Old Nore Point [437 999]. At both of these localities the lower belt of abundant *O. pilula* with *E. scutata* has been observed. Large ammonites (*Parapuzosia*) are present on the platform along the entire length of this cliff sec-tion and are common throughout the Splash Point, Old Nore and Peacehaven beds.   RNM, BY, RDL, CJW

CHAPTER 7

Tertiary deposits: Palaeocene and Eocene

The Tertiary sediments of Sussex comprise clays, with subordinate silts, sands and pebble beds, up to 40 m thick. They are an eastern extension of the strata of this age in the Hampshire Basin. Within the Brighton and Worthing district most of the Tertiary deposits are concealed beneath the drift deposits of the coastal plain and, except in the Worthing and Shoreham Harbour areas, only thin relics of the sequence are preserved. In consequence, the description and interpretation of these beds is based largely on the records of site investigation boreholes.

The most extensive Tertiary deposits are of Palaeocene age and these comprise the Woolwich and Reading Beds. Eocene deposits are present only in the Worthing area, where the lowest beds of the London Clay are preserved in the Worthing Syncline. This structure extends offshore (Curry and Smith, 1975, fig.3) and is probably responsible for the outcrop of Woolwich and Reading Beds beneath Shoreham Harbour. To the east of Shoreham the Woolwich and Reading Beds occur only as small isolated outliers on the dip-slope of the South Downs, but the common presence of Tertiary lithologies in the drift deposits attests to a former widespread cover of these strata.

WOOLWICH AND READING BEDS

A variety of lithologies is present within the Woolwich and Reading Beds, which are up to 30 m thick in the Worthing area. A basal bed of variable thickness (typically up to 2 m) and composed of relatively unabraded flints has been recognised locally; the flints exhibit a dark green glauconitic coating and occur in a sandy or clayey matrix. In places this bed has been secondarily cemented to form a hard ferruginous conglomerate.

In the Worthing area the basal unit has been recorded in only a few of the site-investigation boreholes to have penetrated this level. At East Worthing, one borehole [1683 0359] proved the following sequence:

	Thickness m	Depth m
Drift and Woolwich and Reading Beds (clays)	17.70	17.70
Clay, silty, greyish green, stiff, with fine- to medium-grained gravel	0.75	18.45
Gravel, fine- to coarse-grained, sandy, with flint pebbles and traces of chalk	0.50	18.95
Flint boulders	0.85	19.80
Chalk, weathered	0.88	20.68

The lowest 1.35 m of beds above the Chalk in this borehole are regarded as the local equivalent of the marine 'Bottom Bed' as defined by Hester (1965). In the Falmer area

(p.73), the basal pebble bed and overlying sands probably equate with this bed.

In the Worthing area the clays above the pebble beds, as seen in boreholes, are variously brown or mottled in shades of brown, grey and black. These are succeeded by up to 1 m of lignitic beds, sometimes called 'stromboli', which appear to be persistent throughout the area, typically at 4 to 5 m above the base of the formation. The remainder of the formation apparently consists largely of grey silty clays mottled with red and brown, although intercalations of grey beds have been recognised in boreholes, particularly in the uppermost 10 m or so. Locally the clays are deeply weathered, resulting in loss of red colouration, and are indistinguishable from weathered London Clay.

The beds above the 'Bottom Bed'-equivalent are generally of the terrestrial Reading facies, but C. Reid (in White, 1924, p.65) noted the presence of 'ferruginous concretions containing large oysters and nests of shell-fragments' within red, purple, grey, white and brown mottled clay beneath drift 'in a small opening by the shore' [1782 0346] at South Lancing. It was suggested that this might be the farthest west record in the district indicating a Woolwich (estuarine to marine) facies. Subsequently however, shelly clays, probably of estuarine origin, have been recorded near the top of the Woolwich and Reading Beds, in the Worthing area (pp.72, 75).

Large boulders of hard siliceous fine- to medium-grained sandstone up to about 3 m in diameter are locally common on the surface of the Downs and are known as 'sarsens'. In some cases pebbles and angular pieces of flint are present within the sandstones. A well known variant of this lithology, with abundant well rounded flint pebbles, is the 'Hertfordshire Puddingstone' found to the north and west of London. Although generally distributed as isolated blocks lying on the surface, sarsens are also known to occur embedded in the drift, notably at Black Rock, Brighton [3367 0336], where several such boulders are to be seen in the chalky Head infilling a dry valley. The origin of these boulders is uncertain. Hester (1965) regarded sarsens as being derived from a fluviatile facies of the Woolwich and Reading Beds, termed the 'Reading type'. Within the Brighton district no totally satisfactory source can be identified. Some at least may have been derived from secondarily cemented portions of the formerly more extensive Woolwich and Reading Beds. White (1924, p.68) observed that sarsens were rarely found west of Brighton and it may be significant that the Woolwich and Reading Beds appear — from the limited evidence of the present-day outcrops — to be rather more sandy east of Brighton than farther west. White (1924, pp.68–69) did, however, claim that the lithology of the sarsens could not be matched with 'any of the Eocene sands preserved in Sussex' and that they might have been derived from a younger Tertiary deposit since removed by erosion.

Although it is generally envisaged that the Woolwich and Reading Beds were deposited unconformably on a more or less planar surface of Upper Chalk, the base of these beds is generally highly irregular owing to the development of post-Tertiary solution features in the Chalk surface. The Tertiary sediments have collapsed into these solution hollows and in places, particularly around Brighton and Hove, difficulty is experienced in distinguishing highly disturbed, foundered Woolwich and Reading Beds sediments from Tertiary-rich drift deposits. Within the foundered sediments in the Clifton and Montpelier districts of Brighton a suite of secondary minerals, including selenite and aluminite, has been produced as a result of reactions between groundwaters and the Chalk and Tertiary sediments (Perceval, 1871; Howell, 1872a; 1872b; 1873). Similar deposits have been described from the Upper Chalk – Woolwich and Reading Beds contact at Newhaven (Wilmot and Young, 1985).   RDL, BY

LONDON CLAY

The London Clay is present within synclines to the south-west of Castle Goring [105 055] and beneath the drift in the western part of Worthing. At least 15 m of beds are preserved in the latter structure. This formation consists of olive-grey to medium dark grey, pyritic clays, which weather at the surface to an ochreous and pale grey mottled colour. Sandy intercalations are present towards the base. Gypsum crystals are common near the surface.

The basal bed of the London Clay is typically a pebbly clay, with small rounded black flint pebbles set in greenish grey glauconitic sandy clay. Borehole information indicates that this bed is up to 0.5 m thick. Earlier authors (e.g. White, 1924, fig. 7 and p.68) have taken the 'basement-bed' as a 'compact mass of black and white flint pebbles, mostly under ½ in. diameter, in loamy sand', which was formerly exposed in the top of the Clapham Common brickpit [094 059], just to the west of this district. A maximum thickness of 1.5 m for this bed was recorded by Edwards and Stinton (1971, p.450). Martin (1954) alternatively suggested that this bed might be compared with the Blackheath Beds of north Kent. Recent surveying in the Clapham area suggests, however, that the pebble bed is of superficial origin (Head Gravel) and is possibly largely derived from the basal Woolwich and Reading Beds. Following this conclusion the remainder of the sequence at Clapham needs to be reconsidered. Edwards and Stinton (1971, p.450) described the section as follows:

	Thickness m
4 Brown loam, with abundant, rounded, black and red flint pebbles	about 1.52
3 Yellow-brown clayey silt or fine sand, grey-brown toward the base	about 1.83
2 Blue-grey silty clay, with fish teeth, plant debris, etc. A thin carbonaceous lenticle seen at the top, and brown, soft, calcareous nodules at the base	about 0.84
1 Variegated, red, green and grey massive clay, the upper surface slightly undulose	

[Woolwich and Reading Beds]. Base not seen.   seen 6.10

An earlier description by Martin (1939, p.73) showed beds 2 and 3 to comprise up to 1.8 m of clayey silty sand with a bed of fossiliferous ironstone nodules about 0.15 m thick at the base. Edwards and Stinton (1971, p.451) showed that bed 2 (the 'Black Band') contained a dominantly marine fauna of relatively shallow-water aspect. They considered that bed 2 resembled 'the basement bed of the London Clay at Whitecliff Bay, Isle of Wight (the 'Ditrupa Bed')' but might alternatively be equivalent to the fish-bearing 'Woolwich Bottom Bed' at Herne Bay, Kent. The former correlation now appears to be the correct one and thus it follows that the true basal pebble bed may be locally absent.

Field mapping in the Castle Goring area and elsewhere has shown that it is generally difficult to distinguish the clays of the London Clay from those of the Woolwich and Reading Beds. Where the pebble bed could not be located, silty or sandy beds which were assumed to be equivalent to bed 3 of the above section have been taken as an alternative marker bed for the base of the London Clay.   RDL

DETAILS

Woolwich and Reading Beds

Red-mottled pale grey clays, ochreous pale grey silty clays and brown-grey mottled clays were augered north-west of Hightiten Barn [102 043] and near Holt Farm [105 059]. Sink-holes are present in the drift-covered ground to the south-east of the latter locality.

A well [1066 0454] at Upper Northbrook Farm, which probably started close to the top of the formation, proved 29.6 m of clays beneath 5.5 m of drift and overlying the Chalk.

A borehole [1265 0435] near Durrington provides the best stratigraphical evidence for this area. The abridged log reads:

	Thickness m	Depth m
DRIFT	1.8	1.8
LONDON CLAY		
Clay, brown, shelly at base	7.3	9.1
Sand, green	1.3	10.4
Sand, green, with flints	0.3	10.7
WOOLWICH AND READING BEDS		
Clay, sandy, dark blue	1.2	11.9
Sand, sandy clay and shells	2.1	14.0
Clays, blue, red, brown and grey	20.4	34.4
Clay, black [?lignitic]	2.2	36.6
Clay, brown	2.1	38.7
Clay, green and blue, flinty	2.4	41.1
UPPER CHALK	seen to 35.1	76.2

Here shelly clays were recognised beneath the green sands of the undoubted basal London Clay. This borehole postdates the preparation of the 1:50 000 geological sheet and indicates that the concealed boundary between the Woolwich and Reading Beds and the London Clay should be farther north near this site.

A well [1435 0386] at Southpark Road, Worthing, proved 27.1 m of mottled clay between loamy sands and the Chalk. The record of a well at Newlands Road [1511 0336] shows 30.2 m of clays between the drift and the Chalk.

The top and bottom of the Woolwich and Reading Beds are relatively well defined in the area around Worthing Central railway station [145 034], where numerous trial boreholes have proved red-mottled clays. Farther south, on the north-facing slope of the Teville stream valley [143 030], isolated boreholes indicate the presence of masses of unmapped Tertiary clays which have probably collapsed into solution cavities in the Chalk, the surface of which is locally very irregular.

Numerous boreholes in the Shoreham Harbour area have proved Woolwich and Reading Beds, up to 12 m thick, beneath drift (Thomas and Gray, 1974). At the base a bed of flinty clay up to 1.2 m thick overlies the Upper Chalk; the succeeding brown and grey clays are carbonaceous and contain a lignite bed, typically 0.6 m thick, at levels of 1.2 m to 5.5 m above the Chalk surface.

The recreation ground [2590 0575] at Southern Cross marks the site of a backfilled brickfield excavated in a small concealed outlier of Woolwich and Reading Beds. White (1924, p.65) noted that sand and shelly clay were formerly exposed here beneath the drift. Reid (1890 manuscript) noted dark sandy clay with '*Cyrena, Melania* and *Ostrea*' and sand containing pebbles and large unworn flints. He also recorded that a well sunk in the floor of the pit 'about 15 feet [4.6 m] below the original surface', and probably below the shelly beds, had proved that the Chalk was overlain by Woolwich and Reading Beds comprising sand with flints 6.1 m, beneath sand and clay 3.4 m, in turn overlain by brickearth 2.7 m. To account for the position of this outlier, White suggested that the beds here had been thrown down to the south by a fault situated north of the pit; it is possible, however, that they had collapsed into a solution hollow in the Chalk.

There are no permanent exposures in the two masses of foundered Woolwich and Reading Beds which have been mapped around West Blatchington [272 061; 281 063]. In an earlier revision survey of the area, B. Smith (manuscript notes about 1936) noted clays, sands and ironstones, in addition to abundant flints, in several places; these notes suggest that the Tertiary sediments here are disturbed and may have incorporated later drift sediments in places. In parts of Hove Cemetary [2715 0594] ochreous brown, stoneless, silty clays, known locally as 'snuff', may represent reworked or soliflucted Woolwich and Reading Beds sediments. This material is up to 2 m thick and is commonly overlain by flinty clay-loam, but its relationship to other Tertiary sediments is not clear. Dark clays were noted by Smith in the south-western corner of an old brickyard, the site of which is now occupied by the sports ground [2715 0640] south of Queens Parade, Hangleton.

A large block of ferruginous flint conglomerate in the south-western corner of Hove Park [2868 0602] is known as the 'Goldstone'. It is thought to have come from the basal bed of the Woolwich and Reading Beds, and may have been derived from the outlier that caps the higher ground to the west of the park. Two small outliers of ferruginous sand on Dyke Road, Brighton [2950 0705; 2965 0645] are probably preserved in solution hollows in the Chalk. Reid (1906, p.13) recorded moulds of marine fossils and traces of plants from here.

The sites of former pits for brick-clay may still be recognised in the children's playground adjacent to St Anne's Well Gardens, Brighton [3009 0497]. Plant remains, including leaves and fruit, were recorded from here by Dixon (1878, pp.105–106), and Murchison (1851, p.397) noted that an excavation on the north side of the hill exposed 'from 15 to 20 feet [4.6 to 6.1 m] of mottled plastic-clay with courses (one of which is 3 feet [0.9 m] thick) of black bituminous earth, in parts a lignite'.

White (1924, p.66) described a section exposed in a sewer trench in York Avenue, Hove [approximately 3016 0490] in which the Chalk was overlain by Woolwich and Reading Beds consisting of the following beds in upward succession: hard ochreous clay with flints 0.76 m, lignites and lignitic clays 2.95 m and clay 0.90 m. The chalk immediately beneath the Woolwich and Reading Beds had

been converted partly to gypsum as a result of reaction with ground-waters rich in sulphates from the breakdown of abundant pyrite in the overlying lignitic beds.

Old records suggest that the Woolwich and Reading Beds to the east and north-east of St Anne's Well Gardens have collapsed into solution features in the underlying chalk: in places solution pipes extend for at least 8 m into the chalk. This part of the outcrop is accordingly depicted as 'foundered strata' on the 1:50 000 geological map. Sections seen during the construction of buildings and sewers in the late 19th century were described by Perceval (1871), Howell (1872a; 1872b; 1873) and White (1924, pp.66–67). The following section was recorded by Howell (1878, p.81) at the junction of Clifton Hill and Montpelier Road, Hove [3038 0490] and appears to be typical of the area:

		Thickness m
1	Rich brown, dark grey or ochreous loam, shivered flints, and seams of sand	[0.9]
2	Clay or Brick-earth	[1.2 to 1.8]
3	Breccia and ironstone, with clay, chalk, rubble, rotten flints, sub-sulphate and hydrate of alumina, succeeded [downward] by ochreous loam, containing brecciated masses of indurated clays, gypsum and flints spangled with crystals of selenite, curious stone with a metallic ring containing dark seams of selenite somewhat resembling veined marble, and ferruginous chalk rubble	[2.1 to 2.4]
4	Chalk with flints, the upper portion iron-stained	from [0.9 to 1.2]

The uppermost two divisions probably belong to the drift. The lowest bed, above the Chalk, represents the highly disturbed and collapsed Tertiary Beds, here with included chalk rubble. From Howell's description it is clear that there has been a considerable development of secondary minerals, notably gypsum in the form of selenite, limonite and aluminite ('sub-sulphate and hydrate of alumina' in the above section and also referred to in his descriptions by its obsolete name 'Websterite'). The aluminite occurred as large, solid, nodular masses and also in a soft, friable form. Aluminite was also noted by Howell (1878, p.85) in the railway-cutting [presumed to be approximately 3030 0528] leading to Hove where 'it may be seen in every direction lying immediately below ironstone, embedded in clay resting upon the Chalk'. Both Perceval and Howell described a wood-like form of aluminite occurring in large masses resembling tree trunks.

Basaluminite was identified by Hollingworth and Bannister (1950) as a white, powdery to compact, in some cases nodular mineral, in specimens from Clifton Hill in the British Museum (Natural History) collection. These authors also described white compact nodules, consisting of an intimate mixture of gibbsite and allophane, from Clifton Hill and suggested that the so-called 'collyrite' from Hove mentioned by Dana (1932) was really this material. Allophane was recorded by Perceval and Howell. White (1924, p.66) mentioned diaspore as occurring here.

Around Falmer [354 089] the Woolwich and Reading Beds are preserved as outliers resting on the Chalk at the western end of the Caburn Syncline (Figures 23, 24). Excavations carried out in 1978 during widening of the A27 Lewes to Brighton road west of Park Street [3521 0881] showed the basal pebble bed to be at least 1.5 m thick. The bed consisted mainly of large unworn flints, some with green glauconitic coatings, embedded in a brown, clayey or sandy matrix. Flints coated with black manganese oxides were also common. Hard ferruginous cement and some pockets of cellular limonitic ironstone were noted in places. Other secondary minerals found in parts of these lower beds included allophane, gibbsite and basaluminite. In places the very flinty basal part of the pebble bed was overlain by up to about 1 m of grey to fawn sticky clay containing scattered unworn flints. Overlying these basal beds were up to 2 m of fawn, glauconitic, slightly clayey, fine-grained sand. In all of the sections seen, the beds were disturbed by collapse into solution pipes in the chalk, which were up to at least 5 m across and 8.5 m deep. Nevertheless, the degree of disturbance of the Woolwich and Reading Beds in the Falmer area appears to be much less than in the Brighton area, and in places it has been possible to map separately the basal pebble bed and the overlying sands (Figure 23). The basal pebble bed occupies a wide outcrop north of Falmer, where both iron-stained and glauconite-coated flints are common in the soil.

The former presence of the Woolwich and Reading Beds is suggested by the common occurrence of glauconite-coated flints in the soil on the downland north and east of Falmer, especially around Balmer Huff [3616 1071]. The patch of Clay-with-flints that caps Balmer Huff contains much Tertiary debris and may in part represent a residual outlier of disturbed Woolwich and Reading Beds.

Green glauconite-coated flints are very abundant in the small patches of flinty clay that cap the hills north of Rottingdean [3760 0255] and Saltdean [3885 0255]. Although these deposits closely resemble Clay-with-flints the very high proportion of undoubtedly Tertiary-derived flints suggests that the deposits have a close affinity with the Woolwich and Reading Beds.   RDL, BY

London Clay

In the area to the south-east of Castle Goring [1026 0564] a fine- to medium-grained sand has been mapped. This sediment is probably bed 3 of the sequence given on p.72. The sand is overlain by clayey silts and sandy clays. No pebble bed was found in situ in this area, although pebbles are locally present in the soil. Sandy clays in Goring Wood [0990 0456] are taken to represent the basal London Clay.

A trial borehole [1186 0437] near the junction of Durrington Lane and Littlehampton Road, Durrington proved the sequence which is summarised here:

Figure 23   The Woolwich and Reading Beds of the Falmer area

	Thickness m	Depth m
DRIFT	6.32	6.32
LONDON CLAY		
Clay, silty, and clayey silt, grey-green, very stiff with some shells	2.90	9.22
Band of reddish rock (claystone)	—	—
Clay, silty, green, very stiff, with shells	0.84	10.06
WOOLWICH AND READING BEDS		
Alternations of blue-green and red and grey mottled clays	12.80	22.86

The base of the London Clay has been taken below the lowest shelly clay in this log.

A number of borehole logs near the railway bridge [1472 0338] at Worthing Central Station have recorded the basal beds of the London Clay (depths in metres):

	[1471 0344]	[1472 0341]	[1472 0336]	[1492 0330]
Made ground and drift to	4.6	4.0	4.0	2.6
London Clay to	7.8	5.9	5.6	4.9
Basal bed of London Clay to	8.2[1]	6.1[1]	5.8[1]	5.3[1]
Stiff grey sandy clay	—	to 9.1	to 9.1	to 7.2[2]

1   Grey sandy clay with rounded black pebbles
2   With siltstone fragments and overlying sands with bands of mottled brown and grey sandy clay with siltstone fragments to 9.1 m.

	Depth m
[1477 0326]	
Made ground and drift	4.9
Clay, silty, greenish grey, with shell fragments	6.1
Clays, silty, grey, brown and reddish grey	9.5
Sand, silty	to 10.7

	Depth m
[1503 0343]	
Drift and grey sandy clay (London Clay)	5.8
Silt, clayey, pale brown	6.4
Clay, silty, dark grey, with shells	7.3
Sand, clayey, grey and brown, with layers of silty clay	to 10.7

The shelly clay in the last two logs may be the basal bed of the London Clay on the basis of comparison with those logs which proved the pebble bed horizon (but see discussion below and p.71).

Fossiliferous bluish black sandy clay was recorded by Martin (1937) in spoil from excavations in King Edward Avenue, Worthing [1538 0361] and eastwards. The clays, which were overlain by drift deposits (p.81), contained the following mollusca determined by Wrigley (*in* Martin 1937, p.49): *Melanatria inquinata, Melanopsis buccinoidea, Pitharella rickmani, Tympanotonus funatus, Cyrena cordata, Cyrena cuneiformis, Nucula sp.*, and *Ostrea bellovacina*. Two hinges of *Pitaria* were found, indicative of the London Clay 'basement bed', and a few small well rounded black flint pebbles referable to the same level were also present. Mottled red clays of the Woolwich and Reading Beds were noted towards the eastern end of the section [1569 0368]. Martin took the presence of the thin-shelled *P. rickmani* to indicate a non-marine (i.e. Woolwich Beds) facies and it is probable that part of the fossiliferous sequence lies stratigraphically below the London Clay pebble bed.   RDL

CHAPTER 8

Structure

The Brighton and Worthing district lies on the southern flank of the Wealden anticlinorium which dominates the structure of south-east England. This broad periclinal feature overlies a deep basin of Jurassic sediments and has been modified by faults and folds of varying intensity. Parallels have been drawn between the form of this basin and the inversion structures (so termed) discovered in the North Sea basins (e.g. Kent, 1975). The structural history of the Wealden Basin is not fully understood, although it is apparent that tectonic activity which influenced sedimentation has persisted, albeit sporadically since early Mesozoic times. Widespread unconformities and nonsequences reflect the culminations of these differential movements. On a smaller scale, significant local variations in thickness of various lithological units indicate that deep-seated faulting probably controlled the subsidence of the basin, particularly near its margins. It is now generally accepted that the major faults which have affected the surface strata are related to structures in the Palaeozoic basement rocks. However, not all the surface structures mirror those at depth and it is probable that the contemporary stress-fields and resultant structures varied considerably within the sedimentary fill of the basin. Generally, major faults can only be identified in the more competent strata of Jurassic and early Cretaceous age. The younger strata are locally affected by large folds and it is difficult to relate these to the deep structure except with the aid of seismic profiles. The form of the open folds has probably been influenced by a number of faults at depth. The lowest Mesozoic strata are affected by predominantly west–east faults (Smith, 1985). At higher levels within the basin some of these faults may split or be dissipated, giving rise to folds. The resultant surface structural pattern is consequently more

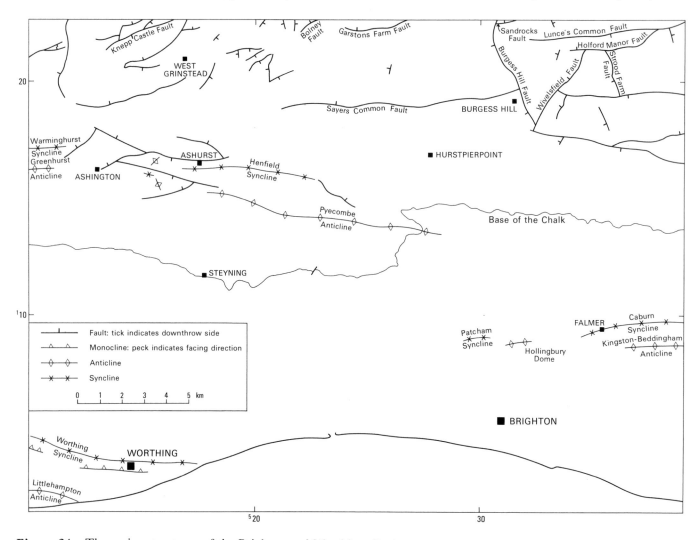

Figure 24   The major structures of the Brighton and Worthing district

diffuse and contains west–east fault plexi, folds with a broadly west–east trend and extensional faults of varying trend. This pattern differs from that postulated by earlier workers, who considered the Weald to show a plexus of *en-échelon* folds with subsidiary faults. Traditionally the major deformation of the Weald has been regarded as part of the mid-Miocene Alpine orogeny. It is difficult, however, to establish the time at which the present inverted form was achieved. Possibly the evidence of deformation and erosion of the Chalk prior to the deposition of the earliest Tertiary formations indicates the initiation of these movements.

The main structural features of this district are shown in Figure 24. It is not possible to construct a contour plot for many of the formations and some minor structures may remain undetected. The most important structures are the anticline–syncline couplets of Pyecombe–Henfield and Littlehampton–Worthing respectively. The Kingston–Beddingham Anticline and Caburn Syncline have a major influence in the Lewes district to the east; the former extends eastwards as the Arlington Anticline and has been linked genetically to the horst at Pevensey which affects Hastings Beds strata (Lake, 1975, p.553).

It will be noted in Figure 24 that the mapped faults are largely restricted to the Wealden strata. The major faults are mainly strike-oriented and, in the extreme north-western area particularly, the trends of some reflect the north-westerly swing of the Lower Greensand crop in the adjacent district. The discovery of the fault plexus between Ashington and Ashurst helps considerably to explain the previously enigmatic collinearity of the Greenhurst Anticline and the Henfield Syncline. It is apparent that the Henfield Syncline is largely fault-controlled, although the complexity of the surrounding fault pattern suggests that the syncline may not simply occupy a modified graben. The existence of the NE–SW-trending fault that impinges on the Greenhurst Anticline to the west of Ashington is somewhat conjectural. An alternative structural explanation for the field relationships in this area would invoke a major unconformity at the base of the Lower Greensand, for which there is no supporting evidence at present. The outcrop pattern of the Weald Clay (Figure 5) suggests the local presence of undetected strike faults; this is a particular problem, especially when considering structures such as the Pyecombe Anticline, where a comparable unconformity might also be inferred from the outcrop pattern to the south-east of Henfield.

DETAILS

Greenhurst Anticline

The maximum recorded dips for the limbs of the Greenhurst Anticline are 25° and 16° to the north and south respectively (White, 1924, p.6). These dips were observed in the Hythe Beds and may have been modified by surficial movements, because the Atherfield Clay downslope shows evidence of minor landslips.

Henfield Syncline

Dip values of up to 40°N and 48°S have been recorded in the Henfield area. The Henfield Syncline may be markedly asymmetrical in cross-section in view of the fault control noted above. A regional dip calculated from the results of the Nep Town Borehole [2112 1562] is about 10°N.

Pyecombe Anticline

A calculated dip for the southern limb of the Pyecombe Anticline, based on outcrop width, the evidence of the Henfield Borehole [1799 1457] and assuming no fault complications, is about 7°S. A dip of 5°N was recorded at the Henfield Brickworks [2197 1434]. As noted above, there is a strong possibility that undetected strike-faults may have affected the Weald Clay in this area.

Worthing Syncline

The Worthing Syncline may be regarded as an extension of the Chichester Syncline, described by Shephard-Thorn and others (1982, fig.3), but separated from it by a structural col near Durrington. The subdrift distribution of the Tertiary deposits demonstrates the marked asymmetry of this fold and the southern limit of these rocks beneath Worthing is defined by a north-facing monocline on the southern side of the syncline. A dip of 25°N was recorded in a water-supply adit [about 1530 0315] near Homefield Park, Worthing. Farther west, in the adjoining district, a dip of 38° N010° was reported by Gaster (1937, p.357) from a chalk-pit [082 043] on Highdown Hill.

Littlehampton Anticline

The presence of Middle Chalk, as shown by fossils of the *T. lata* Zone, beneath the coastal plain west of Worthing, was demonstrated by Martin (1932; 1938). This subcrop, which occupies the core of the Littlehampton Anticline, extends from the foreshore at Goring-by-Sea west-north-westwards at least as far as Wick near the Arun valley in the Chichester district (Martin, 1938, fig.38). Martin (1938, p.202) recorded a dip of 4°S at the coast.

Kingston–Beddingham Anticline

In the Brighton district, the Kingston–Beddingham Anticline has caused Lower Chalk to crop out in the area [387 083] to the north-east of Castle Hill. The anticline is asymmetrical, with a steeper northern limb throughout much of its length. In the Lewes district, dip values of from 15° to 20°N have been recorded in the nearby Kingston area. The westward extension of this structure is somewhat conjectural. The possible link with the fold at Hollingbury has been discussed by Gaster (1951, p.34), who also described the extent of the Caburn Syncline on zonal evidence from the Upper Chalk (but see below).

Hollingbury Dome

The Hollingbury Dome was named the Brighton Dome by Mortimore (1983). It was located by Gaster (1951, p.34), who found evidence of an inlier of *M. cortestudinarium* Zone chalk north-west of Hollingbury Castle; he regarded the fold as a branch of the Kingston–Beddingham Anticline, but it now appears that it is a separate domal structure, flanked by synclines at Patcham (see Gaster, 1951, plate 3) and Falmer. The latter syncline is shown by the presence of Tertiary deposits (Figure 23), albeit in a disturbed state, and may be regarded as part of the Caburn Syncline (Figure 24). No evidence was found during the recent survey to support the presence of the oblique faults projected by Gaster (1951, plate 3; see also Figure 15) near Hollingbury and Falmer.   RDL, RNM

CHAPTER 9

Quaternary deposits

INTRODUCTION

The Quaternary period has been characterised by climatic fluctuations which have ranged from temperate to glacial. Although the Pleistocene glaciers are believed not to have encroached significantly on the Brighton and Worthing district, nivation fields and periglacial activity have probably played a considerable part in the shaping of the landforms. Relatively high sea levels during temperate phases were replaced by low sea levels during cold phases, when water was removed from the hydrological system in the form of ice. Superimposed on these changes of sea level relative to the land there have possibly been regional neotectonic movements.

In the lower reaches of the rivers, oscillatory sea-level changes have resulted in the formation of both river terraces and buried channels. When sea level was low, valleys were subjected to erosion as the rivers regraded their profiles to the lower base level, and during periods of higher sea level aggradation took place. In the hinterland climatic changes caused variations in the amount of run-off and erosion, the eroded materials being fed into the constantly readjusting eustatically-controlled drainage system downstream.

Along the coastal plain of the Brighton and Worthing district much of the Tertiary deposits and a part of the Chalk outcrop are concealed beneath Quaternary deposits. Smaller areas of drift are present on the higher parts of the downland and to the north of the Chalk escarpment. The drift deposits include those of largely solifluction origin (Head, Older Head and Brickearth), river terraces, a suite of raised beach deposits and Flandrian alluvium. Older deposits of somewhat enigmatic origin include the Clay-with-flints and small relict patches of drift which commonly infill pipes in the Chalk.

Table 1 shows the probable chronological inter-relationship of the various drift deposits in the district. This correlation largely follows the regional appraisal by Shephard-Thorn (1975, table 2). Although the events of the late Devensian–Flandrian period are well established, the correlation of the older deposits is uncertain.

The presence of exotic rock types within or below the base of the Raised Beach Deposits has been known for many years and has more recently been the subject of discussion. Kellaway and others (1975) summarised the evidence of large boulders to the west of the district and recorded (1975, p.197) 'numerous boulders (up to about 1 ft [0.3 m] in diameter) of granite, diorite and metamorphic rocks' in the basal layers of the Raised Beach Deposits near the mouth of the River Adur at Lancing. They noted that floating ice had generally been considered to be the means of dispersal of erratic blocks along the channel coast, but concluded that if the boulders were introduced by this agency this must have occurred at a much earlier time than the deposition of the raised beach. The age of the Raised Beach Deposits in this district is here taken as Ipswichian; comparative dating based on racemisation of aminoacids in shells suggests a correlation with oxygen-isotope stage 7 (Davies and Keen, 1985, p.224). The rock-platform beneath the raised beach has a maximum height of 8.5 m above OD at Brighton and the surface elevations of the Second Terrace are broadly

Table 1 Correlation of Quaternary deposits

Stage		River valleys	Coastal plain	Periglacial effects regionally
FLANDRIAN	(warm)	Alluvium Infilling of buried channels	Erosion of cliffs Storm Gravel Beach Deposits Formation of coastal barriers	
DEVENSIAN	(cold)	Cutting of buried channels	Low sea level	Head and Brickearth; solifluction, cryoturbation and valley-bulging ?Older Head
		First Terrace		
IPSWICHIAN	(warm)	Second Terrace	Raised Beach Deposits	
WOLSTONIAN	(cold)	Third Terrace		High-level Head north of the Chalk escarpment
HOXNIAN	(warm)	No evidence		
ANGLIAN	(cold)			
Early Pleistocene				Clay-with-flints

comparable at 5.5 to 9 m above the level of the present-day alluvium. These deposits are probably of roughly similar age and it is assumed that the aggradation of the Second Terrace spanned the interval from late Wolstonian to early Ipswichian; hence an overlap in the times of deposition is possible. Shelly clays which overlie the Raised Beach Deposits west of Worthing (p.81) are possibly comparable with those at Copperas Gap, Portslade (Chapman, 1900), which Kellaway and Shephard-Thorn (1977, p. 64) suggested might be of solifluction origin, perhaps derived from older, higher marine deposits. Alternatively they may be of terrestrial origin.

The age of the valley-bulge structures is conjectural. They are here regarded as formed in Devensian times, penecontemporaneously with the maximum phase of fluvial downcutting, although such movements may have been initiated in the Wolstonian. RDL

CLAY-WITH-FLINTS

The Clay-with-flints is characteristically a dark brown to reddish brown clay or sandy clay in which flint nodules are abundant. The flints are typically fresh or only slightly worn and commonly exhibit brown or black surface-staining owing to the presence of iron and manganese oxides. Pockets of loose brown sand occur locally and fragments of ferruginous sandstone and dark brown ironstone are common. In some outcrops well rounded flint pebbles, some of which show a green glauconitic coating, and blocks of ferruginous flint conglomerate are present. Large boulders of siliceous sandstone (sarsens) up to 2 m in diameter occur in the soil at a number of localities and are believed to have been derived from the Clay-with-flints, though none has been seen in situ in the district. Many of these boulders have been moved from their original positions during land clearance and some have been incorporated into walls.

Small isolated patches of Clay-with-flints are common on the Upper Chalk outcrop. Most of them cap the tops of hills and higher spurs which are probably remnants of the exhumed sub-Tertiary surface (Hodgson and others, 1967). The contact with the underlying Chalk is sharp and commonly irregular, the Clay-with-flints filling hollows and solution pipes. In several places small unmapped pockets of flinty clay, commonly less than 1 m across, can be seen on recently ploughed fields, and many of these appear to be pipe-fillings. Excavations indicate that such solution pipes, though perhaps less than 1 m in diameter, may extend to depths of several metres. Except in solution pipes the Clay-with-flints appears to be a relatively thin deposit, probably rarely exceeding 5 m.

The origin of the Clay-with-flints has attracted discussion from an early date (Jukes-Browne, 1906; Loveday, 1962; Hodgson, Catt and Weir, 1967; Pepper, 1973; Hodgson, Rayner and Catt, 1974). The earliest suggestion that it is a residual deposit produced by in situ solution of the Chalk has been discounted. Jukes-Browne suggested that the origin lay in the reworking of the 'Reading Beds' sediments and recent work (Hodgson and others, 1967; 1974) has given support to this view. Field evidence favours a Tertiary source for much of the Clay-with-flints of the Brighton and Worthing district,

where several masses contain materials derived from nearby Tertiary deposits, including green glauconite-coated flint nodules and pebbles, blocks of hard ferruginous flint conglomerate and dark brown ferruginous sandstone. At Falmer [355 087] and at Telscombe [394 014] in the Eastbourne district, basal Tertiary sands and pebble beds have been disturbed by collapse into solution cavities in the Chalk and pass laterally into material virtually indistinguishable from parts of the Clay-with-flints. Indeed in the south-east of the district, notably around Hove and east of Brighton, it is difficult to differentiate between Clay-with-flints and disturbed Tertiary beds: every gradation appears to exist between the two. BY

Details

The southern part of the Clay-with-flints outcrop at Cissbury Ring [138 079] has been extensively disturbed by Neolithic flint mining and the boundary shown on the map is therefore conjectural. A shallow pit [1384 0730] dug in chalk at Mount Carvey exposed a festoon of cryoturbated Clay-with-flints, 1.8 m wide and 1.3 m deep, immediately north of the main outcrop. The outcrop of flinty loam [128 058] near Durrington Cemetery was classified as Clay-with-flints in the previous editions of the Brighton (318) Sheet, though this deposit is now interpreted as Older Head.

A few rounded flint pebbles were seen in the soil on a small patch of Clay-with-flints [258 068] near Foredown Hospital, Portslade, suggesting the presence of Tertiary pebble bed material within the deposit here. The larger Clay-with-flints outcrop immediately to the south [260 063] may also include a proportion of Tertiary sediments, especially as it lies at the same elevation as the outcrops of foundered Woolwich and Reading Beds a short distance farther east in the West Blatchington area.

The present survey has shown the Clay-with-flints outcrops on Summer Down [265 108], south of Devil's Dyke, to be considerably less extensive than shown on the original Brighton geological sheet. Similarly, on Wolstonbury Hill [2840 1384] the Clay-with-flints has a much more restricted distribution; the outcrop has been much disturbed by the earthworks of the hill fort.

Clay-with-flints forms an extensive spread south of Red Hill. During the widening of Dyke Road, north of the junction with the A2038 road [2854 0810], typical Clay-with-flints up to 1.5 m thick was exposed, resting with an uneven contact on the Upper Chalk. Much Tertiary debris may be present near the southern margin of the outcrop which lies close to a small body of foundered Woolwich and Reading Beds.

A few blocks of ferruginous conglomerate containing green-coated flint pebbles, similar to the basal bed of the Woolwich and Reading Beds at Falmer (see p.73), occur in soil derived from Clay-with-flints at Ditchling Beacon [3316 1306]. Subrounded to well rounded flint pebbles up to 50 mm in diameter are also present here, and a short distance farther east, at Western Brow [3413 1272] such pebbles are locally abundant on the Clay-with-flints. These outcrops range from 221 to 244 m above OD and are the highest occurrences of recognisable Tertiary materials within the Clay-with-flints in the district. Well rounded flint pebbles and relatively unworn flint nodules up to 0.15 m in diameter, both of which exhibit the glauconitic coating characteristic of the basal Tertiary Beds, are common in the Clay-with-flints which caps Balmer Huff [3616 1071]; blocks of dark brown sandstone and ferruginous flint conglomerate were also noted, and augering revealed the presence of pockets of brown coarse-grained sand in the south-eastern corner of the outcrop [3609 1049].

In both the Hollingbury Castle [322 079] and Falmer Hill [347 074] areas the present survey has shown the Clay-with-flints to be much less extensive than shown on previous editions of the Brighton

Figure 25 The relationship of the raised beach cliff-line to the distribution of younger drift deposits

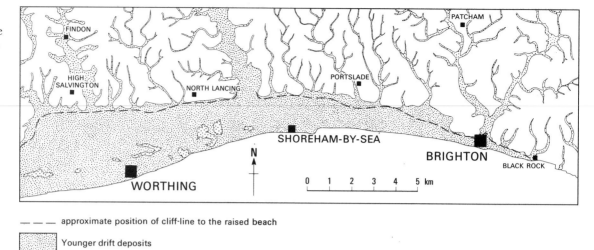

- - - approximate position of cliff-line to the raised beach

Younger drift deposits

Raised Beach Deposits

Sheet. At Falmer Hill no mappable drift is present, though White (1924, p.71) mentioned gravel being worked at the western end of the hill; only small patches of flinty clay occur here and in places flints are common in the soil.

Blocks of dark brown sandstone and ferruginous flint conglomerate with green-coated flint nodules are present in the soil near the radio-mast on Newmarket Hill [3625 0715]. Three small patches of Clay-with-flints have been mapped here, but in addition numerous small pockets and pipe-fillings are present, especially near the summit of the hill [3617 0671]. Cuttings north of the farm buildings at High Hill [3772 0421] expose typical flinty clays up to 4 m thick overlying white chalk. Several large sarsen boulders up to 1 m in diameter standing in front of Balsdean Cottages [3786 0422] may have been obtained from this patch of Clay-with-flints. Sarsens up to 1.5 m in diameter occur on the downland near High Park Corner [3240 1145], near Lower Standean [3185 1175] and around the pond at Stanmer Park [3371 0958]; at the last two localities the boulders have been moved by man to their present positions. BY,RDL

RAISED BEACH DEPOSITS

Beneath a substantial part of the coastal plain of Worthing and Lancing there is an extensive spread of Raised Beach

Deposits which has been largely obscured by more recent drifts. These beach deposits consist of sandy flint gravels and shelly medium-grained sands, resting on a bevelled surface of Chalk and Tertiary deposits. Chalk pebbles are common where the deposits resting on the Chalk have not been decalcified. Organic clays have been recorded above the Raised Beach Deposits in the Worthing area but their origin is not known. The carbonaceous shelly clays which occur beneath the beach deposits 'along the Shoreham road in Hove' (White, 1924, p.76) have not been relocated but are possibly analogous to those at Selsey.

The bedrock surface rises gently to the WNW from at or just above Ordnance Datum in South Lancing to about 6 m above OD at Durrington. This wave-cut platform is delimited on its north side by a fossil cliff-line (Figure 25). Martin (1938) showed that Highdown Hill [093 043] formed a headland on this coastline. North-west of Worthing, the distribution of the beach deposits is similar to that of the overlying Brickearth. The beach deposits are absent in the area immediately adjacent to the coast through loss by erosion.

To the east of the River Adur the bedrock surface beneath

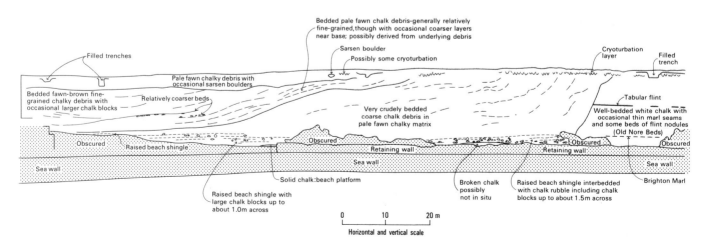

Figure 26 The section in drift deposits at Black Rock, Brighton

the beach deposits commonly lies between 2 and 6 m above OD. However, the preservation of the Raised Beach Deposits is patchy and it is likely that these sediments have been eroded away where channels infilled with Head extend southwards from the dry valleys of the Chalk dip-slope across the coastal plain. Near the Tertiary outcrops to the east of Southwick, the former cliff line has probably been degraded and masked by solifluction deposits.

The exposure at Black Rock [335 033] (Plate 4), detailed below (p.82), shows an oblique section through the fossil cliff cut in Upper Chalk. Thick solifluction deposits of more than one episode are banked against this cliff above the beach deposits (Figure 26). The rock platform lies at 8.8 m above OD, and the beach deposits extend up to 11.9 m above OD. An intertidal molluscan fauna has been obtained from the beach deposits (Shephard-Thorn and Wymer, 1977, p.64), whereas at Copperas Gap, Portslade, a sediment (now thought to have been reworked) containing a fauna characteristic of a slightly deeper-water environment was described by Chapman (1900). These Raised Beach Deposits have been ascribed to the '15-foot' beach or 'Brighton Raised Beach' (at Black Rock) by earlier authors (e.g. Martin, 1937; Shephard-Thorn, 1975). There is no evidence in this district of the higher '100-foot' (or Goodwood) raised beach of Fowler (1932), discussed more recently by Kellaway and Shephard-Thorn (1977) and Shephard-Thorn and others (1982).

In his description of the Raised Beach Deposits of the West Sussex coastal plain to the west of the River Arun, Hodgson (1964, p.554) noted that over the Chalk subcrop the deposits were thin or disturbed. He also remarked that the wave-cut platform was about 1.2 m lower over the Chalk than over the Tertiary clays. This loss of height and the thinness of the beach deposits were believed to be due to differential solution of the Chalk, coupled with frost-heaving and cryoturbation. There are insufficient data to demonstrate these features in this district, although the few logs of boreholes in the Worthing area indicate that the Chalk surface may be slightly elevated with respect to the Tertiary surface farther inland, and the Chalk surface is certainly corroded beneath the drift deposits.

West and Sparks (1960) suggested that the beach deposits were of late Ipswichian age on the evidence of the estuarine and freshwater sediments which underlie the beach at Selsey. Recent evidence (reviewed by Sutcliffe and Kowalski, 1976 and Shotton, 1985) suggests that the period between the Wolstonian and Devensian glaciations included two temperate intervals interspersed with cold ones. Thus the cutting of the wave-cut platform and the deposition on it of marine sands and gravels may represent a more complex sequence of events than a single transgression-regression episode. Chalky flinty clays that have been recorded locally in the Worthing area, above Tertiary bedrock and below the Raised Beach Deposits, but close to the Chalk subcrop, probably reflect an earlier phase of solifluction.   RDL

Details

Trial boreholes in the area [113 047] north of Ham Farm have proved sands and sandy gravels up to 2.5 m thick, overlying the Woolwich and Reading Beds. One borehole [1135 0487] proved the following drift sequence:

	Thickness m	Depth m
Topsoil	0.3	0.3
Clay, sandy, brown, firm (Head)	0.7	1.0
Clay, brown, firm, with flints (Head)	0.6	1.6
Clay, brown, stiff	2.4	4.0
Clay, silty, brown and grey, firm, with shells	0.3	4.3
Sand, medium, dense, grey-blue	1.7	6.0
Woolwich and Reading Beds	—	—

The lowest bed above the Woolwich and Reading Beds is sand of the raised beach. Two nearby boreholes proved peaty silts at the level of the shelly clay in this log and ranging up to 3 m above that of the bedrock surface. A further borehole [1100 0391], near Littlehampton Road, proved the succession:

	Thickness m	Depth m
Made ground and topsoil	0.8	0.8
Clay, pale brown, friable (Brickearth)	0.3	1.1
Clay, grey-brown, firm, with numerous small shells	0.3	1.4
Clay, grey and reddish brown mottled, friable	0.7	2.1
RAISED BEACH DEPOSITS		
Sand, yellowish brown	0.8	2.9
Sand, brown, and rounded flint gravel	0.4	3.3
?WOOLWICH AND READING BEDS	—	—

In the Goring area, the outcrop of the Raised Beach Deposits has been mapped on the presence of abundant rounded flint pebbles in the soil. Thin patches of Brickearth with pebbles derived from the beach beneath are probably present at the surface locally. The gravels were formerly worked in a pit [1135 0265] in Goring Road.

Wells at the Broadwater Pumping Station [1433 0542] in Hill Barn Lane penetrated between 18.0 and 19.8 m of drift deposits overlying the Chalk at 3.9 to 5.8 m above OD. The drift consisted of a basal bed of gravel (possibly Raised Beach Deposits) up to 2.1 m thick overlain by marly clays, 'ballast' and flinty clays (see also White, 1924, p.84). Chalk was formerly exposed at about 30 m OD in the now largely backfilled quarry 150 m to the north, thus demonstrating the presence of the buried cliff to the north of the raised beach.

Trial boreholes in the outcrop area south of Worthing Central Station [145 034] have shown the local presence of thin Brickearth overlying the Raised Beach Deposits. The beach deposits are apparently absent beneath the lower south slope of the Teville stream valley immediately to the south. Beneath the Brickearth to the south of the A259 road the general southern limit of the beach deposits is probably indicated by an impersistent weak break of slope that extends westwards from Worthing to Goring.

Martin (1937) described the Raised Beach Deposits exposed beneath Brickearth in a temporary section [1538 0361 and eastwards] in King Edward Avenue, Worthing. The beach deposits increased in thickness eastwards from 0.6 to 3 m. Martin (1937, p.50) noted that the pebbles were mainly of flint 'but one of quartzite was noticed, and large unworn flints and chalk pebbles and rolled fossils from the Upper Chalk' were common. The fauna determined by Dr L. R. Cox was as follows: *Littorina (Neritoides) littoralis* abundant, *Nucella lapillus*, *?Buccinum undatum*, *Macoma balthica* abundant, *?Mytilus edulis* and *Ostrea sp.* with borings of the sponge *Cliona*.

Up to 1.5 m of medium gravel was noted beneath 1.5 m of fill in a temporary exposure [1755 0359] in South Lancing. The gravels were formerly worked in a pit [1846 0439] near Lancing Station. The Raised Beach Deposits were exposed in temporary sections in North Lancing at the Sports Centre [1870 0566] and at the Sussex

Pad Hotel [1993 0604], close to the inferred cliff-line. At the Sports Centre sandy gravels were interbedded with soliflucted flinty loams, indicating partial recycling of the former deposits.

Trial boreholes at Southlands Hospital [228 061] proved 6.1 m of soliflucted flinty and chalky clays; one deeper bore (with a ground level of 17.1 m above OD) proved sandy gravel between 7.0 and 8.4 m depth, and thus indicated the presence of the former cliff immediately to the north of here. In the area between Cross Road and Southview Road, Southwick, a number of trial boreholes penetrated fine-grained sands with some gravel, beneath the surface mantle of Head; the Chalk surface fell southwards from 5.7 m [2384 0598] to 2.7 m above OD [2419 0561].

Two boreholes [2682 0564; 2676 0561] near Portslade Station proved both flinty and stoneless clays (Head) to overlie sandy gravels (Raised Beach Deposits), which in turn rested on Upper Chalk at 4.8 and 4.5 m above OD respectively. Some of the clays contained shell fragments. Sections of historical interest at Portslade were described by Prestwich (1892), Warren (1897) and Chapman (1900).

A number of the boreholes for the West Street redevelopment in Brighton proved variously flint gravels or sands beneath the Head deposits; one bore [3076 0426] at the northern side of the site encountered the surface of the Upper Chalk at 18.3 m depth (7.0 m above OD). In contrast, no significant drift was encountered at

another site [3090 0435] 150 m to the north-east. Hence the former cliff-line approximately underlies Western Road hereabouts.

The important section at Black Rock [335 033] (Figure 26; Plate 4) is well exposed in the cliff behind Brighton Marina. Here the Brighton Raised Beach comprises sands or sandy flinty gravels with interbedded chalky detritus, up to 3.1 m thick; the gravels also contain ironstones, ferruginous breccias, sarsens and a few igneous and metamorphic rocks. The fragmentary shells recorded by White (1924, p.74) included *Cardium edule*, *Mytilus edulis*, *Littorina obtusata* and *Purpura lapillus*, in association with teeth of horse and fragments of whale bone. Modern cliff recession has destroyed the former eastward extension described by Mantell (1822); then the wave-cut platform mentioned above was probably exposed as low as 4 m above OD at the western (now obscured) part of the section.   RDL

RIVER TERRACE DEPOSITS

In the valleys of the River Adur and its tributaries three terrace levels have been recognised; the ranges of surface level with respect to that of the Flandrian alluvium are as follows: First Terrace 0 to 4 m; Second Terrace 5.5 to 9 m; Third Terrace above 12 m. Of these, the Third and Second, and

Plate 4   The drift deposits at Black Rock. Crudely bedded scree deposits overlie Raised Beach Deposits and are banked against a former sea cliff. (See also Figure 26) [A13417]

the Second and First, have not everywhere been mapped separately. Near the surface the lithologies comprise dominantly silty loams although pebbly sands have been proved locally within individual spreads.

In the middle reaches of the River Adur, between West Grinstead and Henfield, the terrace deposits are generally poorly defined. Where the minor tributary valleys of the River Adur drain north-eastwards across the Weald Clay from the Lower Greensand escarpment between Danhill Farm [108 194] and Warminghurst [117 168], silty loams (Head) commonly flank the lower slopes and infill the secondary embayments. These solifluction deposits merge imperceptibly with the First Terrace deposits of the Adur near West Grinstead, locally incorporating coarser-grained, probably derived, river terrace material. This situation is comparable with that observed by Thurrell and others (1968) in the Haslemere district.

There are two areas of terrace deposits which are not related to the terrace system outlined above. They occur 200 m north-east of Bushovel Farm [1515 1330] and 500 m west of Wappingthorn [1620 1340], at about 60 m and 30 m above present alluvium respectively. The former caps the flat top of a hill. These deposits, which are designated 'River Terrace Deposits, undifferentiated' on the 1:50 000 geological map, are evidently much older than the lower suites of deposits.

Terrace deposits are largely absent where the River Adur passes through a gap in the Upper and Middle Chalk, so that it is not possible to correlate with certainty the Raised Beach Deposits of the coastal plain with the terrace system. However, relative elevations suggest that the Raised Beach Deposits may have been contemporaneous with the Second Terrace (p.78).   RDL

Details

A large bench feature [1620 1340] covered with dark brown to yellow-brown sandy loam and flint gravel is present near Wappingthorn (see above). The brown flint gravel consists of angular clasts between 0.03 and 0.3 m across.

In the Adur valley between West Grinstead and Henfield, the river terraces have been distinguished both on the presence of features and on the local occurrence of pebbly sands within the deposits concerned. The terrace deposits generally consist of silty loams at least 1.4 m thick. Flinty wash, probably reworked from older solifluction deposits, is locally present at surface on these outcrops. In contrast, the adjacent Head deposits consist of silts and clayey silts less than 1 m thick which overlie soft reworked Weald Clay material.

Approximately 1.3 km ESE of Northover Farm [1930 1440] the First Terrace forms a flat bench with a steep slope to the alluvium at its southern extremity. The sandy loam matrix contains angular flint and subrounded sandstone clasts. The sandstone clasts are up to 40 mm in diameter: both yellowish brown, fine-grained sandstone, possibly of Wealden origin, and brown, iron-cemented, coarse-grained material similar to the 'carstone' of the Folkestone Beds are present. In a ditch [1949 1425] on the eastern side of the terrace angular blocks of cemented terrace material were found.

In the railway-cutting [1819 1114] 200 m south of Steyning Station an exposure showed 2.2 m of Third Terrace deposits on Lower Chalk. The top of the Chalk was very irregular and probably cryoturbated. The terrace deposits comprised buff clayey loam, with abundant small angular white flints increasing in abundance towards the top. Small chalk fragments were also present, particularly near the base.

To the north and north-east of Henfield and north of Hurstpierpoint, there are extensive spreads of silty and sandy loams assigned to the Second and Third terraces. No sections were present but flinty loams were recorded in places at 1 to 1.5 m depth. It is possible that these deposits are analogous to the Head deposits mapped to the west near Thakeham [110 173] and thus they may be, in part at least, of solifluction origin.   RDL,BY

OLDER HEAD

In places on the Chalk dip-slope there occur areas of heterogeneous brown flinty clays and flinty loams which appear from their field relationships to be older than the main Head deposits of the district. In the west, in the Clapham and High Salvington areas [108 067; 120 066], spreads of flinty clays and loams below the Clay-with-flints outcrops are grouped with the Older Head; a break of slope is usually present at the boundary with the Clay-with-flints. Elsewhere, Older Head occurs on the lower slopes of dry valleys and locally occupies a gently sloping bench feature near the foot of the slope; these deposits appear to be remnants of earlier fillings of the dry valleys into which the present dry valleys have been cut. No sections have been seen, but the materials at surface and proved by augering resemble the decalcified parts of the much more widespread later Head of the dry valleys and the coastal plain.

Several boreholes on the coastal plain have proved sandy clays between the Chalk bedrock and the Raised Beach Deposits. These are interpreted as early solifluction deposits, preserved as relict masses on the surface of the Chalk or as shallow pipe-fillings. The Raised Beach Deposits are generally regarded as being of Ipswichian age; the underlying head deposits may therefore be of Wolstonian age, and hence may be equivalent to the Older Cherty Head of north Kent, and to the Coombe Rocks which overlie the Slindon deposits in West Sussex, for which Shephard-Thorn (1975, p.545) suggested a Wolstonian date. No evidence has been obtained to date the Older Head seen at outcrop in the district.

Details

In the Clapham [108 067] and High Salvington [120 066] areas, solifluction and downwash from outcrops of Clay-with-flints have produced spreads of flinty clays and loams which are classified as Older Head. In Clapham Wood the dry valleys appear to have been incised into the surface on which the Older Head was deposited. On the slopes south of High Salvington a mantle of brown flinty loam extends downslope from the Clay-with-flints outcrop to the coastal plain; in this case delineation of the Older Head is arbitrary. In the old chalk-pit [1275 0620] at Mill Lane, High Salvington, joints are infilled with brown clay and in places the same clay has been injected along bedding planes. This clay may be a representative of the Older Head emplaced by cryoturbation and its presence may indicate that the Older Head formerly blanketed the adjacent ground.

At Lychpole Farm [1565 0765], Sompting, and at Hazelholt Bottom [2320 0875], north-west of Mile Oak, deposits of Older Head rest on terrace-like features at the foot of the valley sides, adjoining the newer Head in the valley bottoms. Similarly, in the dry valley [3820 0455; 3860 0445] north-east of Balsdean Farm, flinty loam forms prominent terrace features near the foot of the south-facing valley side. A well marked break of slope forms a conspicuous back feature and there is a clear step down to the present valley floor. The Older Head terrace feature ranges in height from about 43 m to almost 60 m above OD, and is bisected by a small incised tributary dry valley filled with younger Head.   RDL,BY

HEAD AND HEAD GRAVEL

The term 'Head' is applied here to generally unstratified deposits, commonly of solifluction origin, which occur widely in the river valleys and on the coastal plain. Although the various lithologies reflect the local parent material, wind-blown deposits may have been incorporated into these sediments. The Head deposits of the coastal plain and Chalk dip-slope were classified as 'Coombe Deposits' on the earlier published one-inch geological sheet.

Near Castle Goring [1026 0564] and westwards, soliflucted pebbly loams, probably derived from the Woolwich and Reading Beds (see p.72), have been classified as 'Head Gravel'. Thin flinty gravels which overlie the Lower Greensand near Heath Common [110 145] and at Sandgate Park [101 140] were previously mapped as 'Plateau Gravel', but these are too thin to be distinguished on the current geological map. These gravels also contain fragments of ferruginous sandstone and have a fine- to coarse-grained sandy matrix (White, 1924, p.71); the rarity of stratification points to an origin by solifluction.

The Head deposits present to the north of the Chalk scarp occur both in association with the modern drainage system and on isolated low hills with a crudely terrace-like surface expression. The latter examples presumably relate to a much older and subsequently dissected solifluction sheet.

The sediments consist dominantly of homogeneous, brown, silty or sandy loams. In the northern part of the Weald Clay outcrop, clayey loams are locally common, particularly in the minor tributary valleys where the local parent bedrock material makes a large contribution. In many cases the Head deposits which occur on valley sides merge imperceptibly with the terrace loams (p.83) so that the distinction of these deposits is made difficult.

Patches of angular or worn, nodular, patinated flints together with a few sandstone fragments are common on the interfluves and these are probably directly related to the older solifluction sheet mentioned above. They are most common on the higher ground but have also been washed downslope and incorporated in the younger lower-lying drift deposits.

The dry valleys of the dip-slope of the Chalk downland are underlain by channels filled with weakly bedded chalk and flint detritus in a soft marly matrix, mainly of solifluction origin. Near the surface this material is patchily decalcified to form a brown flinty loam. A concentration of angular flint fragments locally marks the base of the decalcified zone. Towards the flanks of the larger valleys, soft putty chalk debris present at the surface may represent local solifluction scree deposits, but the bulk of the deposits that occur in the dry valleys are probably related to major solifluction flows; crude bedding structures within these deposits reflect intermittent phases of subaqueous deposition or the pulsatory movement of individual solifluction lobes.

The thickness of these deposits is difficult to determine because few borehole logs distinguish accurately the rubbly chalky fill of the dry valleys from the bedrock beneath, which is commonly shattered by penecontemporaneous frost-action. The form and depth of the channels may be seen however in cross-section in the cliffs to the east of Brighton. Here the channels are up to 15 m deep and locally extend down almost to foreshore level.

The exposure at Black Rock [335 033] (Figure 26) shows the composite nature of the Head deposits which overlie the Raised Beach Deposits (p.82) here. The material near the exhumed cliff comprises coarse chalk talus which grades upwards and westwards into finer-grained slope deposits that show steep depositional dips. A series of fine-grained chalky solifluction deposits are banked against these sediments at the west end of the section. They appear to represent the solifluction lobe of the Sheepcote valley. A coarser-grained solifluction deposit with sizeable sarsens, ironstones and flints overlies these sediments. The mammalian bones which have been collected from these Head deposits include *Mammuthus primigenius, Coelodonta antiquitatis, Cervus elaphus, Equus caballus, Hippopotamus amphibius* and *Sus scrofa* (White, 1924, p.80).

The Head deposits of the coastal plain are broadly similar to those of the Chalk dip-slope, but where they are at the surface or beneath permeable drift deposits, such as brickearth, the effects of decalcification have been so pervasive as to produce compact flinty loam or clay; the flints in such deposits are generally patinated and fractured and the matrix is dark brown or reddish brown.

These deposits occur at the foot of the Chalk dip-slope, typically up to 6 m thick, and they extend beneath the Brickearth (p.85) to the south, where they overlie the Raised Beach Deposits. In some boreholes comparable lithologies have also been recorded beneath the Raised Beach Deposits, indicating an earlier phase of deposition (p.83).   RDL

Details

The flinty loams that cap Spear Hill [1345 1740] at about 44 m above OD, and the flinty wash which is present at Dial Post [155 195] at about 31 m above OD, probably relate to a formerly extensive high-level solifluction sheet, perhaps comparable in age with the Third Terrace. Other examples at lower topographical levels, such as that [138 187] near Oakwood (up to 22 m above OD), relate to the Second Terrace, whereas the most extensive Head deposits that flank the modern valleys generally merge with the First Terrace.

A marked bench feature on the western flank of Findon valley is underlain by soft, putty chalk and chalk rubble [122 076 to 127 066]. This may be localised scree material and perhaps conceals a feature related to marls present within the Chalk.

A track-cutting [1460 0753] exposed 0.6 m of brown, flinty clay overlying 1.2 m of chalk rubble at the head of a tributary valley to Deep Bottom. The chalky material showed involution festoon structures 0.3 to 0.6 m wide, and, locally, crude stratification. The festoon structures were sharply truncated at the base of the decalcified material.

Ditch sections [1007 0604 to 1044 0598] to the north-west of Holt Farm showed that the Head generally consists of 1 to 1.5 m of compact flinty loam overlying 0.5 m of ochreous flinty clay. Cryoturbated wedges of the bedrock (Woolwich and Reading Beds) were observed locally. Silcreted chalk fragments were noted beneath the drift in a nearby ditch-cut [1007 0609].

Site investigation boreholes for a building development [113 048] north of Ham Farm proved between 2.3 and 5.5 m of flinty, sandy clays overlying Raised Beach Deposits. Other trial boreholes for a site [1155 0435] to the east of Ham Farm proved between 1.4 and 2.4 m of sandy clays (Brickearth) overlying chalky Head deposits, indicating minimal decalcification of the lower lithology. Site investigation boreholes at Nelson Road [1202 0355], Durrington, proved up to 6 m of sandy calcareous clay with chalk and flint fragments overlying Chalk and beneath 1 to 2 m of Brickearth.

In the West Tarring area, where the Brickearth is locally less than 1 m thick, the chalky Head beneath is decalcified in the upper part to form a brown very flinty clay. At Broadwater the limited information suggests that the surficial decalcified zone is between 0.7 and 1.5 m thick. On the southern slope of the Teville stream valley [around 144 030], the Raised Beach Deposits are apparently generally absent and this feature is largely due to the increased thickness of Head deposits present beneath the Brickearth.

A former pit [143 052] near the Warren exposed 4.3 m of Coombe Deposits, with common large unworn flints and chalk fragments (Holmes, 1936, in manuscript).

In the area [165 045] to the south of Sompting the Head consists of brown, silty loam with generally small angular flints. This lithology appears intermediate between the Brickearth and the Head deposits typical of north Worthing.

Chalky solifluction deposits occur beneath the alluvial deposits of the Adur valley (Figure 28) although in the Shoreham area they are apparently largely absent beneath the coastal strip south of the railway line. In the area to the north, boreholes for the A27 river crossing showed that they are present where the bedrock surface lies above 10 m below OD.

In the Southwick area the Head is typically between 1 and 7 m thick. Thicker sequences occur where the channels associated with the dry valleys of the Chalk dip-slope extend across the coastal plain. Similar conditions prevail eastwards. Thus up to 15.3 m of flinty marls were proved in boreholes near Portslade Station, to the south of the dry valley which runs through Hangleton.

Up to 6.7 m of brown stony clay was penetrated in boreholes [2733 0540] in Portland Road, Hove. This site lies close to the cliff-line of the raised beach and this thickness probably represents the aggradation of materials near the foot of this feature. Comparable examples elsewhere have been described on pp.81–82.   RDL, BY

BRICKEARTH

In this district Brickearth deposits are confined to the coastal plain west of Brighton. The Brickearth is a buff or brown, generally structureless, non-calcareous loam or silt. The basal part of the deposit characteristically contains material derived from the underlying stratum; thus pellets of chalk are common in the lower part where it rests on the Chalk, for example in the Worthing area adjacent to the coast. At higher levels lenses of small angular flints are locally present, and in places the Brickearth interfingers with, or passes imperceptibly into, the coarse-grained Head deposits.

Borehole evidence in the vicinity of Worthing indicates that north of the railway line the Brickearth generally overlies coarse solifluction deposits (Head) which, in turn, rest on Raised Beach Deposits. Here the Brickearth is about 1.5 to 2 m thick, although locally thicknesses of only 0.6 m have been recorded. To the south of the railway, the Brickearth is 3 to 6 m thick in the coastal strip near the town centre, generally with a corresponding reduction in the combined thickness of the underlying drifts. Elsewhere in the district thicknesses rarely exceed 2 to 3 m. The basal surface

is commonly irregular because of solution and cryoturbation of the underlying deposits.

Early descriptions of the deposit were published by Murchison (1851) and Godwin-Austen (1857). The remains of bear, horse, mammoth and whale have been recorded from the Brickearth between the River Adur and Brighton (Howell, 1873; White, 1924). No definitive age has been obtained for the Brickearth of the Brighton and Worthing district, although a late Devensian to early Flandrian age is accepted for the deposits in general.

The origin of Brickearth in south-east England has been discussed by a number of authors, for example Dines and others (1954). The deposit in this district was probably formed by solifluction, representing a distal form of the Head deposits described above. The parent material of the Brickearth is, however, in doubt, in view of the low silt content of the Chalk and the small present-day outcrop area of the dominantly clayey Tertiary formations. It is possible that a significant proportion of the silt material is of aeolian origin.   RDL, BY

ALLUVIUM

In the hinterland the alluvium of the River Adur and other streams consists of dominantly soft, brown and grey, freshwater silts and silty clays with peaty intercalations, and has a thin basal lag gravel. The floodplain of the River Adur is narrow where the river flows over Wealden strata, but it spreads west and south of Henfield until it is 2 km wide on the Gault near Steyning. The alluvium then narrows to 0.4 to 1.2 km where the river passes through a prominent gap in the Chalk downland, and widens to about 2 km again on the drift-covered coastal plain near Shoreham.

The alluvium fills a channel, the base of which is graded to a lower sea level than that of the present day. Near the mouth of the River Adur the lowest part of the channel lies at 23 m below OD. Here the buried channel follows a different alignment to that of the present river (Figure 27), and meets the coast near New Salts Farm.

In the Shoreham area and particularly near the course of the buried channel, the alluvium includes shelly fine-grained sands, possibly deposited in a tidal-flat environment. In the coastal strip near the A259 road at Shoreham the alluvial sands and clays are replaced laterally by sandy gravels derived from or forming part of the storm beach (Figure 28). The progradation of the storm beach deposits, in response to the rising Flandrian sea level, caused the progressive ponding back of the Adur drainage in the broad alluvial tract immediately to the north.   RDL, BY

Details

Up to 10.5 m of alluvium has been proved in the Teville stream valley, in a borehole [1688 0362] at East Worthing which showed the typical presence of a basal sandy gravel 1.3 m thick. At the industrial estate to the north-west, boreholes [around 156 042] have proved between 2 and 5 m of alluvium, which is locally underlain by chalky solifluction deposits.

The alluvium at South Lancing near Old Salts Farm [1927 0446] has an undulating and locally hummocky surface. Augering proved

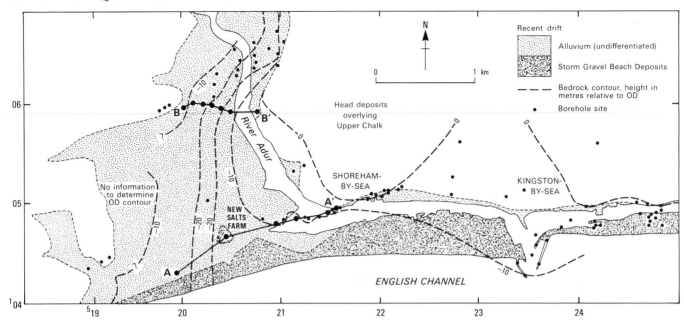

Figure 27   The bedrock surface beneath drift deposits at the mouth of the River Adur
(see also Figure 28)

up to 1.4 m of soft silty clays in the low-lying areas, but on the rises a thin clayey wash was shown to overlie brown sandy silts and clayey silts. This relationship has probably resulted from differential compaction of the alluvium, coupled with a certain amount of wastage of clay material from the higher ground.

Evidence for the buried channel of the River Adur in the Bramber area was provided by a trial borehole [1931 1010] made for the Bramber-Steyning By-pass 500 m SSE of Beeding Bridge. The sequence proved was as follows:

	Thickness m	Depth m
ALLUVIUM		
Topsoil	0.30	0.30
Clay, brown-mottled, stiff, sandy in parts	2.14	2.44
Clay, silty, organic, blue, very soft to soft	5.48	7.92
Sand, fine- to medium-grained, silty in parts, with traces of peat	8.84	16.76
Clay, silty, brown, firm	0.92	17.68
Clay, sandy, stony, grey, firm	0.61	18.29
Gravel, very coarse, compact	1.22	19.51
Flints with chalk fragments, compact	1.22	20.73
UPPER CHALK		
Chalk, weathered to sound	3.65	24.38

The sandy beds above 16.76 m depth resemble those recorded downstream, but the absence of shelly material in this and adjacent boreholes suggests that here they are of freshwater origin.   RDL

STORM GRAVEL BEACH DEPOSITS

Storm Gravel Beach Deposits consist of shingle which has been thrown into ridges above normal high tide levels by wave action. Between Worthing and Kemp Town the coast is fringed by a nearly continuous narrow belt of Storm Gravel Beach shingle. East of the entrance to Shoreham harbour, the storm beach shingle is largely concealed beneath

made ground on which Brighton Power Station and several industrial premises are built. The information from boreholes shows that the Storm Gravel Beach Deposits extend northwards beneath the Alluvium in the vicinity of the A259 coast road (Figure 28). The shingle is composed almost exclusively of rounded flint pebbles between 0.01 and 0.1 m in diameter. Wheeler (1902, p.183) noted the presence of scattered quartzite pebbles at Shoreham, though it is possible that these and other 'exotic' pebbles originated as ship's ballast. The longshore drift of shingle along this coast is eastward and much of the flint shingle has presumably been derived from the Pleistocene deposits of the coastal plain both within and to the west of the district.

Various accounts provide a picture of the changing pattern of the Storm Gravel Beach Deposits. A full account of the historical development of the Adur mouth and Shoreham Beach was given by Ward (1922, pp.100–105). The shingle spit of Shoreham Beach has moved repeatedly in past centuries. In the mid-17th century it appears to have lain close to its present position, but for some time between 1698 and 1760 the river mouth became established at New Shoreham, approximately 1.5 km west of its present position. In 1760 an artificial cut was made near the earlier mouth opposite Kingston. Longshore drifting of shingle caused a progressive eastward shift of this outlet until in 1810 the river mouth lay south of Portslade. In 1816 the Kingston outlet [235 045] was reopened and was made permanent by harbour works constructed in 1821. Wheeler (1902, pp.181–182) described the landward encroachment of the shingle bank near Lancing [190 038], where between 1875 and 1891 the advance was between 21 and 98 m. Carey and Oliver (1918, p.95) recounted the effects of a gale in 1913 on Shoreham Beach approximately 1.7 km west of the harbour entrance. Today much of Shoreham Beach is covered by houses: the river frontage is largely protected by harbour walls and groynes have been constructed on the seaward side.

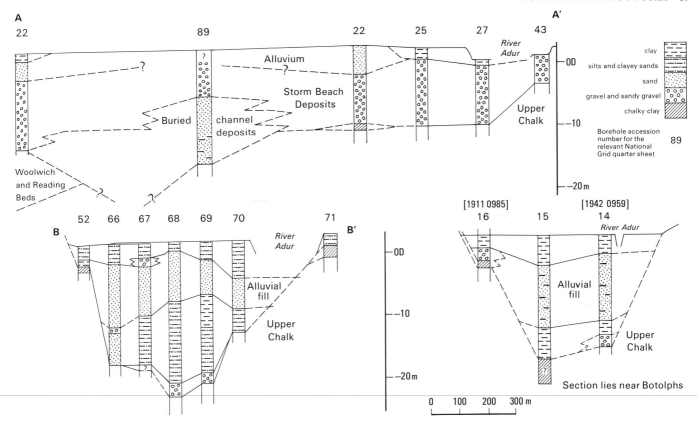

Figure 28 Sections through drift deposits at Shoreham-by-Sea (for locations of sections AA', BB', see Figure 27)

MARINE BEACH DEPOSITS

The Marine Beach Deposits consist largely of flint shingle like that of the Storm Gravel Beach Deposits into which they pass. They are extensive below high water mark from the western edge of the district to Kemp Town, but east of Brighton Marina only small areas of beach deposits are present on the wave-cut platform at the foot of the Chalk cliffs. On a number of beaches, notably at Worthing and Shoreham, the flint shingle of the beach gives way to sand at lower levels. Along almost the entire length of the coast groynes have been erected to retain the beach deposits, which then protect the land behind against erosion by the sea. Between Brighton Marina [345 031] and Saltdean [3859 0170] the cliffs are protected by a concrete sea-wall. The design and construction of the sea defences for the Brighton district have been described by Wheeler (1902, pp.180–189). A study of coastal erosion (East Sussex County Council, 1977) indicates that between 1973 and 1975 there was an overall gain of beach material at the western end of Brighton beach, with no net change at the eastern end. The long-term effect of the construction of the Marina on coastal erosion and deposition cannot yet be evaluated, but a build-up of shingle is taking place to the west of the western breakwater.   BY

SUPERFICIAL STRUCTURES

It is probable that the less competent strata in the district have been disturbed locally by superficial movements under the force of gravity. In the west, small landslips have affected parts of the outcrop of the Atherfield Clay, where relatively steep slopes are present. Farther east, landslips have occurred between Upper Chancton Farm [1337 1442] and Abbott's Farm [1431 1436] on the Weald Clay scarp slope below the Lower Greensand outcrop; relatively recent mass movement has produced a hummocky topography, where back scarps and toes of slips are distinguishable; much of the movement has probably resulted from shallow mudslides, although there may have been some rotational failures. Other smaller and less clear examples of landslips have affected the Gault, such as that at a site [1368 1287] east of Rokers and another [1430 1275] near Weppons Farm. In the latter case the Upper Greensand was also involved in the disturbance, which probably included mudflows.

Cambering and valley-bulging have resulted from periglacial conditions within the district. Cambering has developed best where permeable, moderately hard formations overlie argillaceous sequences and cap the higher ground. Valleyward attenuation of the weaker clay has caused the harder formations to drape downslope and to fracture into fault-bounded blocks. In the valley-floors lateral pressures have formed anticlinorial structures (or valley-bulges). Inconsistent dip values and vectors at any one locality may indicate the presence of bulges and examples occur in the Weald Clay in the Adur valley near Bay Bridge [164 207]. Bulges have been recognised in valleys of both steep and shallow profiles and probably occur widely in the Chalk as well as in clay formations. They are, however, difficult to recognise in the Chalk, particularly where deep weathering and frost action have destroyed the stratification. In the Chalk cliffs to the east of Brighton minor disruption of the bedding near exposures of channels filled with solifluction material may be ascribed to valley-bulging.

The upper part of the Chalk has been greatly dissolved during periods of cold climate, both at outcrop and beneath thin overlying drift and solid deposits. This process was most effective in the valleys beneath the present-day Head deposits and also where the contemporary surface run-off was directed along the margins of the Tertiary outcrops. Oscillatory water-table levels probably enhanced this process. As a consequence, the fractures in the Chalk were enlarged and formed conduits for surface drainage and its transported sediment. The resultant pipes, which are filled with superficial deposits, continue to provide sumps for excess surface water at the present day. At the surface these solution hollows (or sink-holes) form roughly circular depressions which are lined with remobilised sediments. The depths of some pipes probably exceed 15 m and, in extreme cases, 25 m. Examples are present near Holt Farm [105 059], and others, with no surface expression, probably occur at the margins of the Tertiary outcrop beneath the drift of the coastal plain. In the Brighton area, solution features are widespread; the Tertiary deposits have been extensively disturbed (p.72) and have been classified as areas of foundered strata on the published geological map.   BY, RDL

MADE GROUND

Areas of made ground occur widely in the district but they are most common near the urban areas of Worthing and Brighton. Sites for the disposal of domestic refuse include those at Small Dole [205 125], in the lower reaches of the Teville valley, East Worthing [170 037], and at the head of Sheepcote Valley [341 048]. A former dump at Black Rock [3360 0337] was described by White (1924, p.97). Other ancient sites are not well documented; for example, the records of trenches dug in Brighton for the installation of the main sewerage system at the end of the last century indicate the presence of localised dumps of waste material. It was not possible to map such occurrences.

Excavations for quarrying and for the construction of railways and roads have also provided materials for nearby disposal. There are dumps of quarry waste adjacent to the sand-pits at Washington [130 137]. Much chalk debris was dumped near the railway-cuttings between Clayton Tunnel [2926 1204] and Patcham [2973 0916] and beneath the railway yards [310 052] north of Brighton Station. Other areas of made ground occur on the west side of the River Adur at Shoreham [210 050] and above the shingle spit east of the river mouth [250 048]. The latter comprises mainly gravel and earth fill.   BY

CHAPTER 10

Economic geology

HYDROGEOLOGY

Within the Brighton and Worthing district the dominant source of supply is from groundwater contained in permeable strata; no major water supplies are at present derived from impounded surface water. The Lower and Upper Tunbridge Wells Sands are capable of yielding useful supplies of groundwater, although their outcrop in the district is very limited, and little use has been made of these resources. In the Lower Greensand, the sandstone formations such as the Folkestone Beds form useful aquifers, but they are thin at outcrop and the aquifers have not been extensively used. The most important aquifer is the Chalk. The abstraction from licensed sources has been recorded at 300 megalitres (Ml) per year or greater; the total abstraction from the Chalk in 1977 amounted to some 34 000 Ml.

The mean annual rainfall over the Tunbridge Wells Sand and Lower Greensand outcrops is of the order of 780 mm, and the annual infiltration about 150 mm. The mean annual rainfall over the Chalk outcrop is about 865 mm, attaining more than 1000 mm over the higher ground of the escarpment. Infiltration into the Chalk is on average about 380 mm per year, although this is much reduced in urban areas and where the outcrop is overlain by brickearth and alluvium. The valley of the River Adur is floored with thick alluvium where it crosses the Chalk outcrop, and there is probably little direct hydraulic continuity between the aquifer and the river.

The general groundwater conditions and details of wells in this district have been summarised in previous Geological Survey publications by Whitaker and Reid (1899), White (1924), Buchan and others (1942), and Robertson and others (1964). Further hydrological information was published by the Sussex River Authority (1970). The Brighton district lies within the Hydrogeological Map of the South Downs and adjacent parts of the Weald, published on a scale of 1:100 000 by the Institute of Geological Sciences (1978).

Tunbridge Wells Sand

The Tunbridge Wells Sand crops out over a small area in the north-east corner of the district. Its usefulness as an aquifer is limited by silty horizons and by the presence of the Grinstead Clay which forms an aquiclude separating the Lower Tunbridge Wells Sand from the upper formation. Local 'perched' water tables are common.

There are only two boreholes in this district for which yields are recorded, both of the order of 440 cubic metres per day (m³/d). These are rather higher than the yields normally obtained from the more extensive outcrops of this aquifer in the Lewes district. Boreholes constructed in the Tunbridge Wells Sand require sand screens. Development of the completed borehole is usually by surging and pumping. Where silty beds are encountered, problems may arise with the ingress of fines to the borehole, and it is advisable to line out such strata where possible.

There is little information on groundwater quality. However, on the basis of Tunbridge Wells Sand groundwaters beyond the confines of the district, the total hardness is likely to be within the range 60 to 100 milligrams per litre (mg/l), and the chloride-ion concentration 25 to 40 mg/l. Where the Weald Clay confines the Tunbridge Wells Sand, the total hardness may be less than 20 mg/l.

Weald Clay

Some of the thin limestones and sandy beds in the Weald Clay yield small quantities of groundwater. The water-bearing strata tend to be discontinuous and the natural replenishment is limited. In consequence, even where the initial yield is substantial, it is possible for the pumping rate to diminish with time. Of eleven boreholes for which records are available, the yields ranged from nil to 32 m³/d, with a mean of 17 m³/d. The greatest depth to which any of these boreholes were sunk was 53 m, the shallowest 23 m.

The groundwater within the Weald Clay is usually very soft, with a total hardness of the order of 25 to 50 mg/l. Where the limestone strata are intersected, the hardness may be 180 mg/l or more. The chloride-ion concentration may be high, in some cases exceeding 500 mg/l. Iron also presents a problem, with concentrations commonly greater than 0.5 mg/l.

Lower Greensand

Of the four divisions recognised in the Lower Greensand in the Brighton district, the Hythe Beds (or their lateral equivalent) and the Folkestone Beds form useful aquifers. The Sandgate Beds locally yield groundwater, but generally act as an aquitard. The Atherfield Clay is an aquiclude.

Despite differences in lithology between the Hythe Beds (interbedded sands and calcareous sandstones) and the Folkestone Beds (relatively poorly bedded sands), the yields of groundwater from both are very similar. The mean yield of a 300 mm diameter borehole penetrating a saturated thickness of 10 m in either aquifer is of the order of 35 m³/d per metre of drawdown. There is a 25 per cent chance of a similar borehole yielding 100 m³/d per metre of drawdown. However, yields tend to be much lower where the finer grain sizes of sand are encountered.

Boreholes in the Hythe Beds and Folkestone Beds generally require sand screens. Methods for the design of sand screens and filter packs were described by Monkhouse (1974). Development of the completed borehole is usually carried out by surging and pumping; the use of hydrochloric acid is not recommended.

The quality of the Lower Greensand groundwater is normally good. The total hardness in the Hythe Beds ranges from 110 to 290 mg/l and in the Folkestone Beds from 55 to 200 mg/l (Table 2). The chloride-ion concentration is normally within the range 20 to 35 mg/l. Iron can be a problem, values in excess of 1.0 mg/l being not uncommon.

In 1978, the (former) Central Water Planning Unit constructed an experimental borehole at the Sompting pumping station [166 064] to prove the presence of potable groundwater in the Lower Greensand at depth. Although the Hythe Beds could not be distinguished, it was shown that an abstraction borehole would be capable of yielding in excess of 2.5 Ml/d from a thickness of 35 m of the Folkestone Beds beneath 400 m of cover comprising Chalk, Upper Greensand and Gault (Monkhouse, 1980). The groundwater was potable, with a total hardness of 60 mg/l and a chloride-ion concentration of 9 mg/l; total iron was very high at 5.1 mg/l, but of this only 0.08 mg/l was in solution.

Gault

The Gault will not normally yield groundwater, but acts as an aquiclude between the Lower Greensand below and the Upper Greensand and Chalk above.

Upper Greensand

Where the Upper Greensand is thickest, between Washington [122 128] and the River Adur, successful boreholes may be sunk. A borehole of 300 mm diameter can yield as much as 700 m^3/d per metre of drawdown. The sands are, however, generally poorly consolidated and require the use of sand screens. Where the grain-size is very fine there are problems, both in the design of the sand screens and their associated filter packs, and in development of the completed boreholes.

East of the River Adur, the Upper Greensand becomes much attenuated, and the aquifer at outcrop rarely yields supplies greater than a few cubic metres per day.

The Upper Greensand is sometimes exploited in conjunction with the Lower Chalk. However, boreholes attempting to draw groundwater from both formations simultaneously are not recommended, since the methods normally used for developing the completed borehole (acid treatment for the Chalk, surging and pumping for the sands) are not mutually compatible. It is more advantageous to construct the borehole in the Upper Greensand, where pumping will induce a downward seepage from the Lower Chalk.

There are few groundwater analyses available from the Upper Greensand, but the indications are that the groundwater is commonly harder than that in the Lower Chalk, in many cases exceeding 400 mg/l.

Chalk

There are 22 public supply pumping stations within the Chalk of the Brighton and Worthing district. More than 45 per cent of the annual mean replenishment to the aquifer is pumped into supply. The management of the groundwater resources requires that a substantial part of the annual replenishment is permitted to discharge naturally to the sea in order to prevent large-scale intrusion of sea-water (see below), and in consequence the amount of potable groundwater still available for further extraction is thought to be small.

Table 2 Representative analyses of groundwaters from the aquifers in the Brighton and Worthing district

Location	Stanhope Lodge	Sompting	Sompting	Shoreham	Mile Oak	Randolph's	Goldstone	Patcham	Balsdean	Newmarket
National Grid reference	112 056	166 064	166 064	211 068	243 080	279 157	284 066	294 092	378 046	381 091
Analyst	SWA	SWA	SWA	SWA	SWA	Lewes	SWA	SWA	SWA	SWA
Date	1978*	12.8.78	1978*	1978*	1978*	29.3.45	1978*	1978*	1978*	1978*
Aquifer	UCk	FB	UCk	UCk	UCk	LGS	UCk	UCk	UCk	UCk
Total solid residue (180°C)	—	102	—	—	—	274	—	—	—	—
Chlorine as chlorides	24	9	26	37	25	27	31	24	43	24
Total hardness	256	60	226	240	222	181	259	212	219	229
Non-carbonate hardness	—	6	—	—	—	43	—	—	—	—
Carbonate hardness	—	54	—	—	—	138	—	—	—	—
Alkalinity	226	54	189	193	179	—	210	181	185	196
pH	7.4	6.6	7.4	7.4	7.4	7.6	7.2	7.4	7.4	7.4
Nitrates as N	5.2	0.2	6.1	6.4	5.1	11.4	8.5	4.5	5.6	5.1
Total iron	—	5.1	—	—	—	0.29	—	—	—	—
Sulphate as SO$_4$	9.6	13	12.2	25	21.6	—	22	15.6	12	16.9
Fluoride as F	—	0.03	—	—	—	0.7	—	—	—	—

Aquifer: UCk = Upper Chalk
      FB = Folkestone Beds
      LGS = Lower Greensand

Analyst: SWA = Southern Water Authority, Falmer
      Lewes = Public Analyst, Lewes

* indicates analysis comprises mean value for year

The matrix of the Chalk has only limited permeability. Essentially, groundwater yielded to boreholes is stored in, and flows through, fissure systems within the aquifer. These fissures are generally small, a millimetre or less in width, and few reach as much as 10 mm. The density of the fissuring varies from one area to another and experience has shown that the transmissivity tends to be significantly greater beneath the lower ground of the larger valleys, probably owing to the local enlargement of the fissures along the valley axes. Thus many of the high-yield pumping stations are sited at the southern ends of the Findon and Adur valleys and in the Falmer and Patcham valleys. The density of the fissuring decreases also with depth, and it has been shown on the coast that little groundwater flow occurs at depths greater than 100 m beneath the water table (Monkhouse and Fleet, 1975).

The lower part of the Lower Chalk (the Chalk Marl) tends to act as an aquitard, but the upper part (the Grey Chalk) may be productive. Hydrogeologically, there appears to be little difference between the Middle and the Upper Chalk.

The transmissivity of the Chalk is commonly of the order of 250 square metres per day (m²/d) in the valley areas, whereas beneath the higher ground the value may be 50 m²/d or less. Yields from boreholes vary accordingly. The mean yield of a 300 mm diameter borehole penetrating 50 m thickness of chalk beneath the water table is approximately 160 m³/d per metre of drawdown. There is theoretically a 25 per cent chance of a similar borehole yielding 630 m³/d per metre of drawdown, but it is not unusual for boreholes to yield little or no water, particularly in high-ground areas.

In the past the larger pumping stations were based upon excavated shafts of 3 m diameter and more. Horizontal adits, some of them several hundred metres long, were driven at levels below the water table to increase the yield. At present, it is less expensive to drill one or several boreholes of diameters up to 915 mm. During drilling, a slurry is formed of the drilling fluid and crushed chalk, and this coats the borehole wall, tending to block the fissures. Newly drilled boreholes are treated with hydrochloric acid to break down this wall-cake, thereby in many cases increasing borehole yields dramatically, in some cases by 100 per cent or more.

The quality of the Chalk groundwater is usually very good. For 31 sites for which full analyses are available, total hardness ranges from 168 to 392 mg/l, with a mean of 254 mg/l. Carbonate hardness ranges from 117 to 244 mg/l, with a mean of 190 mg/l. The chloride-ion concentration in uncontaminated chalk groundwater is normally in the range 20 to 30 mg/l.

The Chalk adjacent to the coast is vulnerable to saline intrusion, and the extent and the rapidity of the intrusion is related to the nature of the fissuring and local pumping regimes. In the neighbourhood of the pumping station at Goldstone [284 066], saline intrusion takes place in response to heavy pumping, but the salinity increases only slowly. This indicates the presence of a network of relatively small fissures that permits only a slow groundwater flow. In contrast, heavy pumping at Balsdean [378 046] produces a rapid reaction, saline water issuing within hours from discrete fissures. In this case, there appears to be a small number of relatively large fissures connected directly to the sea. Changes in salinity in a number of coastal boreholes have been noted in response to pumping at stations as much as 6 km inland (Monkhouse and Fleet, 1975). The salinity in these coastal boreholes also varies seasonally in proportion to changes in groundwater level inland, and diurnally in response to the tide.

Woolwich and Reading Beds

A little groundwater can be obtained from the basal beds of the drift-covered Woolwich and Reading Beds between Durrington [105 053] and the coast near South Lancing [185 037] but the main hydrogeological significance of the formation lies in its effect on the underlying Chalk, the permeability of which is low. The main natural discharge of the Chalk catchment lying to the north of the Tertiary outcrop appears to be channelled through the area where the Chalk and the sea are in hydraulic continuity on the coast between South Lancing and Shoreham. The small outliers of Tertiary strata east of the River Adur have little hydrogeological significance.

The chalybeate spring which formerly issued from the Woolwich and Reading Beds at St Anne's Well, Hove [2997 0493], was first mentioned and developed as a spa by Dr Richard Russell in about 1750. A stone well-head now marks the site of the spa. The spring appears to have continued in use until the early 1900's and by the 1930s the flow had virtually ceased. Analyses of the water include one dating from 1805, which recorded sulphates of calcium, iron, magnesium and sodium, and dissolved carbon dioxide.

Drift

Little groundwater is extracted from superficial deposits in this district. The drift cover is usually thin, with permeable strata commonly present beneath the drift at relatively shallow depths.   RAM

SAND AND GRAVEL

The Folkestone Beds provide an important source of sand throughout the Weald. In the Brighton and Worthing district they are worked at four large pits near Washington (Figure 29). The sand is relatively loose, easily worked without blasting, and the outcrop is wide enough in most places to accommodate fairly large-scale quarrying operations. Attempts to work below the water table by open-pit methods have shown that heavy pumping is necessary and this factor will probably limit the depths of working; no sand has yet been worked by dredging in this district.

Two of the pits in the Folkestone Beds have washing facilities and all four produce unwashed material. The unwashed sand is normally screened dry at a coarse size to remove any ironstone fragments and lumps of clay, after which it is sold as a building sand, which complies with British Standard 1200, for use in mortar. Typical particle size distributions for two samples of sand (A and B) from Sandgate Pit [1049 1407] are as follows:

Sieve size mm	Weight passing per cent	
	A	B
5.0	100	100
2.36	99	100
1.18	85	97
0.60	70	76
0.30	10	12
0.15	2	2

The washing equipment is used to remove fine particles to produce a concreting sand with a size range corresponding to that of Zone 3 in BS 882.

Within the Brighton and Worthing district, sand and gravel occur in the terraces and alluvium deposited by the River Adur, and in drift deposits underlying the coastal urban areas. However, although Head Gravel has been successfully worked farther west near Chichester, there are no sand or gravel workings in drift deposits in the present district.

CHALK AND CEMENT

Within the district, chalk is worked for agricultural use at Washington [1219 1213] and Newtimber [2782 1374], and

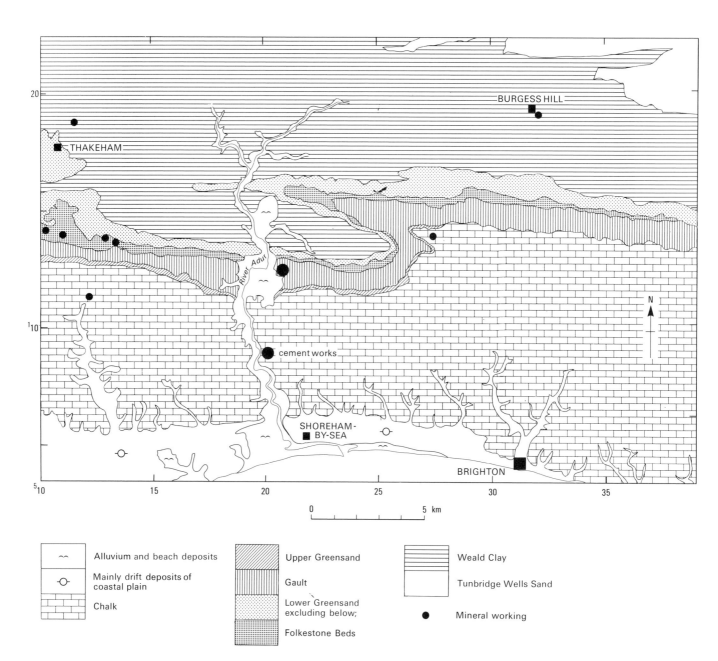

Figure 29   Locations of mineral workings

on a larger scale for cement manufacture at Shoreham [203 088].

Chalk is used in agriculture mainly to reduce soil acidity; it is applied to the land in a finely divided form which is easily spread and readily absorbed. Chalk can absorb large amounts of water and under wet conditions the quarried material becomes so sticky that it cannot be crushed or screened without prior drying, which is generally considered to be too expensive; also vehicles can move only with difficulty in the quarry. Hence the working of chalk for agriculture is usually an intermittent operation, confined to periods of dry weather in summer.

Cement is made by heat treatment of a mixture containing approximately 78 per cent of calcium carbonate, together with silica and alumina, which is usually produced by mixing appropriate quantities of limestone with clay or shale. At Shoreham Cement Works, which has an annual capacity of 300 000 tonnes of cement clinker, Middle and Upper Chalk from a large pit at Upper Beeding and clay from a pit [2100 1240] in the Gault at Small Dole provide the main raw materials. The chalk, which contains 14 to 18 per cent of water when mined, is mixed with additional water and about 25 per cent of its weight of clay in wash mills. Flint, which constitutes about 5 per cent of the chalk, is readily removed from the resulting slurry at this stage. Until 1982 the slurry was fed directly to the kiln, as is usual in the 'wet process' for cement making. Subsequently, in order to minimise fuel costs, a filtration system was installed to reduce the water content of the kiln feed, thus effectively converting the original 'wet process' to a 'semi-wet process'.

The Shoreham chalk quarry is worked in benches by means of a face shovel, with the assistance of explosives in the deeper parts. The broken material is loaded on to dump trucks for transport to the works. In the clay-pit, initial extraction is by bulldozer or scraper, after which the broken clay is loaded on to a conveyor belt for transport to a transfer point from which it is hauled by road to the plant.

CLAY

The district contains several deposits which have been used for the manufacture of coarse clay products. At the present time, Weald Clay is extracted near Thakeham at the Laybrook Works [118 188] of Ibstock Brick Hudsons Ltd., and at the Keymer Works [325 189] of Maidenhead Brick and Tile Co. Ltd, at Burgess Hill (Figure 29). At Laybrook the Weald Clay does not possess any significant impurities that might affect its performance as a brick clay and a variety of medium, dark and light multi-clamp stocks are produced, suitable for all situations and degrees of exposure. The soft-mud forming process is employed, followed by pressing, and the green bricks are clamp fired in the traditional way, with the addition of high carbon power station grit to the blended clay to provide inherent fuel.

At Burgess Hill the Weald Clay is used almost exclusively to produce handmade plain roofing tiles and fittings in a variety of natural hues and sandfaced. Their durability is very good and the tiles blend in well with local architecture. They have been used sucessfully in the re-roofing of many older buildings.

Impurities in the Weald Clay include calcite, siderite, pyrite and gypsum, as well as ostracod-bearing horizons; the last are occasionally troublesome in brick-making and are avoided, but generally the deposit is well suited to clay-brick manufacture by methods ranging from extrusion to soft-mud forming. The alumina content of the Weald Clay used in brick-making is about 20 per cent and a high iron-oxide content (7 to 8 per cent) is common. Vitrification ranges are narrow or fairly narrow and care is taken not to over-fire the bricks, as evolved gases can otherwise burst the vitrified surface skin. The Weald Clay generally has a broad particle-size distribution but some very fine-grained clay seams are characteristic. These exhibit high shrinkage during drying and firing and low porosity in the fired products; but the effects can be offset by the incorporation of coarser sediments. In general, drying shrinkage is very low and compressive strength is high in machine-made bricks from Weald Clay.

PMH

REFERENCES

ALLEN, J. R. L. and NARAYAN, J. 1964. Cross-stratified units, some with silt bands, in the Folkestone Beds (Lower Greensand) of south east England. *Geol. Mijnbouw*, Vol. 44, 451–461.

ALLEN, P. 1949. Wealden petrology: the Top Ashdown Pebble Bed and the Top Ashdown Sandstone. *Q. J. Geol. Soc. London*, Vol. 104, 257–321.

— 1959. The Wealden environment: Anglo-Paris Basin. *Philos. Trans. R. Soc.*, Vol. B242, 283–346.

— 1975. Wealden of the Weald: a new model. *Proc. Geol. Assoc.*, Vol. 86, 389–437.

— 1976. Wealden of the Weald: a new model. Correspondence. *Proc. Geol. Assoc.*, Vol. 87, 427–442.

— 1981. Pursuit of Wealden models. *J. Geol. Soc. London*, Vol. 138, 375–405.

AMÉDRO, F. and MANIA, J. 1976. L'Aptien du Boulonnais. *Ann. Soc. Géol. Nord.*, Vol. 96, 207–216.

ANDERSON, F. W. 1940. Ostracod zones of the Wealden and Purbeck. *Adv. Sci.*, London, Vol. 1, 259.

— 1962. Correlation of the Upper Purbeck Beds of England with the German Wealden. *Liverpool and Manchester Geol. J.*, Vol. 3, 21–32.

— 1985. Ostracod faunas in the Purbeck and Wealden of England. *J. Micropalaeontol.*, Vol. 4, 1–68.

— BAZLEY, R. A. B. and SHEPHARD-THORN, E. R. 1967. The sedimentary and faunal sequence of the Wadhurst Clay (Wealden) in boreholes at Wadhurst Park, Sussex. *Bull. Geol. Surv. G.B.*, No. 27, 171–235.

— — 1971. The Purbeck Beds of the Weald (England). *Bull. Geol. Surv. G.B.*, No. 34.

ANDERSON, I. D. 1968. The Gault Clay–Folkestone Beds junction in West Sussex, southeast England. *Proc. Geol. Assoc.*, Vol. 97, 45–58.

ARKELL, W. J. 1933. *The Jurassic system in Great Britain.* (Oxford: Clarendon Press.)

BAILEY, H. W., GALE, A. S., MORTIMORE, R. N., SWIECICKI, A. and WOOD, C. J. 1983. The Coniacian–Maastrichtian stages of the United Kingdom, with particular reference to southern England. *Newsl. Stratig.*, Vol. 12, 19–42.

— — — — 1984. Biostratigraphical criteria for the recognition of the Coniacian to Maastrichtian Stage boundaries in the Chalk of north-west Europe, with particular reference to southern England. *Bull. Geol. Soc. Denmark*, Vol. 33, 31–39.

BARROIS, C. 1876. Recherches sur le Terrain Crétace supérieur de l'Angleterre et de l'Irland. *Mem. Soc. Géol. Nord.*, Vol. 1, 234.

BLACK, M. 1972, 1973 and 1975. British Lower Cretaceous Coccoliths, Pts 1, 2 and 3. Gault Clay. *Monogr. Palaeontogr. Soc.*, 1–142.

BRISTOW, C. R. and MORTER, A. A. 1983. Field meeting: a traverse of the Weald, 6 June 1982. *Proc. Geol. Assoc.*, Vol. 94, 377–381.

— — and WILKINSON, I. P. In press. The stratigraphy and palaeontology of the Lower Greensand of the Hoes Farm Borehole, near Petworth, Sussex. *Proc. Geol. Assoc.*

— and WYATT, R. J. 1983. Geological notes and local details for 1:10 000 sheets TQ 01 NW, NE, SW and SE (Pulborough and Storrington). (Keyworth: Institute of Geological Sciences.)

BROMLEY, R. G. 1978. Hardground diagenesis in *Encyclopedia of earth sciences, VI The encyclopedia of sedimentology.* FAIRBRIDGE, R. W. and BOURGEOIS, J. (editors) (Stroudsburg.)

— and GALE, A. S. 1982. The lithostratigraphy of the English Chalk Rock. *Cretaceous Res.*, Vol. 3, 273–306.

BRYDONE, R. M. 1914. The zone of *Offaster pilula* in the South English Chalk. Part 1. *Geol. Mag.*, Vol. 51, 359–369.

— 1915. The *Marsupites* Chalk of Brighton. *Geol. Mag.*, Vol. 52, 12–15.

— 1939. *The Chalk zone of Offaster pilula.* 3–8. (London: Dulau & Co Ltd.)

BUCHAN, S., ROBBIE, J. A., BUTLER, A. J., HOLMES, S. C. A. and MORRIS, L. S. O. 1942. Water supply of SE England from underground sources. *Wartime Pamph.*, No. 15, Part VI.

BULL, A. J. 1936. Studies in the geomorphology of the South Downs (Eastbourne to the Arun gap). *Proc. Geol. Assoc.*, Vol. 47, 99–127.

CALLOMON, J. H. 1955. The ammonite succession in the Oxford Clay and Kellaways Beds at Kidlington, Oxfordshire, and the zones of the Callovian Stage. *Philos. Trans. R. Soc. London*, Vol. 239B, 215–264.

— 1968. The Kellaways Beds and the Oxford Clay. 264–290 in The Geology of the East Midlands SYLVESTER-BRADLEY, P. C. and FORD, T. D. (editors). (Leicester: University Press.)

CAREY, A. E. and OLIVER, F. W. 1918. *Tidal lands.* (Blackie & Son.)

CARTER, D. J. and HART, M. B. 1977. Aspects of mid-Cretaceous stratigraphical micropalaeontology. *Bull. Br. Mus. Nat. Hist. (Geol.)*, Vol. 29, 1–135.

CASEY, R. 1961. The stratigraphical palaeontology of the Lower Greensand. *Palaeontol.*, Vol. 3, 487–621.

— 1963. The dawn of the Cretaceous period in Britain. *Bull. South-east Union Sci. Soc.*, No. 117, 15 pp.

— 1965. A monograph of the Ammonoidea of the Lower Greensand. Part 6. *Monogr. Palaeontogr. Soc.*, 399–546.

— 1966. 56–59, 102–113 *in* Geology of the country around Canterbury and Folkestone. SMART, J. G. O., BISSON, G. and WORSSAM, B. C. *Mem. Geol. Surv. G.B.*

— 1978. A monograph of the Ammonoidea of the Lower Greensand. Part 8. *Monogr. Palaeontogr. Soc.*

CHALONER, W. G. 1962. Rhaeto-Liassic plants from the Henfield Borehole. *Bull. Geol. Surv. G.B.*, No. 19, 16–28.

CHAPMAN, F. 1900. The Raised Beach and Rubble Drift at Aldrington between Hove and Portslade-by-Sea, Sussex, with notes on the microzoa. *Proc. Geol. Assoc.*, Vol. 16, 259–270.

CHATEAUNEUF, J. J. and FAUCONNIER, D. 1979. Étude palynoplanctologique de L'Albien stratotypique à partir de trois sondages du réservoir Aube. *Les Stratotypes Français*, Vol. 5. (Paris: C.N.R.S.)

COOKSON, I. C. and HUGHES, N. F. 1964. Microplankton from

the Cambridge Greensand (Mid-Cretaceous). *Palaeontol.*, Vol. 7, 37–59.

COPE, J. C. W. 1978. The ammonite faunas and stratigraphy of the upper part of the Upper Kimmeridge Clay of Dorset. *Palaeontol.*, Vol. 21, 469–533.

COX, B. M. and GALLOIS, R. W. 1981. The stratigraphy of the Kimmeridge Clay of the Dorset type area and its correlation with some other Kimmeridgian sequences. *Rep. Inst. Geol. Sci.*, No. 80/4.

CURRY, D. and SMITH, A. J. 1975. New discoveries concerning the geology of the central and eastern parts of the English Channel. *Philos. Trans. R. Soc. London*, Vol. A279, 155–167.

DANA, E. S. 1932. *A textbook of mineralogy* (4th edition). Revised by the late W. E. Ford.

DAVEY, R. J. and VERDIER, J. P. 1971. An investigation of microplankton assemblages from the Albian of the Paris Basin. *Verh. K. Ned. Akad. Van Wetens*, Vol. 26, No. 2, 57 pp.

— — 1973. An investigation of microplankton assemblages from latest Albian (Vraconian) sediments. *Rev. Espanola de Micropal.*, Vol. 5, No. 2, 173–212.

DAVIES, K. H. and KEEN, D. H. 1985. The age of Pleistocene marine deposits at Portland, Dorset. *Proc. Geol. Assoc.*, Vol. 96, 217–225.

DESTOMBES, P. 1973. Hoplitidae et zonation nouvelle de l'Albien inférieur de Bully—St Martin (Bray occidental). *C. R. Hebd. Séanc. Acad. Sci. Paris*, Vol. 277, 2145–2148.

— 1979. Les ammonites de l'Albien inférieur et moyen dans le stratotype de l'Albien: Gisements, Paléontologie, Biozonation. 51–194 in L'Albien de l'Aube. RAT, P. and others. *Les Stratotypes Français*, No. 5.

DINES, H. G., HOLMES, S. C. A. and ROBBIE, J. A. 1954. Second Ed. 1971. Geology of the country around Chatham. *Mem. Geol. Surv. G.B.*

DIXON, F. 1850. *The geology and fossils of the Tertiary and Cretaceous formations of Sussex* (1st edition).

— 1878. *The geology and fossils of the Tertiary and Cretaceous formations of Sussex* (2nd edition) revised by T. R. Jones and others.

EAST SUSSEX COUNTY COUNCIL. 1977. *Report on the problems of coastal erosion.* East Sussex County Council Planning Department.

EDMUNDS, F. H. 1928. Wells and springs of Sussex. *Mem. Geol. Surv. G.B.*

— 1930. The Coombe Rock of the Hampshire and Sussex coast. *Summ. Prog. Geol. Surv. G.B.*, No. 2, 63–68.

EDWARDS, N. and STINTON, F. C. 1971. A fish fauna from the Lower Tertiary Marine Bed, Clapham Common, West Sussex. *Proc. Geol. Assoc.*, Vol. 82, 449–454.

ERNST, G. 1971. Biometrische Untersuchungen über die Ontogenie und Phylogenie der *Offaster/Galeola*-Stammersreihe (Echin.) aus der nordwest-europäischen Oberkreide. *Neues Jahr. Geol. Paläont. Abh.*, Vol. 139, 169–225.

FALCON, N. L. and KENT, P. E. 1960. Geological results of petroleum exploration in Britain 1945–1957. *Mem. Geol. Soc. London*, No. 2, 1–56.

FLETCHER, T. P. and WOOD, C. J. 1978. Chapter 15, Cretaceous rocks. 84–215 in Geology of the Causeway Coast. Vol. 2. WILSON, H. E. and MANNING, P. I. *Mem. Geol. Surv. North. Irel.*, Sheet 7.

FOWLER, J. 1932. The 'one hundred foot' raised beach between Arundel and Chichester, Sussex. *Q. J. Geol. Soc. London*, Vol. 88, 84–99.

FRIEG, C. and PRICE, R. J. 1981. The subgeneric classification of *Arenobulimina*. 42–77 in *Aspects of micropalaeontology*. BANNER, F. T. and LORD, A. R. (editors). (George Allen and Unwin.)

GALLOIS, R. W. and MORTER, A. A. 1982. The stratigraphy of the Gault of East Anglia. *Proc. Geol. Assoc.*, Vol. 93, 351–368.

GASTER, C. T. A. 1924. The Chalk of the Worthing District, Sussex. *Proc. Geol. Assoc.*, Vol. 35, 89–110.

— 1929. Chalk Zones in the neighbourhood of Shoreham, Brighton and Newhaven, Sussex. *Proc. Geol. Assoc.*, Vol. 39, 328–340.

— 1937. The stratigraphy of the Chalk of Sussex, Part 1. West Central area—Arun gap to valley of the Adur, with zonal map. *Proc. Geol. Assoc.*, Vol. 48, 356–373.

— 1951. The stratigraphy of the Chalk of Sussex, Part IV. East central area—between the valley of the Adur and Seaford, with zonal map. *Proc. Geol. Assoc.*, Vol. 62, 31–64.

GILBERT, E. W. 1954. *Brighton Old Ocean's Bauble.* 275 pp. London.

GODWIN-AUSTEN, R. A. C. 1857. On the newer Tertiary deposits of the Sussex coast. *Q. J. Geol. Soc. London*, Vol. 13, 40–72.

GOSSLING, F. 1929. The geology of the country around Reigate. *Proc. Geol. Assoc.*, Vol. 40, 197–259.

HANCOCK, J. M. (editor). 1965. The Gault of the Weald: a symposium. *Proc. Geol. Assoc.*, Vol. 76, 243–260.

HARRIS, C. S. 1982. *Albian microbiostratigraphy (Foraminifera and Ostracoda) of S. E. England and adjacent areas.* PhD thesis, Council of National Academic awards at Plymouth.

HART, M. B. 1969. Discussion in The correlation of the Lower Chalk of South-East England. KENNEDY, W. J. *Proc. Geol. Assoc.*, Vol. 80, 459–551, discussion, 551–560.

— 1974. A correlation of the macrofaunal and microfaunal zonations of the Gault Clay in southeastern England. 267–288 in The Boreal Lower Cretaceous. CASEY, R. C. and RAWSON, P. F. (editors). Geological Journal, Special Issue No. 5. (Liverpool: Seel House Press.)

— BAILEY, H. W., FLETCHER, B. N., PRICE, R. and SWEICICKI, A. 1981. Cretaceous (foraminifera). 149–227 in *Stratigraphical atlas of fossil foraminifera.* JENKINS, D. G. and MURRAY, J. W. (Chichester: Ellis Horwood and British Micropalaeontological Society.)

HESTER, S. W. 1965. Stratigraphy and palaeogeography of the Woolwich and Reading Beds. *Bull. Geol. Surv. G.B.*, No. 23, 117–137.

HODGSON, J. M. 1964. The low-level Pleistocene marine sands and gravels of the West Sussex Coastal Plain. *Proc. Geol. Assoc.*, Vol. 75, 547–561.

— 1967. Soils of the West Sussex Coastal Plain. *Bull. Soil Survey of Great Britain*, No. 3.

— CATT, J. A. and WEIR, A. H. 1967. The origin and development of Clay-with-flints and associated soil horizons on the South Downs. *J. Soil Sci.*, Vol. 18, No. 1, 85–102.

— RAYNER, J. H. and CATT, J. A. 1974. The geomorphological significance of the Clay-with-flints on the South Downs. *Trans. Inst. Br. Geogr.*, Vol. 61, 119–129.

HOLLINGWORTH, S. E. and BANNISTER, F. A. 1950. Basaluminite and hydrobasaluminite, two new minerals from Northamptonshire. *Min. Mag.*, Vol. 29, 1–17.

HOLLIS, J. D. 1971.   Report of project meeting to Small Dole, Sussex. *Tertiary Times*, Vol. 1, 108–109.

HOLMES, S. C. A. 1959.   In *Summ. Prog. Geol. Surv. G.B. for 1958*, No. 28.

HOWELL, J. 1872a.   On the minerals lately found in the drainage-works at Brighton. *Rep. Br. Assoc. Brighton, 1872*, 108–109.

— 1872b.   On Super-Cretaceous formations in the neighbourhood of Brighton. *Rep. Br. Assoc. Brighton, 1872*, 109–111.

— 1873.   On the geology of Brighton; Part 1. *Proc. Geol. Assoc.*, Vol. 3, 168–188.

— 1878.   The geology of Brighton; Part II. *Proc. Geol. Assoc.*, Vol. 5, 80–90.

HOWITT, F. 1964.   Stratigraphy and structure of the Purbeck inliers of Sussex (England). *Q. J. Geol. Soc. London*, Vol. 120, 77–113.

INSTITUTE OF GEOLOGICAL SCIENCES. 1974.   I.G.S. boreholes 1973. *Rep. Inst. Geol. Sci.*, No. 74/7.

— 1978.   I.G.S. boreholes 1976. *Rep. Inst. Geol. Sci.*, No. 77/10.

JEFFERIES, R. P. S. 1961.   The palaeoecology of the *Actinocamax plenus* Subzone (Turonian) in the Anglo-Paris Basin. *Palaeontol.*, Vol. 4, 609–647.

— 1963.   The stratigraphy of the *Actinocamax plenus* Subzone (Turonian) in the Anglo-Paris Basin. *Proc. Geol. Assoc.*, Vol. 74, 1–33.

JUKES-BROWNE, A. J. 1906.   The Clay-with-flints; its origin and distribution. *Q. J. Geol. Soc. London*, Vol. 62, 132–164.

— and HILL, W. 1900.   Cretaceous rocks of Britain. Vol. 1: The Gault and Upper Greensand of England. With contributions by W. Hill and E. T. Newton. *Mem. Geol. Surv. G.B.*

— — 1903.   The Cretaceous rocks of Britain. Vol. 2: The Lower and Middle Chalk of England. *Mem. Geol. Surv. G.B.*

— — 1904.   The Cretaceous rocks of Britain, Vol. 3: The Upper Chalk of England. *Mem. Geol. Surv. G.B.*

KAUFFMAN, E. G. 1977.   Systematic, biostratigraphic and biogeographic relationships between Middle Cretaceous Euamerican and North Pacific Inoceramidae. *Spec. Pap. Pal. Soc. Jpn*, (Hokkaido Symposium) Vol. 1, No. 21, 169–212.

— 1979 (for 1976).   British Middle Cretaceous inoceramid biostratigraphy. *Ann. Mus. Nat. Hist. Nice*, Vol. 4, IV 1 to 12.

KELLAWAY, G. A., REDDING, J. H., SHEPHARD-THORN, E. R. and DESTOMBES, J. P. 1975.   The Quaternary history of the English Channel. *Philos. Trans. R. Soc. London*, Vol. A279, 189–218.

— and SHEPHARD-THORN, E. R. 1977.   Raised beaches of West Sussex. 62–71 in *Guidebook for Excursion A5, South-east England and the Thames Valley*. International Union for Quaternary Research.

KEMP, E. M. 1970.   Aptian and Albian miospores from southern England. *Paleontographica*, Series B, Vol. 131, 73–143.

KEMPER, E. 1982a.   Zur Gliederung der Schichtenfolge Apt–Unter-Alb. *Geol. Jahrb.*, A65, 21–33.

—1982b.   Die Aucellinen des Apt und Unter-Alb Nordwestdeutschlands. *Geol. Jahrb.*, A65, 579–595.

KENNEDY, W. J. 1969.   The correlation of the Lower Chalk of south-east England. *Proc. Geol. Assoc.*, Vol. 80, 459–551.

— and HANCOCK, J. M. 1979.   The mid-Cretaceous of the United Kingdom. *Ann. Mus. Nat. Hist. Nice*, Vol. 4, V1 to V72.

— and MACDOUGALL, J. D. S. 1969.   Crustacean burrows in the Weald Clay (Lower Cretaceous) of south-eastern England and their environmental significance. *Palaeontol.*, Vol. 12, 459–471.

KENT, P. E. 1949.   A structure contour map of the surface of the buried pre-Permian rocks of England and Wales. *Proc. Geol. Assoc.*, Vol. 60, 87–104.

— 1975.   The tectonic development of Great Britain and the surrounding seas. 3–28 in *Petroleum and the continental shelf of North-west Europe*. WOODLAND, A. W. (editor). (London: Applied Science Publishers.)

KING, W. B. R. 1954.   The geological history of the English Channel. *Q. J. Geol. Soc. London*, Vol. 110, 77–101.

KIRKALDY, J. F. 1933.   The Sandgate Beds of the Western Weald. *Proc. Geol. Assoc.*, Vol. 43, 270–311.

— 1935.   The base of the Gault in Sussex. *Q. J. Geol. Soc. London*, Vol. 91, 519–537.

— 1937.   The overstep of the Sandgate Beds in the Eastern Weald. *Q. J. Geol. Soc. London*, Vol. 93, 94–126.

— and BULL, A. J. 1937.   Field meeting at Henfield and Bramber. *Proc. Geol. Assoc.*, Vol. 47, 346–348.

— — 1940.   The geomorphology of the rivers of the southern Weald. *Proc. Geol. Assoc.*, Vol. 51, 115–149.

LAKE, R. D. 1975.   The structure of the Weald—a review. *Proc. Geol. Assoc.*, Vol. 86, 549–558.

— and HOLLIDAY, D. W. 1978.   Purbeck Beds of the Broadoak Borehole, Sussex. 1–12 in *The Broadoak Borehole. Rep. Inst. Geol. Sci.*, No. 78/3.

— and THURRELL, R. G. 1974.   The sedimentary sequence of the Wealden Beds in boreholes near Cuckfield, Sussex. *Rep. Inst. Geol. Sci.*, No. 74/2.

— and YOUNG, B. 1978.   Boreholes in the Wealden Beds of the Hailsham area, Sussex. *Rep. Inst. Geol. Sci.*, No. 78/23.

— YOUNG, B., WOOD, C. J. and MORTIMORE, R. N. 1987. The geology of the country around Lewes. *Mem. Br. Geol. Surv.*, Sheet 319.

LEES, G. M. and COX, P. T. 1937.   The geological basis of the present search for oil in Great Britain by the D'Arcy Exploration Company Limited. *J. Geol. Soc. London*, Vol. 93, 156–194.

LOVEDAY, J. A. 1962.   Plateau deposits of the southern Chiltern Hills. *Proc. Geol. Assoc.*, Vol. 73, 83–101.

MANTELL, G. A. 1818.   A sketch of the geological structure of the south-eastern part of Sussex. *Gleaners Portfolio or Provincial Magazine*. 8, (Lewes.)

— 1822.   *The fossils of the South Downs; or illustrations of the geology of Sussex*. (London.)

— 1827.   *Illustrations of the geology of Sussex, containing a general view of the geological relations of the south-eastern part of England*. (London.)

— 1829.   A tabular arrangement of the organic remains of the county of Sussex. *Trans. Geol. Soc.*, Ser. 2, Vol. 3, 210.

— 1830.   A sketch of the geological structure of the Rape of Bramber. i–xv in *Parochial topography of the Rape of Bramber*. CARTWRIGHT. Forming Vol. ii part 2 of *Western Sussex*. DALLAWAY (Fol. London.)

— 1833.   *The geology of the south-east of England*. (London.)

— 1835.   Geology and mineralogy of Sussex. 8–29 in *History of Sussex*. Vol. i. HORSFIELD (Lewes and London.)

— 1836.   *Descriptive catalogue of the objects of natural history etc. (chiefly discovered in Sussex), in the museum attached to the Sussex Scientific and Literary Institute at Brighton* (6th edition).

— 1846. Descriptions of some fossil fruits from the Chalk formation of the south and east of England. *Q. J. Geol. Soc. London*. Vol. 2, 51.

MARTIN, A. J. 1967. Bathonian sedimentation in southern England. *Proc. Geol. Assoc.*, Vol. 78, 473–488.

MARTIN, E. A. 1929. The Pleistocene cliff-formation of Brighton. *S. East. Nat. London*, 60–72.

MARTIN, E. C. 1932. Chalk zones in the foreshore between Worthing and Felpham, Sussex. *Proc. Geol. Assoc.*, Vol. 43, 201–211.

— 1937. A section in the Woolwich and Reading Beds, and in the '15-foot' raised beach at Worthing, Sussex. *Proc. Geol. Assoc.*, Vol. 48, 48–51.

— 1938. The Littlehampton and Portsdown Chalk inliers and their relation to the raised beaches of West Sussex. *Proc. Geol. Assoc.*, Vol. 49, 198–212.

— 1939. Report of field meeting at Highdown Hill, Clapham and Angmering, West Sussex. *Proc. Geol. Assoc.*, Vol. 50, 72–76.

— 1954. Field meeting at Highdown Hill, Clapham and Storrington, West Sussex. *Proc. Geol. Assoc.*, Vol. 65, 377–382.

MARTIN, P. J. 1828. *A geological memoir on a part of western Sussex.* (London.)

MIDDLEMISS, F. A. 1962. Brachiopods and shorelines in the Lower Cretaceous. *Ann. Mag. Nat. Hist.*, Ser. 13, Vol. 4, 613–626.

— 1973. The geographical distribution of Lower Cretaceous Terebratulacea in western Europe. 111–120 in *The Boreal Lower Cretaceous*. CASEY, R. and RAWSON, P. F. (editors). Geological Journal, Special Issue No. 5. (Liverpool: Seel House Press.)

MILBOURNE, R. A. 1955. The Gault at Greatness Lane, Sevenoaks, Kent. *Proc. Geol. Assoc.*, Vol. 66, 235–242.

— 1961. Field meeting in the Gault at Small Dole, near Henfield, Sussex. *Proc. Geol. Assoc.*, Vol. 72, 135–138.

— 1962. Notes on the Gault near Sevenoaks, Kent. *Proc. Geol. Assoc.*, Vol. 72, 437–443.

— 1963. The Gault at Ford Place, Wrotham, Kent. *Proc. Geol. Assoc.*, Vol. 74, 55–79.

MONKHOUSE, R. A. 1974. The use and design of sand screens and filter packs for abstraction wells. *Water Servs.*, Vol. 78, (939), 160–163.

— 1980. An exploratory borehole to the Lower Greensand at Sompting, Sussex. *Tech. Note Centr. Water Plann. Unit*, No. 33. 18 pp.

— and FLEET, M. 1975. A geophysical investigation of saline water in the Chalk of the South Coast of England. *Q. J. Eng. Geol.*, Vol. 8, 291–302.

MORTER, A. A. 1984. Purbeck–Wealden mollusca and their relationship to ostracod biostratigraphy, stratigraphical correlation and palaeoecology in the Weald and adjacent areas. *Proc. Geol Assoc.*, Vol. 95, 217–234.

— and WOOD, C. J. 1983. The biostratigraphy of Upper Albian–Lower Cenomanian *Aucellina* in Europe. *Zitteliana*, Vol. 10, 515–529.

MORTIMORE, R. N. 1979. The relationship of stratigraphy and tectonofacies to the physical properties of the White Chalk of Sussex. Unpublished PhD thesis, Brighton Polytechnic.

— 1983. The stratigraphy and sedimentation of the Turonian–Campanian in the southern province of England. *Zitteliana*, Vol. 10, 22–41.

— 1985. Controls on Upper Cretaceous sedimentation in the South Downs with particular reference to flint distribution. In *The scientific study of flint and chert: papers from the Fourth International Flint Symposium, Vol. 1.* SIEVEKING, G. DE G. and HART, M. B. (editors). (Cambridge University Press.)

— 1986. Stratigraphy of the Upper Cretaceous White Chalk of Sussex. *Proc. Geol. Assoc.*, Vol. 97, 97–139.

MUIR-WOOD, H. M. 1936. A monograph of the brachiopoda of the British Great Oolite. *Monogr. Palaeontogr. Soc.*, Pt 1, 1–144.

MURCHISON, R. I. 1851. On the distribution of the flint drift of the south-east of England on the flanks of the Weald, and over the surface of the South and North Downs. *Q. J. Geol. Soc. London*, Vol. 7, 349–398.

NARAYAN, J. 1963. Cross-stratification and palaeogeography of the Lower Greensand of south-east England and Bas-Boulonnais, France. *Nature London*, Vol. 199, 1246–1247.

— 1971. Sedimentary structures in the Lower Greensand of the Weald, England and Bas-Boulonnais, France. *Sediment. Geol.*, Vol. 6, 73–109.

NEAVERSON, E. 1925. The zones of the Oxford Clay near Peterborough. *Proc. Geol. Assoc.*, Vol. 36, 27–37.

OWEN, H. G. 1958. Lower Gault sections in the northern Weald and the zoning of the Lower Gault. *Proc. Geol. Assoc.*, Vol. 69, 148–165.

— 1960. The Gault-Lower Greensand junction and the Lower Gault of the Maidstone By-pass (East section), Kent. *Proc. Geol. Assoc.*, Vol. 71, 364–378.

— 1962. The brachiopod genus *Cyclothyris*. *Bull. Br. Mus. Nat. Hist. (Geol.)*, Vol. 7, No. 2.

— 1963. Some sections in the Lower Gault of the Weald. *Proc. Geol. Assoc.*, Vol. 74, 35–53.

— 1965. Some Lower Cretaceous Terebratelloidea. *Bull. Br. Mus. Nat. Hist. (Geol.)*, Vol. 11, No. 2.

— 1971. Middle Albian stratigraphy in the Anglo-Paris Basin. *Bull. Br. Mus. Nat. Hist. (Geol.)*, Supplement 8, 164 pp.

— 1975. The stratigraphy of the Gault and Upper Greensand of the Weald. *Proc. Geol. Assoc.*, Vol. 86, 475–498.

— 1979. Ammonite zonal stratigraphy in the Albian of North Germany and its setting in the Hoplitinid Faunal Province. *Aspekte der Kreide Europas*, IUGS Series A, No. 6, 563–588.

— 1984. The Albian Stage; European province chronology and ammonite zonation. *Cretaceous Res.*, Vol. 5, 329–344.

PATTERSON, C. 1966. British Wealden sharks. *Bull. Br. Mus. Nat. Hist. (Geol.)*, Vol. 11, No. 7, 281–350.

PECK, R. E. 1973. *Applinocrinus*, a new genus of Cretaceous microcrinoids and its distribution in North America. *J. Palaeontol.*, Vol. 47, 94–100.

PENN, I. E., MERRIMAN, R. J. and WYATT, R. J. 1979. The Bathonian strata of the Bath-Frome area. *Rep. Inst. Geol. Sci.*, No. 78/22.

PEPPER, D. M. 1973. A comparison of the 'Argile à silex' of northern France with the 'Clay-with-flints' of southern England. *Proc. Geol. Assoc.*, Vol. 84, 331–352.

PERCEVAL, S. G. 1871. On the occurrence of Websterite at Brighton. *Geol. Mag.*, Vol. 8, 121–122.

PRESTWICH, J. 1854. On the structure of the strata between the London Clay and the Chalk in the London and Hampshire Tertiary systems. *Q. J. Geol. Soc. London*, Vol. 10, 75–157.

— 1859. On the westward extension of the old raised beach of Brighton; and on the extent of the sea-bed of the same period. *Q. J. Geol. Soc. London*, Vol. 15, 215–221.

— 1892. The raised beaches and Head or rubble-drift of the south of England: their relation to the valley drifts and to the glacial period; and as a late post-Glacial submergence. *Q. J. Geol. Soc. London*, Vol. 48, 263–344.

PRICE, F. G. H. 1874. On the Gault of Folkestone. *Q. J. Geol. Soc. London*, Vol. 30, 342–368.

— 1876. On the Lower Greensand and Gault of Folkestone. *Proc. Geol. Assoc.*, Vol. 4, 135–150.

— 1879. *The Gault.* (London: Taylor and Frances.)

PRICE, R. J. 1976. Palaeoenvironmental interpretations in the Albian of western and southern Europe, as shown by the distribution of selected foraminifers. 625–648 in *Maritime Sediments Spec. Pub.* No. 1. SCHAFER, C. T. and PELLETIER, B. R. (editors).

— 1977. The stratigraphical zonation of the Albian sediments of north-west Europe, as based on foraminifera. *Proc. Geol. Assoc.*, Vol. 88, 65–91.

REEVES, J. W. 1947. 82–85 in Whitsun field meeting to the Central Weald, the Henfield neighbourhood. *Proc. Geol. Assoc.*, Vol. 58.

— 1949. Surface problems in the search for oil in Sussex. *Proc. Geol. Assoc.*, Vol. 59 (for 1948), 234–269.

— 1953. The Wivelsfield Sand. *Proc. Geol. Assoc.*, Vol. 64, 269–275.

— 1958. Subdivision of the Weald Clay in Sussex. *Proc. Geol. Assoc.*, Vol. 69, 1–16.

REID, C. 1892. The Pleistocene deposits of the Sussex coast and their equivalents in other districts. *Q. J. Geol. Soc. London*, Vol. 48, 344–361.

— 1903. The geology of the country near Chichester. *Mem. Geol. Surv. G.B.*

— 1906. In *Victorian history of Sussex.*

ROBERTSON, A. S. and others. 1964. Records of wells in the area of New Series One-Inch (Geological) Brighton (318) Sheet. *Water Supply Pap. Geol. Surv. G.B.*

ROWE, A. W. 1900. The zones of the White Chalk of the English coast. Part 1. Kent and Sussex. *Proc. Geol. Assoc.*, Vol. 16, 289–368.

SHEPHARD-THORN, E. R. 1975. The Quaternary of the Weald—a review. *Proc. Geol. Assoc.*, Vol. 86, 537–547.

— BERRY, F. G. and WYATT, R. J. 1982. Geological notes and local details for 1:10 000 sheets SU 80 NW, NE, SW and SE; SU 90 NW, NE, SW and SE; TQ 00 NW, SW (West Sussex coastal plain between Chichester and Littlehampton). (Keyworth: Institute of Geological Sciences.)

— and WYMER, J. J. 1977. *South east England and the Thames Valley. Guidebook for excursion A5.* International Union for Quaternary Research.

SHOTTON, F. W. 1985. IGCP 24: Quaternary glaciation in the Northern Hemisphere final report. *Quaternary Newsl.*, No. 45, 28–36.

SMART, J. G. O., BISSON, G. and WORSSAM, B. C. 1966. Geology of the country around Canterbury and Folkestone. *Mem. Geol. Surv. G.B.*

SMITH, B. 1936. Levels in the raised beach, Black Rock, Brighton. *Geol. Mag.*, Vol. 73, 423–426.

SMITH, N. J. P. (compiler). 1985. *Map 2: Contours on the top of the pre-Permian surface of the United Kingdom (South).* (Keyworth: British Geological Survey.)

SPATH, L. F. 1923a. Excursion to Folkestone with notes on the zones of the Gault. *Proc. Geol. Assoc.*, Vol. 34, 70–76.

— 1923b. On the ammonite horizons of the Gault and contiguous deposits. *Summ. Prog. Geol. Surv. G.B.* (for 1922), 139–149.

— 1926. On the zones of the Cenomanian and the uppermost Albian. *Proc. Geol. Assoc.*, Vol. 37, 420–432.

— 1941. A monograph of the ammonoidea of the Gault. *Monogr. Palaeontogr. Soc.*, part XIV, 668.

SUSSEX RIVER AUTHORITY. 1970. *Water for Sussex: A report on the first periodic survey of water resources.* 243 pp.

SUTCLIFFE, A. J. and KOWALSKI, K. 1976. Pleistocene rodents of the British Isles. *Bull. Br. Mus. Nat. Hist. (Geol.)*, Vol. 27, 31–147.

TAITT, A. H. and KENT, P. E. 1958. *Deep boreholes at Portsdown (Hants) and Henfield (Sussex).* (London: British Petroleum Co. Ltd.)

TAYLOR, R. J. 1981. Lower Cretaceous (Ryazanian to Albian) calcareous nannofossils. 40–80 in *A stratigraphical index of calcareous nannofossils.* LORD, A. R. (editor). (Chichester: Ellis Horwood and British Micropalaeontological Society.)

THOMAS, L. P. and GRAY, D. A. 1974. Concealed Eocene outcrop beneath Shoreham Harbour, Sussex. *Geol. Mag.*, Vol. 111, 125–132.

THURRELL, R. G., WORSSAM, B. C. and EDMONDS, E. A. 1968. Geology of the country around Haslemere. *Mem. Geol. Surv. G.B.*

TOPLEY, W. 1875. The geology of the Weald. *Mem. Geol. Surv. G.B.*

WARD, E. M. 1922. *English coastal evolution.* (London: Methuen.)

WARREN, S. H. 1897. Note on a section of the Pleistocene rubble drift near Portslade, Sussex. *Geol. Mag.*, Vol. 34, 302–304.

WARRINGTON, G. 1983. Mesozoic micropalaeontological studies. Appendix 4 in WHITTAKER, A. and GREEN, G. W. Geology of the country around Weston-super-Mare. *Mem. Geol. Surv. G.B.*

WEST, R. G. and SPARKS, B. W. 1960. Coastal interglacial deposits of the English Channel. *Philos. Trans. R. Soc. London*, Vol. B243, 45–133.

WHEELER, W. H. 1902. *The sea coast.* (London: Longmans Green & Co.)

WHITAKER, W. and REID, C. 1899. The water supply of Sussex from underground sources. *Mem. Geol. Surv. G.B.*

WHITE, H. J. O. 1921. Geology of the Isle of Wight. *Mem. Geol. Surv. G.B.*

— 1924. The geology of the country near Brighton and Worthing. *Mem. Geol. Surv. G.B.*

— 1926. The geology of the country near Lewes. *Mem. Geol. Surv. G.B.*

WILKINSON, I. P. and MORTER, A. A. 1981. The biostratigraphical zonation of the East Anglian Gault by Ostracoda. 161–176 in *Microfossils from Recent and fossil shelf seas.* NEALE, J. W. and BRASIER, M. D. (editors). (Chichester: Ellis Horwood and British Micropalaeontological Society.)

WILMOT, R. D. and YOUNG, B. 1985. Aluminite and other aluminium minerals from Newhaven, Sussex: the first occurrence of Nordstrandite in Great Britain. *Proc. Geol. Assoc.*, Vol. 96, 47–52.

WIMBLEDON, W. A. 1980. In *A correlation of Jurassic rocks in the British Isles Part Two: Middle and Upper Jurassic.* COPE, J. C. W. AND OTHERS. *Spec. Rep. Geol. Soc. London*, No. 15.

— and COPE, J. C. W. 1978. The ammonite zonation of the

English Portland Beds and the zones of the Portlandian Stage. *J. Geol. Soc. London*, Vol. 135, 183–190.

— and HUNT, C. O. 1983. The Portland–Purbeck junction (Portlandian–Berriasian) in the Weald, and correlation of latest Jurassic–early Cretaceous rocks in southern England. *Geol. Mag.*, Vol. 120, 267–280.

WOOLDRIDGE, S. W. and LINTON, D. L. 1955. *Structure, surface and drainage in south-east England*. 176 pp. (London.)

WORRALL, G. A. 1954. The Lower Greensand in East Kent. *Proc. Geol. Assoc.*, Vol. 65, 185–202.

— 1957. The mineralogy of some Lower Greensand borehole samples in Kent. *Proc. Geol. Assoc.*, Vol. 67, 138–141.

WORSSAM, B. C. 1969. Written discussion of Reeves, J. W. 1968. Subdivision of the Weald Clay in North Sussex, in Surrey and Kent. *Proc. Geol. Assoc.*, Vol. 79, 457–476. Discussion Vol. 80, 381–383.

— 1978. The stratigraphy of the Weald Clay. *Rep. Inst. Geol. Sci.*, No. 78/11.

YOUNG, B. 1977. In *Annual Report for 1976*. (London: Institute of Geological Sciences.)

— 1978. The Upper Greensand of Eastbourne, Sussex. 48–52 in *Guide book to South East England excursion, Sixth International Clay Conference*. (Oxford.)

— HIGHLEY, D. E. and MORGAN, D. J. 1979. Calcium montmorillonite (fuller's earth) deposits in the Lower Greensand of the Tillington area, West Sussex. *Open-file Rep. Inst. Geol. Sci.*, No. 1979/1.

— and MONKHOUSE, R. A. 1980. The geology and hydrogeology of the Lower Greensand of the Sompting Borehole, West Sussex. *Proc. Geol. Assoc.*, Vol. 91, 307–313.

— and MORGAN, D. J. 1981. The Aptian Lower Greensand fuller's earth beds of Bognor Common, West Sussex. *Proc. Geol. Assoc.*, Vol. 92, 33–37.

— — and HIGHLEY, D. E. 1978. New fuller's earth occurrences in the Lower Greensand of southeastern England. *Trans. Inst. Min. Metal.*, Vol. 87, B93–96.

ZEIGHAMPOUR, M. R. 1981. Biozonation du Crétace (Albien-Santonien) à partir des coccolithes des Craies de Hautes-Normandie (France). *Revue de Micropaléontologie*, Vol. 24, 172–186.

APPENDIX 1

Borehole records

For each borehole the BGS registration number and National Grid reference are given, together with an outline log. References are given to any published accounts of the boreholes. Detailed logs are held at the British Geological Survey, Keyworth, Nottingham NG12 5GG, where they may be inspected by appointment. Specimens from all these boreholes are held in the BGS National Geosciences Data Centre, Keyworth where they may also be examined by arrangement.

Chanctonbury: BGS (TQ 11 SW 28) [1445 1215]

	Thickness m	Depth m
Lower Chalk	67.32	67.32
Upper Greensand	15.68	83.00
Gault	seen to 18.21	101.21

Nep Town: BGS (TQ 21 NW 1) [2112 1562]

Lower Greensand		
Folkestone Beds	6.27	6.27
'Undivided'	70.53	76.80
Weald Clay	seen to 72.55	149.35

(Institute of Geological Sciences, 1978)

Plumpton: BGS (TQ 31 SE 1) [3545 1350]

Lower Chalk	29.24	29.24
Gault	seen to 0.06	29.30

This record supersedes that previously published (Institute of Geological Sciences, 1974)

Sompting: Central Water Planning Unit (TQ 10 NE 80) [1661 0636]

Upper and Middle Chalk, undivided	225.0	225.0
Lower Chalk	100.0	325.0
Upper Greensand	25.0	350.0
Gault	54.0	404.0
Lower Greensand		
Folkestone Beds	35.1	439.1
'Undivided'	13.9	453.0
Atherfield Clay	3.5	456.5
Weald Clay	seen to 0.5	457.0

(Young and Monkhouse, 1980)

Steyning Station: BGS (TQ 11 SE 58) [1818 1130]

	Thickness m	Depth m
Lower Chalk	2.02	2.02
Upper Greensand	seen to 8.64	10.66

(Institute of Geological Sciences, 1974)

Streat: BGS (TQ 31 SW 1) [3492 1485]

Lower Greensand		
Folkestone Beds	3.00	3.00
'Undivided'	66.65	69.65
Weald Clay	seen to 25.85	95.50

(Institute of Geological Sciences, 1978)

Thakeham: BGS (TQ 11 NW 17) [1084 1765]

Lower Greensand		
Hythe Beds	24.03	24.03
Atherfield Clay	9.47	33.50
Weald Clay	seen to 3.02	36.52

Washington: BGS (TQ 11 SW 1) [1264 1345]

Lower Greensand		
Folkestone Beds	38.41	38.41
'Undivided'	57.22	95.63
Weald Clay	seen to 46.41	142.04

(Institute of Geological Sciences, 1978)

APPENDIX 2

List of Geological Survey photographs

Copies of the photographs are deposited for reference in the British Geological Survey library at the Keyworth Office, Keyworth, Nottingham NG12 5GG. Prints and slides may be purchased. The more recent photographs listed below were taken by Mr C. J. Jeffery and are available in colour and black and white. They belong to Series A.

TOPOGRAPHY AND MISCELLANEOUS

13312   Common land on Weald Clay, Ditchling Common [3375 1805].

13321   Weald Clay country with escarpment of Large-'*Paludina*' limestone, Holmbush House, Ashington [1365 1687].

13322   Large-'*Paludina*' limestone scarp, Gallops Farm, Streat [352 177].

13329   Ironstone scarp in Weald Clay, Wivelsfield Green [3520 1980].

13330   Lower Greensand scarp and Weald Clay lowlands, Upper Chancton Farm, Wiston [1340 1445].

13332   View across the Greenhurst Anticline, Warminghurst [1170 1684].

13333   Lower Greensand ridge, Henfield [2190 1500].

13340-1   South Downs from Streat church [3506 1515].

13363   Pastureland on Gault outcrop near Plumpton [3509 1420].

13368   Upper Greensand scenery with spring, Whitelands, Clayton [3145 1400].

13369   Spring rising near base of Upper Greensand, Whitelands, Clayton [3145 1400].

13372   Upper Greensand used as a building stone, Aburton Farm, Edburton [2343 1145].

13374   South Downs escarpment from Rock Common Sand Pit, Washington [1263 1363].

13375   Ouse valley and Mount Caburn from Kingston ridge, Lewes [3845 0812].

13376   Firle Beacon and South Downs escarpment from Kingston ridge, Lewes [3845 0812].

13377-8   South Downs escarpment near Poynings [2669 1196; 2671 1189].

13379   Chalk escarpment at Steyning [165 104].

13380   South Downs escarpment at Devil's Dyke, Poynings [2582 1106].

13381   Adur valley and South Downs escarpment [2087 1220].

13382   South Downs escarpment and Chanctonbury Ring [117 128].

13383-4   Chalk dip-slope scenery, High Park Corner, Ditchling Beacon [3240 1135].

13385   Cissbury Ring and Lychpole Hill—secondary escarpment [1652 0888].

13399   View across Woolwich and Reading Beds outlier, Falmer [3552 0784].

13403   Coastal plain and Chalk dip-slope from Highdown Hill [0923 0447].

13404   River Adur and coastal plain near Lancing [2122 0678].

13405-6   Devil's Dyke, Poynings [2671 1189; 2586 1081].

13420   Central Weald from Ditchling Beacon [3340 1300].

13421   View across Weald from Devil's Dyke Hotel [2582 1106].

CRETACEOUS: WEALDEN

13313   Weald Clay mudstones, Keymer brick-works, Burgess Hill [3275 1905].

13318   Sandstone in Weald Clay, Lidde Hill Farm, Henfield [2114 1751].

13324   Large-'*Paludina*' limestone, Marchants Farm, Streat [3498 1621].

CRETACEOUS: LOWER GREENSAND

13334   Sunken lane in Lower Greensand, Warminghurst [1169 1677].

13335   Old stone pit in Lower Greensand, Little Thakeham [1078 1576].

13336   River-cliff in Lower Greensand, Lashmars Hall, Henfield [1947 1620].

13337-8   Old stone-pit in Lower Greensand, Stonepit Lane, Henfield [2010 1623].

13342   Folkestone Beds overlain by Gault, Streat Sand Pit [3499 1481].

13343   Folkestone Beds, Streat Sand Pit [3498 1478].

13344   Folkestone Beds overlain by Head, Streat Sand Pit [3485 1481].

13346   Folkestone Beds, Hassocks [3012 1535].

13347   Ferruginous staining in Folkestone Beds, Slabcrete Quarry, Washington [1365 1347].

13348   Cross-bedding in Folkestone Beds, Slabcrete Quarry, Washington [1340 1347].

13349   Folkestone Beds, Slabcrete Quarry, Washington [1292 1347].

13350   Folkestone Beds, Slabcrete Quarry, Washington [1300 1344].

13352-3   Folkestone Beds, Rock Common Quarry, Washington [1260 1355].

13354   Ferruginous staining in Folkestone Beds, Rock Common Quarry, Washington [1266 1345].

13355   Folkestone Beds, Rock Common Quarry, Washington [1266 1345].

13356   Folkestone Beds, R.M.C. Sand Pit, Sullington [1113 1400].

13357   Folkestone Beds in old sand-pit, Heath Common, Washington [1100 1504].

13358   Pipeclay seams in Folkestone Beds in old sand-pit, Heath Common, Washington [1100 1504].

13359-61   Folkestone Beds, Sandgate Pit, Storrington [1037 1409; 1047 1400].

13362   Cross-bedding in Folkestone Beds, Sandgate Pit, Storrington [1037 1407].

CRETACEOUS: GAULT AND UPPER GREENSAND

13364   Pit in Gault, Small Dole, Henfield [2057 1235].

13370   Upper Greensand in roadside, Poynings [2626 1198].

13371   Upper Greensand, Fulking [2469 1139].
13373   Upper Greensand in house foundation, Mouse Lane, Steyning [1728 1157].

CRETACEOUS: CHALK

13387-8   Plenus Marls and Melbourn Rock, Newtimber Limeworks [2765 1368; 2778 1374].
13390   Small faults in Upper Chalk, Shoreham Cement Works Quarry [2093 0897].
13391   Normal fault and solution cavity in Upper Chalk, Shoreham Cement Works Quarry [2087 0909].
13392   Solution cavity in Upper Chalk, Shoreham Cement Works Quarry [2087 0909].
13393   Upper Chalk and Head deposits, Rottingdean cliffs [3709 0209].

PALAEOCENE

13396   Ferruginous flint conglomerate, The Goldstone, Hove Park [2868 0602].
13397-8   Woolwich and Reading Beds on Upper Chalk, Falmer [3538 0886].
13401   Sarsen boulders, Stanmer [3370 0959].

QUATERNARY

13331   Landslips on Weald Clay and Atherfield Clay, Upper Chancton Farm, Wiston [1345 1450].
13407   Cryoturbation lobes in Head deposits, Shoreham Cement Works Quarry [2082 0890].
13408   Cryoturbation lobes in Upper Chalk, Roedean [3440 0315].
13412   Drift deposits in dry valley and valley-bulge structure in Upper Chalk, Saltdean cliffs [3850 0178].
13413-4   Head filling dry valley in Upper Chalk, Saltdean cliffs [3809 0205; 3799 0196].
13415   Disintegrated chalk at margin of dry valley, Rottingdean [3695 0215].
13416   Brighton Raised Beach at Black Rock, Brighton [3365 0336].

13417   Drift deposits banked against old sea-cliff, Black Rock, Brighton [3371 0335].
13418-9   Drift deposits, Black Rock, Brighton [3363 0336].

ECONOMIC PRODUCTS

13314   Loading clay from stockpits, Keymer brick-works, Burgess Hill [3232 1915].
13315-6   Brick and tile kilns, Keymer brick-works, Burgess Hill [3217 1925].
13317   Local building stones, Ewhurst Manor, Shermanbury [2114 1902].
13319   Ripple-marked Weald Clay sandstone paving, Joles Farm, Partridge Green [1886 1976].
13320   Ripple-marked Weald Clay sandstone roofing, Westmeston church [3390 1363].
13323   Large-'*Paludina*' limestone in wall, Marchants Farm, Streat [3498 1621].
13325-6   Large-'*Paludina*' limestone as building stone, East Chiltington church [3699 1512].
13327   Local building stones, Holy Sepulchre Church, Warminghurst [1170 1686].
13328   'Sussex Marble' font, Woodmancote church [2310 1500].
13339   Local building stones, St Andrew's Church, Steyning [1790 1140].
13345   Lower Greensand carstone as building stone, Erskine Nursery, Hurstpierpoint [2799 1603].
13351   Folkestone Beds in Rock Common Sand Pit, Washington [1263 1363].
13365   Small Dole Clay Pit, conveyor belt system [2057 1235].
13366   Small Dole Clay Pit, processing plant [2056 1237].
13367   Small Dole Clay Pit, slurry tank [2056 1237].
13386   Spring from near base of Chalk, Fulking [2468 1132].
13389   Shoreham Cement Works [2000 0860].
13394-5   Local building stones, Sompting church [1615 0564].
13402   Site of chalybeate spring, St Anne's Well, Hove [2997 0493].

APPENDIX 3

List of 1:10 000 maps

The following is a list of 1:10 000 geological maps included in the areas of 1:50 000 Geological Sheets 318 and 333, with the names of the surveyors and the dates of the survey of each map. The surveyors were C. R. Bristow, R. A. Ellison, R. W. Gallois, R. D. Lake, T. E. Lawson, D. Millward, R. G. Thurrell and B. Young.

Manuscript copies of the maps are deposited for public reference in the library of the British Geological Survey at Keyworth. Uncoloured dyeline copies of these maps are available for purchase from the British Geological Survey, Keyworth, Nottingham NG12 5GG.

TQ 10 NW	Findon Lake	1979
TQ 10 NE	North Lancing Young	1979
TQ 10 SW	West Worthing Lake	1979
TQ 10 SE	Worthing Lake	1979
TQ 11 NW	Ashington Thurrell and Lake	1964 & 1978
TQ 11 NE	Ashurst Thurrell, Lake and Lawson	1964, 1976 & 1978
TQ 11 SW	Washington Ellison	1978
TQ 11 SE	Steyning Millward	1976–77
TQ 12 SW	Shipley Thurrell	1964
TQ 12 SE	West Grinstead Thurrell	1964
TQ 20 NW and part of TQ 20 SW	Shoreham-by-Sea Lawson and Young	1976 & 1979
TQ 20 NE and part of TQ 20 SE	Hove Lawson and Young	1976 & 1978–79
TQ 21 NW	Henfield Gallois, Thurrell, Lawson and Young	1962, 1964 & 1975–76
TQ 21 NE	Hurstpierpoint Young and Lawson	1975–77
TQ 21 SW	Small Dole Lawson	1975
TQ 21 SE	Poynings Young	1975 & 1977
TQ 22 SW	Cowfold Thurrell	1962
TQ 22 SE	Bolney Thurrell and Gallois	1963–64
TQ 30 NW	Hollingbury Young	1978
TQ 30 NE	Falmer Lake and Young	1973 & 1978
TQ 30 SW	Brighton Young	1978
TQ 30 SE	Rottingdean Lake and Young	1973 & 1978
TQ 31 NW	Burgess Hill Young	1975 & 1977
TQ 31 NE	Plumpton Green Bristow, Lake and Young	1972, 1973 & 1975
TQ 31 SW	Westmeston Young	1975
TQ 31 SE	Plumpton Lake and Young	1972–73
TQ 32 SW	Haywards Heath Gallois	1963–64
TQ 32 SE	Scaynes Hill Gallois	1964

FOSSIL INDEX

GENERAL INDEX

BRITISH GEOLOGICAL SURVEY

Keyworth, Nottingham NG12 5GG

Murchison House, West Mains Road,
Edinburgh EH9 3LA

The full range of Survey publications is available
through the Sales Desks at Keyworth and
Murchison House. Selected items are stocked by
the Geological Museum Bookshop, Exhibition
Road, London SW7 2DE; all other items may be
obtained through the BGS London Information
Office in the Geological Museum. All the books
are listed in HMSO's Sectional List 45. Maps are
listed in the BGS Map Catalogue and Ordnance
Survey's Trade Catalogue. They can be bought
from Ordnance Survey Agents as well as from
BGS.

*The British Geological Survey carries out the geological
survey of Great Britain and Northern Ireland (the latter as
an agency service for the government of Northern Ireland),
and of the surrounding continental shelf, as well as its
basic research projects. It also undertakes programmes of
British technical aid in geology in developing countries as
arranged by the Overseas Development Administration.*

*The British Geological Survey is a component body of the
Natural Environment Research Council.*

Maps and diagrams in this book use topography
based on Ordnance Survey mapping

HER MAJESTY'S STATIONERY OFFICE

HMSO publications are available from:

HMSO Publications Centre
(Mail and telephone orders)
PO Box 276, London SW8 5DT
Telephone orders (01) 622 3316
General enquiries (01) 211 5656
Queueing system in operation for both numbers

HMSO Bookshops
49 High Holborn, London WC1V 6HB
  (01) 211 5656 (Counter service only)
258 Broad Street, Birmingham B1 2HE
  (021) 643 3740
Southey House, 33 Wine Street, Bristol BS1 2BQ
  (0272) 264306
9 Princess Street, Manchester M60 8AS
  (061) 834 7201
80 Chichester Street, Belfast BT1 4JY
  (0232) 238451
71 Lothian Road, Edinburgh EH3 9AZ
  (031) 228 4181

HMSO's Accredited Agents
(see Yellow Pages)

And through good booksellers